General Principles of Sampling
Associated Materials (second

Methods for the Examination of Waters and Associated Materials

London: HMSO

ISBN 0 11 752364 X

Acknowledgement is made to the World Health Organization (European Region) for permission to use material from their publication "Manual of Analysis for Water Pollution Control".

In this document, mention has been made to proprietary brands of equipment which authors have found suitable. The use of the equipment is not obligatory and the Standing Committee of Analysts does not endorse their use. It is up to users to decide which equipment to use and assess the performance obtained.

HMSO

Standing order service

Placing a standing order with HMSO BOOKS enables a customer to receive other titles in this series automatically as published.

This saves the time, trouble and expense of placing individual orders and avoids the problem of knowing when to do so.

For details please write to HMSO BOOKS, Publications Centre, PO Box 276, London SW8 5DT.

The standing order service also enables customers to receive automatically as published all material of their choice which additionally saves extensive catalogue research. The scope and selectivity of the service has been extended by new techniques, and there are more than 3,500 classifications to choose from. A special leaflet describing the service in detail may be obtained on request.

General Principles of Sampling Waters and Associated Materials (second edition) 1996; Estimation of Flow and Load 1996

Methods for the Examination of Waters and Associated Materials

This booklet contains two related parts in this series.

CONTENTS

About this series

Introduction

This booklet is part of a series intended to provide authoritative guidance on recommended methods of sampling and analysis for determining the quality of drinking water, groundwater, river and seawater, waste water and effluents as well as sewage sludges, sediments and biota. In addition, short reviews of the more important analytical techniques of interest to the water and sewage industries are included.

Performance of methods

Ideally, all methods should be fully evaluated with results from performance tests reported for most parameters. These methods should be capable of establishing, within specified or pre-determined and acceptable limits of deviation and detection, whether or not any sample contains concentrations of parameters above those of interest.

For a method to be considered fully evaluated, individual results encompassing at least ten degrees of freedom from at least three laboratories should be reported. The specifications of performance generally relate to maximum tolerable values for total error (random and systematic errors), systematic error (bias), total standard deviation and limit of detection. Often, full evaluation is not possible and only limited performance data may be available. An indication of the status of methods is usually shown at the front of publications on whether or not methods have undergone full performance testing.

In addition, good laboratory practice and analytical quality control are essential if satisfactory results are to be achieved.

Standing Committee of Analysts

The preparation of booklets in the series 'Methods for the Examination of Waters and Associated Materials' and their continuous revision is the responsibility of the Standing Committee of Analysts. This committee was established in 1972 by the Department of the Environment and is managed by the Drinking Water Inspectorate. At present, there are nine working groups, each responsible for one section or aspect of water quality analysis. They are:

- 1.0 General principles of sampling and accuracy of results
- 2.0 Microbiological methods
- 3.0 Empirical and physical methods
- 4.0 Metals and metalloids
- 5.0 General non-metallic substances
- 6.0 Organic impurities
- 7.0 Biological monitoring
- 8.0 Sewage works control methods and biodegradability
- 9.0 Radiochemical methods

The actual methods and reviews are produced by smaller panels of experts in the appropriate field, in co-operation with the working group and main committee. The names of members associated with methods are usually listed at the back of booklets.

Publication of new or revised methods will be notified to the technical press. An index of methods and the more important parameters and topics is available from HMSO (ISBN 0 11 752669 X).

Every effort is made to avoid errors appearing in the published text. If however, any are found, please notify the Secretary.

Dr D WESTWOOD
Secretary

22 January 1995

Warning to Users

The procedures described in this booklet should only be carried out under the proper supervision of competent, trained analysts in properly equipped laboratories.

All possible safety precautions should be followed and appropriate regulatory requirements complied with. This should include compliance with The Health and Safety at Work etc Act 1974 and any regulations made under the Act, and the Control of Substances Hazardous to Health Regulations 1988 SI 1988/1657. Where particular or exceptional hazards exist in carrying out the procedures described in this booklet then specific attention is noted. Numerous publications are available giving practical details on first aid and laboratory safety and these should be consulted and be readily accessible to all analysts. Amongst such publications are those produced by the Royal Society of Chemistry, namely 'Safe Practices in Chemical Laboratories' and 'Hazards in the Chemical Laboratory', 5th edition, 1992; by Member Societies of the Microbiological Consultative Committee, 'Guidelines for Microbiological Safety', 1986, Portland Press, Colchester; and by the Public Health Laboratory Service 'Safety Precautions, Notes for Guidance'. Another useful publication is produced by the Department of Health entitled 'Good Laboratory Practice'.

CONTENTS

1 Introduction

1.1 Aim of this publication

Large amounts of time, money and effort are involved in the sampling and examination of waters, effluents and other types of samples to provide information on their qualities. It is clearly desirable that such work be planned so that the required information is obtained with adequate accuracy and maximum efficiency. The aim of this publication is, therefore, to provide general advice on the design of measurement programmes.

1.2 Topics considered

The main topics discussed in the following sections are:

i.   definition of the information required from the measurement programme;

ii.   collection of samples; and

iii. examination of samples.

In addition, certain statistical techniques are involved in (ii) and (iii), and for those readers unfamiliar with such techniques, a simplified account of their basic concepts and methods will be found in Chapter 3. The important aspects of data-handling and interpretation are not included. A few introductory words on the above sections will help to indicate their scope and relation to other publications in this series.

If the information required on quality is not carefully defined, it is obvious that measurement programmes may be inappropriate or inefficient or both. Definition of the required information and other important points are discussed in Chapter 2.

Given a clear statement of the information required, decisions must be made on where and when samples are to be obtained, and on the procedures and equipment used to collect and transport the samples to the location where they will be examined. However, it is stressed that, for many of the applications with which this publication is concerned, a number of factors can lead to grossly unrepresentative samples. To control such errors, several important principles should always be borne in mind and applied as appropriate; those principles are described in Chapter 4. Detailed recommendations on sampling procedures for individual determinands are given in other parts of this series of publications dealing with the examination procedures for the various determinands.

The examination procedures applied to samples will also introduce errors in the results. The procedures must, therefore, be chosen so that they are capable of the required accuracy, and tests to ensure that accuracy is achieved are also necessary. These topics are discussed in references 1–5.

1.3 How to use this book

The first four chapters deal with general principles of sampling waters and associated materials. These are therefore aimed at all readers who may be involved in any sampling exercises. Chapters 6 to 13 are concerned with sampling in specific circumstances, and contain greater detail appropriate to their particular subjects. Readers intending to sample rivers, lakes, seawater, precipitation, potable water or any other materials covered, should therefore consult the appropriate chapters. Finally, Chapter 5 should be consulted for details of sample storage and preservation techniques. Table 1 in this chapter is a comprehensive summary of suitable techniques, listed by determinand.

Inevitably some techniques are appropriate to more than one type of water or material. To avoid duplication as much as possible, cross-references to other chapters are given where necessary.

2 Definition of the required information

2.1 General principles

Defining the required information need not, in principle, involve questions of sampling and examination. However, it is always sensible to consider the practical aspects of these topics when planning a measurement programme.

The cost of sampling and examination often increases markedly as the required information becomes more exacting, for example as greater accuracy, measurement of smaller concentrations or greater numbers of samples are requested. Care is needed to ensure that the cost of the measurement programme does not exceed its potential benefits. A formal cost-benefit analysis will often be difficult, and may be impossible, but the concept is important, and it is a sound approach not to make the required information more exacting than is necessary.

2.2 Points to be considered

The required information should be defined as precisely as possible. While individual measurement programmes should be planned to achieve their specific objectives, the following general points should normally be considered:

i.   the matrix to be sampled and the determinands of interest should be specified;

ii.   the required analytical sensitivity and accuracy should be stated so that appropriate methods of sampling and analysis may be used;

iii. the time-scale or sampling frequency should be decided on, so that appropriate numbers of samples are taken for analysis;

iv.   an indication should be given on how quality is to be expressed (for example, as an average or median or maximum), and the tolerable uncertainty on any such parameters should be stated so that, again, appropriate sampling and analytical techniques may be used; and

v.   an indication should be given as to how the data will be used, so that suitable data-handling techniques may be employed.

2.3 Defining the determinands of interest

The quality parameters must be defined unambiguously so that appropriate sampling and analytical techniques can be ensured. The following aspects should be considered:

i.   Many substances can exist in water in a variety of different chemical and physical forms, and the response of an analytical method may depend on the particular form or forms present in the sample. Careful choice of method is therefore necessary.

ii.   Some quality parameters are often expressed in such a way that one parameter represents a whole class of compounds, a number of which may be present in samples. For such parameters, it may be useful to specify the individual compounds of interest so that appropriate analytical methods can be selected. However, circumstances can arise in which the measurement of a whole class of compounds is required, for example total organic carbon.

iii. Some quality parameters are overall properties of a sample rather than a particular substance, such as biochemical oxygen demand, colour, turbidity, and taste and odour. Some of these parameters may be observer dependent, while others, though capable of accurate measurement, may often be assessed empirically for simplicity. A few, such as biochemical and chemical oxygen demand, are not only empirical but highly dependent on the method used. Great care is necessary with these empirical tests, not only to ensure that the test is done reproducibly, but also that the correct variant is used to ensure comparability with other analyses.

2.4 Requirements for analytical results

2.4.1 Range of concentrations to be determined

The concentration range of interest can markedly affect the choice of analytical method. The most important point is to specify the lowest concentration of interest, because this will govern the limit of detection required of the analytical method. However, it must be borne in mind that demands for extremely low limits will often require greater analytical sophistication and effort. As a general rule, a lower limit of about 10% of the smallest concentration of importance is reasonable. Existing standards for water quality can be of value in choosing the lower limits for analysis, but when such standards do not exist, a lower limit must still be specified. Sometimes, quality standards, which have been arrived at by applying large safety factors to toxicological studies, are below the limit of detection of most analytical methods. In some cases this difficulty can be overcome by use of very large samples.

2.4.2 Accuracy required of analytical results

The following points should be noted.

i.   It is usually important to specify separate values for systematic and random errors because their effects differ.

ii. The expression of tolerable error is often of the form 'the error should not exceed a given proportion (for example 10%) of the result'. Such statements overlook the fact that analytical errors (expressed as a proportion of the result) increase markedly as the limit of detection of the analytical method is approached. For example, at the limit of the detection, the random error (95% confidence limits) is approximately 50% of the limit.

Further, as concentrations decrease towards the limit of detection, it is often the case that the tolerable percentage error increases. It may therefore be better to use statements of the form: 'the error should not exceed c mg/l or p% of the concentration, whichever is the greater'. The values of c and p for both random and systematic errors are chosen for the particular application.

iii. Random errors can be defined quantitatively only for a given confidence level (see Chapter 3), and this must be chosen appropriately. The 95% confidence level is often used, but greater confidence levels (such as 99%) may sometimes be necessary, for example in controlling some crucial aspect of water quality.

The analyst is advised, whenever possible, to consult the user of the data to ensure that the analyst understands why the analysis is being made and the recipient of the analysis understands what that analysis actually determines. Sometimes an alternative determinand may be more useful or give the same information at less cost. Speed may often be more important than great accuracy, though on other occasions the converse applies.

2.4.3 Procedure when maximum reliability is required

There may be occasions when the final analytical result must be as accurate as possible. In such an event, the analyst should consider all the methods available, with their precision and bias, and extraction efficiencies if relevant. If possible, two or more suitable methods differing in technique should be selected. These should then be used to analyse the sample at least in duplicate, along with controls and, if appropriate, spiked samples (although these do not always detect some forms of interference). Multiple samples may be useful where representativeness of a single one is in question. The results, with their standard deviations, should then be compared (allowing for any known bias). Ideally, there should be a range of complete overlap from all the methods. If there is no overlap, reconsider the methods used, the sampling and sample stability.

3 Statistical aspects of sampling

3.1   Introduction

Most investigations of water quality, whether they are concerned with chemical concentrations, or with population densities of biological organisms, have to face two difficulties which complicate the task of drawing correct conclusions from the experimental results.

i.   The quantity of water actually examined is usually only a minute fraction of that for which information is being sought. The sampling scheme must therefore recognise and attempt to allow for possible variability, both throughout the body of water and through time.

ii. For many determinands the procedures for collecting and examining samples are not free from error. The accuracy may be limited by technology or expense; whatever the reason, the possible sizes of the errors must be considered in interpreting the results of measurements.

Commonsense can go some way towards surmounting these difficulties. Just the recognition of their existence may be enough, if all that is needed is a purely qualitative assessment. Often, however, some kind of quantitative statement is required of the inaccuracies or uncertainties associated with the results. This may be in order to draw objective conclusions, to assess the relative risks of alternative decisions, or to ensure that the results of one investigation may be validly compared with those of another.

These needs can be met by establishing what are essentially common sense notions of uncertainty in an unambiguous mathematical framework. This is the function of statistics. Statistical methods aid the interpretation of data that are subject to random or systematic variability. Such methods provide a way of dealing with the difficulties outlined in (i) and (ii) above. This is true whatever the scale of the investigation. A proper statistical assessment is required for even the simplest monitoring regime, if a purely subjective interpretation is to be avoided.

This section does not attempt to survey the whole subject of statistics, nor even just the parts of it which are relevant to water analysis. The objective is to direct readers to the statistical approach, so that they are encouraged to apply it and can recognise when to seek further help elsewhere. The need for specialised advice will always remain, for an important aspect of applied statistics is the right choice of method for the particular situation.

3.2 The statistical approach

3.2.1 Types of variation

Statistics deals with two kinds of error; random variation and systematic effects. A set of measurements varying in a haphazard and unpredictable manner about some central value would be exhibiting random variability. If, however, those measurements taken on day 1 show a persistent tendency to be higher (say) than those taken on day 2, they would be indicating a systematic difference between days 1 and 2. One of the general purposes of statistical analysis is to distinguish systematic differences or trends from the background of random variability. This task arises frequently in questions such as:

'Is the average concentration of nitrate in River X greater than in River Y?'

'Is the bacterial population density in the water leaving the sewage works below a predetermined limit?'

If the nitrate levels in each of the two rivers vary from place to place or at different times, and the laboratory cannot determine nitrate without experimental errors then the answer must take into account the uncertainties from these sources. Similar remarks may be made about the bacterial counts.

In other situations the question of interest may be posed differently: 'what is the average density of *E. coli* in this stream?' or 'Within what range may the bacterial density be reasonably assumed to lie?'. The answer to these questions demands knowledge of the size and type of randomness in the samples and methods of measurement.

3.2.2 Random variability

The way random variability is dealt with statistically can be introduced by some simple examples. In the two following examples, suppose that the difficulties associated with sampling from an inhomogeneous body of water may be ignored, and that the only statistical problems are ones of repeatability within the laboratory. Two examples of typical data are presented in Figures 1 and 2.

Figure 1 shows the results of a trial of a new method for determination of magnesium. Under normal laboratory conditions 30 analyses were performed on portions of a well mixed synthetic solution. The results are presented in histogram form.

Figure 2 shows the counts of micro-organism *M*, observed in 20 successive dips of a 10 ml trap into a well stirred bucket of water from River *T*. A histogram is shown.

Both sets of results show a scatter which is typical of many kinds of scientific observations. The result from the magnesium determination is not exactly the same every time, nor is the micro-organism count. Each is subject to random variability, which governs precision and is a quantitative measure of the variability of observations. If the random variability in a set of results is high, then the precision will be low, and vice versa.

There is one important difference between Figures 1 and 2. Each chemical result, while there may be no merit in trying to express it to more than three significant digits, can in principle take any value on a continuous scale. In contrast for each microbiological result, the counts are integers. Histograms provide a convenient way of summarising both kinds of data.

In both figures there is a tendency for the data to cluster about a "central" region. It is useful to be able to define the 'middle' of the data in an unambiguous way and a number of measures like the mode (the most frequently occurring value) or the median (the value exceeded by half the data) are useful in certain circumstances. However, by far the most widely used is the arithmetic mean or 'average'. It is commonly denoted by a bar: thus $\bar{x}$ is the average of a set of x-values.

The other essential requirement is to know how spread out the data values are. Measures which summarise this are called measures of dispersion. Again, there is a choice of such measures, but the one of fundamental importance is the standard deviation, s (or similarly, the variance, s^2).

The means and standard deviations for the two illustrations are shown in Figures 1 and 2.

If another set of 30 magnesium analyses were performed, this would almost certainly produce a different set of data, a somewhat different looking histogram and different values of $\bar{x}$ and s. Any one such set of data is called a sample. For different samples, the histograms will probably be different in detail but roughly similar in general shape. Note the word 'sample' has similar meanings in both the experimental sciences and statistics. In the former it refers to 'a portion of the material of interest'; in the latter it means 'a subset of data values from the whole set of possible values'.

3.2.3 Populations and probability distributions

The concept of a population is central to the whole of statistical reasoning. The assumption is made that the results of an experiment, such as those outlined in Figures 1 and 2, have arisen from a process which produces individual results in random order but which has an inbuilt propensity to generate results of different sizes in particular relative proportions. For example, suppose the experiment consists of rolling a pair of dice in the hope of getting a double six. Provided the dice are not loaded, it is reasonable to imagine the underlying process as generating successes and failures in the ratio 1:35. This is not to say that in 36 experiments there will be exactly 1 success and 35 failures; that would be rather fortuitous. However, there will be an underlying tendency for the results to be generated in these relative proportions in the long run.

An equivalent but slightly different view is to imagine the results being drawn randomly from a very large body of data containing particular proportions of results of different sizes. In some applications this set may physically exist, as for example when sampling fish from a certain reservoir at a given time (the set then being the entire stock of fish in the reservoir). In other cases, the set is purely conceptual, as it is in the dice example. Whether the process idea or the large set idea is preferred, the totality of possible experimental results, together with their relative frequency weightings, is known as the Population.

These ideas are expressed in a more tangible mathematical way with the help of probability distributions. Probability distributions suitable for the data in Figures 1 and 2 are shown in Figures 3 and 4. One way to interpret the continuous distribution in Figure 3 is in terms of areas. The total area under the curve is arranged to be unity, and the area between two particular values of x is the probability that a result will fall in that interval. The height of the curve at any point is known as the probability density.

In the case of Figure 4, the distribution is discrete, and the vertical axis measures probability directly as there are now definite non-zero probabilities of observing the discrete values 0, 1, 2, 3, etc.

The probability distributions of Figures 3 and 4 each come from a family of distributions, that is distributions which all have the same general mathematical form and are specified by particular values of the parameters in the general equation. Figure 3 shows a Normal distribution; this is characterised by two parameters, μ and σ. Note that population parameters are usually denoted by Greek letters, and sample statistics by Roman letters. The Poisson distribution of Figure 4 contains one parameter, λ. There are a number of other commonly occurring families of distributions; the following remarks apply equally to all of them.

Just as the mean and standard deviation are used to summarise a sample of data, so it is possible to introduce these concepts to describe a population. In this context the terms population mean and population standard deviation are used. Knowing the mathematical expression for a particular probability distribution, it is possible to calculate the population mean and standard deviation in terms of the distribution's parameters. Thus in the case of the Normal distribution (Figure 3) the mean is μ and standard deviation, σ. For the distribution in Figure 4 the mean can be shown to be λ and the standard deviation, λ.

A probability distribution can be regarded as a mathematical model of a system showing random variability. It is a convenient foundation on which further argument may be developed, but precisely because the variation is random, data from the system hardly ever fit the model exactly. This inability of the data (certainly with small samples) to provide conclusive corroboration of the assumed model heightens the importance of being able to justify the underlying assumptions. This can be attempted at two levels. At a general level, rejection of the notions of population and distribution leads directly to the attitude that experimental results are special to the particular occasion on which they were obtained and all inferences from the particular to the general are impossible. This would be to deny the purpose of obtaining the results in the first place. For example, there would be no point in counting the bacteria in a 2 ml sample of water from the sewage works if the count could give no information at all about the bacterial density in water other than the 2 ml sample.

At the level of the particular application, the choice of distributional form must be justified afresh each time. There will of course be occasions when it is obvious, but both the choice and the strength of reasoning to support it can vary from situation to situation. For example, on the evidence of the data alone in Figure 1, there is scant justification for choosing the Normal distribution, though in cases like this it is often possible to draw upon previous evidence of Normality. A more practical point is that the Normal curve is very well understood mathematically and in the absence of better suggestions it is a good one to opt for. The Normal curve is in fact one of the most useful and widely used distributions because many situations yield data values which are nearly Normal for practical purposes. The immense convenience of the Normality assumption should not, however, be interpreted as a licence for its indiscriminate acceptance.

For the data in Figure 2 the case is less in doubt. Provided the micro-organisms are small and independent, the choice of the Poisson distribution can be given a theoretical justification.

3.2.4 Systematic errors

So far the discussion has concentrated on random or haphazard errors. Measurements may, however, also be subject to systematic error, or bias as it is often known. Systematic error will be described here using the example in Figure 1.

In the discussion of population and distribution, μ was introduced as the conceptual mean of the population of experimental observations. Suppose now it is revealed that the synthetic solution used for the trial had been carefully made up to a magnesium concentration of 5 mg/l. It would appear from the results that μ is less than 5. This cannot be stated unequivocally because it is suggested only by sample data. If however the true μ was less than 5, the distribution would no longer be centred about the hoped-for value and the new method of magnesium determination is said to show a systematic error. In this case, the systematic error would be synonymous with what chemists call incomplete recovery.

The recovery of the method would not be improved just by doing more analyses. This would, however, improve the precision of estimation of μ. This illustrates the crucial difference between random and systematic errors. In the long run the former tend to balance each other out; the latter maintain a constant influence.

3.2.5 Estimation

Very often the purpose of making measurements on a sample of water is to infer properties of the body of water from which the sample was drawn. In statistical terms, the experimental results have to be used to estimate the values of parameters describing the probability distribution of the underlying population.

Consider again the examples in Figures 1 and 2. Assuming in each case that the sample values have arisen from a probability distribution of a specified family but of unknown parameter values, the next step is to use the data to try to estimate what the values of the parameters are. It so happens in the first example that the sample mean and standard deviation, $\bar{x}$ and s, provide estimates of the population mean and standard deviation, μ and σ, which themselves define the Normally distributed population. It is also the case that the mean in the second example supplies the best estimate of the Poisson parameter. Common sense suggests that this should be so, and much of basic statistical methodology is indeed essentially common sense in a mathematical framework. It should be noted that the estimation of population parameters from sample statistics is not always so trivial as illustrated here.

Having estimated the parameters, the population (as it is believed to be) is now completely described, and so probabilistic statements can be made about it. For example it can be derived for the magnesium determination experiment that the chances of seeing an individual result lower than 2.5 mg/l are 0.011, or about 1 in 90. It is interesting to note that such a statement could not have been made from these data without the construction of a probability distribution. The sample itself contained no results below 2.91 mg/l. This kind of information which can now be gained has been bought at the price of the assumptions which were made about the distributional form and—the biggest assumption of all—that the population is a good enough model of the system which operates in the real laboratory.

3.2.6 Interval estimates

Estimation, as so far described, has been concerned with making a single 'best guess' about each unknown parameter. This is called a point estimate. A point estimate of a parameter will rarely be exactly right and so it is more informative to have in addition to this estimate a measure of the range within which the parameter is believed to lie. For example, an assertion that the magnesium concentration is likely to lie in the range 4.27 to 4.87 mg/l clearly provides much more information than does the single point estimate of 4.57 mg/1. A range such as this is called an interval estimate.

The most widely used method of interval estimation is that of confidence limits, and in order to explain this concept it is convenient to return to the example given in Figure 2. The population model adopted there enables formulae to be derived for any chosen probability α (say 99%), by which an interval (a, b) can be calculated from the sample data so that the interval is likely to include the true value of λ at the probability level α. As the numerical values of the data will vary from sample to sample, so too will a and b. The formulae are designed to have the property that the interval they produce will contain λ on a proportion α of occasions, in the long run. A numerical illustration will clarify this:

α	a	b
0.95	1.22	2.43
0.99	1.08	2.67

The interval (1.22, 2.43) is called the 95% confidence interval for λ, and (1.08, 2.67) the 99% confidence interval. The end points are often referred to as confidence limits. The confidence level may be set at any value, but it is obvious that the greater the desired confidence the wider will be the corresponding interval, as the example illustrates.

Great care must be taken in the interpretation of confidence statements. To quote the 95% confidence limits for λ as 1.22 and 2.43 means that one is 95% confident that λ lies in the interval from 1.22 to 2.43. This is equivalent to saying that the probability of the interval covering the true value of λ is 0.95. Expressed in another way, if a large number of samples were taken from the population and a confidence interval for λ calculated for each, then on average 95% of the intervals would contain λ. The confidence statement does **not** mean that the probability that λ lies in any particular interval is 0.95, although this may seem to be saying the same thing. This last statement is incorrect because λ is a parameter, and so for a given population it has a fixed value which is either inside the interval or outside it. It cannot be inside a given interval for 95% of the time.

All experimental measurements are subject to random error, and any result derived from these measurements, whether a mean or an estimate of variance, will therefore also contain an element of uncertainty. Only by using confidence intervals (or the related techniques of hypothesis testing) is it possible to quantify the doubt surrounding an estimate and hence make rational decisions in the face of uncertainty.

3.2.7 Testing hypotheses

The discussion of the data in Figure 1 in connection with systematic error raises another point. Is the difference between the sample mean of 4.57 mg/l and the nominal concentration of 5.00 mg/l for the synthetic solution attributable to the method of analysis not recovering all the magnesium (that is, having a μ less than 5.00), or is the difference attributable purely to the random variability of the determinations?

Statistics has a well developed set of techniques for dealing with questions such as this. Under the hypothesis that μ really was 5.00, what would be the probability of observing an $\bar{x}$ equal to 4.57 or less? Assuming the Normal probability model discussed in Section 3.2.3, this can be shown to be between 1 in 100 and 1 in 200. On the other hand, if the alternative explanation is that μ really is less than 5.00, the probability of observing $\bar{x}$ <4.57 is larger. How much larger this is depends on how small μ really is.

The striking difference between the chance of observing $\bar{x}$ <4.57 under the null hypothesis, as it is usually known, and the chance of observing it under the alternative leads to rejection of the null hypothesis at the 1% significance level. If the case was less clear-cut, and there was say a 1 in 10 chance of observing the data under the null hypothesis, it might well be decided that the hypothesis ought to stand. At precisely what level of probability a hypothesis should be accepted or rejected is a matter of judgement and context; traditionally, the rejection levels 5%, 1% and 0.1% are commonly used criteria of increasing significance.

3.2.8 Explanatory variables

The discussion so far has dwelt entirely on the case of a single variable (magnesium analysis, or micro-organism count) which is subject to random variation from sample to sample. In many statistical applications the situation is complicated by the presence of other measurable variables which influence the original variable being considered. These are known as explanatory variables. In a study of oxygen demand in a river, for example, suitable explanatory variables might be the time of day and the distance downstream from a fixed reference point. Oxygen demand will of course also be subject to random fluctuations in addition to the systematic influences of time and distance. Thus, the statistical problem is to identify the systematic effects in the presence of random variation. The fundamental task consists of estimating certain parameters and then testing various hypotheses about them.

3.2.9 The planning of experiments

The supporting nature of the role played by applied statistics in scientific investigations has already been stressed. Statistics simply provides the quantitative means of dealing with problems and ideas which are largely already embedded in scientific method in general. This is especially true in experimental design. Scientists embark on experiments seeking information about the effects of certain factors and if they plan an experiment (or series of experiments) with their objectives clearly in mind, the statistician will probably find their design basically satisfactory. Statistical considerations can help to extract the maximum quantity of information from a given amount of experimental effort; for example 3 replicates from each of 6 batches might give a more precise estimate of within-batch variability than would 2 replicates from each of 9 batches.

Suppose, for example single nitrate values are obtained at 3 depths at each of 4 sites in a lake. If the assumption can be made that the depth effect and the site effect (if they exist) operate independently, it is possible to test whether either effect is significant. But if it is felt that a depth/site interaction may exist, it is no longer possible to assess the depth and site effects unless repeat samples are taken at some of the depth/site locations.

3.3   Further reading

Among the 'paperback' statistics texts for the layman are the ones by Moroney (6) and Cormack (7). Both of these would be good for anyone seeking a fuller introduction than that given in Section 3.2. For specialist texts written for analysts see refs 5 and 8.

From the many works written for scientists, the respective motivations, ie the chemical industry and biology, in refs 1, 8 and 9, suit the two background disciplines involved in water examination. It is not however suggested that chemists should exclusively read the first two references and biologists the latter.

Experimental design has a succinct chapter in ref 7 but is not extensively treated in refs 8 and 9. The reader who wishes to pursue this topic further should turn to ref 10 which itself contains a short general bibliography on this topic.

The Association of Public Analysts has produced a protocol for Analytical Quality Assurance (AQA)(3). The following references contain useful information (4, 11).

For statistical planning for the optimum number of samples and general programming see ref 12.

4   Sampling

4.1   Introduction

The aim of this chapter is to discuss the factors of general significance in sampling. The emphasis is placed on principles because it is impossible to give definite practical advice that is suitable for all situations. Much of the discussion will also apply to short term and research programmes.

The basic aim of sampling is to collect samples (usually extremely small fractions) of water of interest, whose quality represents the quality of that water. To achieve that aim two aspects of sampling should be considered. Firstly, a set of samples must provide a true representation of the temporal and spatial variations of the quality of the water body for the duration of the measurement programme. To achieve this, the sampling location and the time and frequency of sampling must be considered. Secondly, all the determinands of interest in the sample must have the same values as the water body being sampled at the point and time of collection. Thus, it is important to consider the method of sample collection and transportation, storage and preservation of samples. *In-situ* measurements commonly ensure that the second criterion is met, but the choice of sampling positions and the times and frequencies of measurements remains just as important.

The requirements for sampling given above involve the logical, sequential consideration of several factors discussed in Sections 4.3 and 4.4. Figure 5 summarises the order in which it is recommended those factors be considered when designing sampling programmes. The figure gives initial priority to the need for the fullest possible definition of the objectives of the sampling programme. Thereafter, a logical sequence is followed, and this should be continually reviewed in the light of the sampling experience.

The prominence given to definition of objectives also implies the early involvement of statistical techniques in the design of the programme. This is necessary, not only to formulate confidence limits on mean results for example, but also to assist in the objective choice between sampling strategies.

Many other publications deal with the design of sampling programmes and some useful discussions are given in refs 4, and 13–20. In addition, the proceedings of two conferences contain many papers of interest (21, 22).

4.2 Safety aspects of sampling

It is not the purpose of this document to provide a comprehensive treatise on safety when sampling. A number of specialised publications deal with safety aspects, and these should be consulted. See, for example, the 'Warning to Users' at the start of this book. However, a few general points are given.

Those involved in sampling waters and effluents can encounter a wide range of conditions and be subject to a variety of safety and health risks, and efforts should be made to minimise these.

Sampling from potentially unsafe sites such as insecure river banks should be avoided. If unavoidable, the operation should be carried out by more than one person and appropriate safety precautions taken. Reasonable access to the sampling location in all weathers is important and is essential for routine sampling. If instruments or other equipment are installed on a river bank, locations subject to flooding or vandalism should be avoided; appropriate precautions should be taken where this cannot be achieved.

When samples are to be taken by wading into streams, rivers, ponds or estuaries, the sampler should take into account the possible presence of soft mud, quicksands, deep holes and swift currents. A wading rod or similar probing instrument is essential to safe wading.

Traffic can be a serious hazard when working from bridges, and when sampling from bridges over navigable streams. Care must also be taken not to cause injury to others below.

Many other situations arise during the sampling of water when precautions have to be taken to avoid accidents. Suitable safety equipment should always be used when working from boats or other vessels, and a watch should be kept on weather conditions. Care should be taken when using electrical equipment near water, and samplers should always be aware of the hazards of toxic or flammable materials, risks of infection from sewage-associated materials, and dangers from low oxygen levels, toxic vapours and gases, steam and hot discharges, etc.

Further discussion of the safety aspects of sampling can be found in refs 23 (natural waters), 24 (potable water treatment plant), 25 (sewage and industrial effluent treatment plant) and 26 (sewers and sewage treatment plant) and also in the later chapters of this book.

4.3 Sampling position

In choosing the exact position from which samples are required, two aspects are generally involved

i.   the location within the system

ii.   the exact position of the chosen location.

Some general principles relevant to these aspects are described in Sections 4.3.1 and 4.3.2.

4.3.1 Objectives

The objectives of the programme should usually be stated in such a way that the locations for sampling are at least approximately defined. If this is not so, the objectives should be reviewed before attempting to select any locations. Sometimes the objectives will precisely define sampling locations; for example, if it is required to measure the efficiency of a treatment plant, sampling locations before and after the plant would be chosen. Similarly if it was desired to determine the effect of an effluent discharge on a receiving stream, sampling locations upstream and downstream of the receiving discharge would be required. Often, however, the stated objectives will only give a general idea of the sampling locations, for example, quality measurement in an entire river basin or within the potable water distribution system of a large area.

It is important that the sampling locations are chosen so that the objectives of the programme are achieved. The nature and extent of spatial heterogeneity may vary with time, (for example, due to seasonal or biological effects) and can also differ markedly between systems of the same type. Thus, it is very difficult to give detailed advice on the choice of sampling locations, and the value of local knowledge and understanding of the system as well as investigations of its spatial heterogeneity cannot be over-emphasized. However, some general points worth considering are given in Sections 4.3.1.1 to 4.3.1.6. Figure 6 summarises the order of the points raised in those sections and Section 4.3.2.

It will sometimes be necessary to take samples from several locations in order to obtain the required information, for example, when the average quality through a heterogeneous system is of interest. Analytical effort may then be saved by combining the individual samples in appropriate proportions. Certain precautions must be taken when carrying out this operation (see Section 4.6).

4.3.1.1 Importance of spatial distribution of determinands

Problems arise in selecting suitable sampling locations whenever the determinands are not homogeneously distributed throughout the water of interest. There are two main causes of heterogeneous distribution of quality within water systems.

First, the system is composed of two or more waters of different composition which are (i) unmixed or (ii) in the course of mixing. Examples of (i) are the vertical, thermal stratification of lakes and reservoirs, and the stratification of salt water and freshwater in estuaries. Case (ii) is exemplified by a river downstream of an effluent or tributary and in industrial plant where one liquid stream is injected into another. The second type of heterogeneity is distinguished by the non-homogeneous distribution of certain determinands in an otherwise homogeneous water system. Again, two cases are possible. First, undissolved materials tend to be heterogeneously distributed if their densities differ from that of water. Thus, oil tends to float on water surfaces, while suspended solids tend to sink. The second case arises when chemical and/or biochemical reactions occur to different extents in different parts of the system of interest, for example, the dissolved oxygen downstream of an effluent of high biochemical oxygen demand, the growth of algae in the upper layers of water bodies with consequent changes in certain chemical determinands such as pH and silica.

A fuller discussion of incompletely mixed waters and inhomogeneously distributed determinands is given in ref. 4.

The objectives of the sampling programme may sometimes dictate a particular approach to the selection of sampling locations. For example, in sampling benthic organisms within rivers or reservoirs, it may be necessary to select the sites in a statistically random manner. The efficiency of such selection will be optimised by prior recourse to statistical advice and by recognition of the requirements of the statistical analyses to be performed.

4.3.1.2 Checking spatial distribution of determinands

When no detailed knowledge is available for a particular system, preliminary tests to assess the degree of non-homogeneity are useful. These investigations should be preceded by a careful reconnaissance of the system. Land or boat inspection could be used, and aerial inspection can be of great value for large areas such as river basins (27). Tests to assess the degree of heterogeneity commonly consist in collecting samples—preferably simultaneously to avoid complications from temporal variations—from a number of points throughout the system of interest. It is useful in such tests to measure dissolved oxygen, electrical conductivity, pH and temperature. Continuously analysing instruments also allow results to be obtained rapidly (28–30). Vertical net hauls allow at least horizontal variations of zooplankton to be simply studied. Review of inter-relations in such data, may allow simple field tests to serve as guides to sampling organisms which are difficult to sample, for example, free swimming invertebrates. Thus it would be unreasonable to set fish traps in anoxic zones of reservoirs.

The use of tracer techniques with dyes or radioactive materials is also of value when studying mixing processes in bodies of water (14, 31–38).

When planning such tests, it should be remembered that the degree of heterogeneity may depend on the determinand. A maximum amount of useful information is likely to be obtained if the preliminary investigations are planned statistically. Examples of this approach have been described for groundwater (39, 40), lakes (41), rivers (42) and estuaries (43).

Investigations of heterogeneity should preferably be made on several occasions to check if it varies with time. For example, lakes or reservoirs, though stratified in summer, usually de-stratify in autumn in temperate climates. Similarly, the degree of heterogeneity in a river cross section may depend on flow, and the rate of dispersion of an effluent into a river may vary with discharge and the temperature difference between the two waters. Climatic information (such as wind-speed and direction and solar radiation) may be useful in assessing any variations of heterogeneity with time.

The degree of heterogeneity may depend on direction. For example, lakes can be stratified vertically but be essentially homogeneous horizontally. The converse is also known.

4.3.1.3 Sampling near boundaries of water systems

In general, sampling locations near the boundaries of water systems are best avoided except when these regions are of direct interest. The quality at such locations is often not representative of the vast bulk of the water and there is also the possibility of sample contamination for example, by materials forming or deposited on the boundaries. The chemical and/or biological reactions causing the heterogeneity discussed above are often confined to boundaries of the system of interest. For example, samples should not usually be taken near the banks or bottoms of rivers or reservoirs and the walls of pipes, channels and process units. Disturbance of flow at such boundaries may well markedly influence such factors as deposition of particles or gas exchange, particularly if a free surface is also disturbed in this latter instance.

4.3.1.4 Need to consider rate of flow

For many purposes, it is necessary to know the rate of flow at the time of sampling. Thus, sampling locations should generally be chosen so that the corresponding discharges are known or can be estimated. Should such a location be a weir, for example, where it may not be desirable to sample because of the effects of re-aeration, then another site should be selected, preferably as close as possible so that the flow data are still relevant.

Sampling sites may have to be arranged so as to allow particular elements of water to be traced through a system. Hence, such locations must be chosen so as to take account of the residence time within the system under investigation. The number and/or distribution of such sampling sites will also be strongly influenced by the rate of processes taking place within the water element being monitored. Automatic sampling or *in-situ* monitoring may be of considerable assistance in such investigations.

4.3.1.5 Accessibility of sampling locations

Sampling locations should generally be chosen on the basis of their suitability for providing valid samples. Convenience of access should be a secondary consideration when the validity of samples is important. If an accessible location is known or suspected to give invalid samples, an alternative location should usually be sought. Given that valid samples may be obtained, it may be useful for instance, to be able to sample in the centre of a river from a bridge, or to choose a site with vehicle access if a number of bulky samples are to be transported or any on-site handling is to be undertaken. Bridge sampling may not, however, be desirable in biological investigations, for instance, due to the possibility of anomalous flow conditions and their effects on bottom deposits, or to the effect of shadows. Within distribution systems and treatment plants, the choice of sampling location may initially be restricted to the sites provided. However, if these are not satisfactory, alternative locations should be arranged.

4.3.1.6　Biological measurements

When sampling for properties associated with substrates, consideration must be given to the nature of the substrate, the manner in which organisms, for instance, are related to it, and the general relationship of substrate to the water body. For example, it would not be appropriate to sample for photosynthetic periphyton at depths that are inadequately illuminated. For substrates and/or organisms which are not easily sampled, artificial substrates may be substituted if the organisms of interest will colonise them. Such devices need to be located where they are relevant, retrievable and protected from damage whether elemental, accidental or deliberate. It should be noted that the organisms colonising artificial substrates and the relative species abundance of these organisms may be quite different from those present in the natural substratum at the same locality.

For invertebrate benthic sampling in relation to biological monitoring of water quality, the stations selected should have similar characteristics in terms of current velocity, depth and nature of substratum as all these are important in determining community structure in addition to water quality.

4.3.2　Sampling position at a given location

When the desired location has been selected, the position at that location from which to sample must also be decided on. For example, the location may be a bridge over a river downstream of an effluent discharge; the position(s) within the river cross-section at that location would then need to be chosen. Similarly, when the location is the centre of a reservoir, the sampling depth at that point needs to be chosen.

If there is any possibility of non-homogeneous distribution of the determinands of interest at the chosen location, experimental tests of the nature and magnitude of any heterogeneity should be made (44, 45). Factors affecting the degree of heterogeneity may vary with time, and it is desirable, therefore, to make the tests on several occasions. If such tests show that the determinands are distributed homogeneously, one position for sampling will suffice. Otherwise it is best to seek another location where the determinands are homogeneously distributed. For example, homogeneity may be produced by weirs in rivers and by certain components in treatment plants. If it is not possible to find a suitable sampling location, samples should be taken from sufficient positions at the chosen location to ensure valid results. A minimum of three positions may suffice for water flowing in pipes and channels, but more positions may be needed in more complicated systems such as large rivers and estuaries. For flowing systems, for example in rivers and pipes, the individual results may need to be weighted according to the velocity at each position.

When considering the spatial distribution of sampling positions, it is helpful to character-ise hydraulic conditions approximately as:

i.　homogeneous,

ii.　stratified,

iii.　plug-flow,

iv.　longitudinal mixing,

v.　lateral and longitudinal mixing,

vi.　patchiness, for example in the distribution of zooplankton.

The number of sampling positions needed to obtain the required information tends to be smallest for (i), and greatest for (vi).

Problems in selecting sampling positions can arise in many types of water systems, particularly those in which water is flowing in a channel or pipe. As an example, consider the lateral and vertical mixing of an effluent or tributary with the main river. Such mixing can be rather slow, particularly if the two waters being mixed differ appreciably in temperature. Thus, a uniform cross-sectional distribution of quality may be obtained only after a considerable distance (sometimes many kilometres) downstream of the confluence. If one sampling position is used at a non-homogeneous location, variations in results may well reflect different rates of mixing, rather than true variations in overall quality (see Figure 7). The choice of sampling position(s) for a given location on a river is, therefore, important. This is especially true if it is desired to avoid multi-point sampling, for example if a continuous water quality monitoring instrument is to be installed. Useful discussions of mixing in rivers will be found in refs 14, 46 and 47.

4.3.2.1   Accuracy of location

It is usually essential to locate the correct sampling site accurately and in such a way that it can be found again should it be necessary to re-sample the same site. Information on methods of doing this is contained in refs 8 and 48, and in Chapter 6.

4.3.3   Sampling from various types of water systems

Considerations relevant to the sampling position in various types of waters are dealt with in Chapters 6–13.

4.4   Time and frequency of sampling

4.4.1   Nature of the problem

When the quality of a water or effluent at one particular time is of interest, there is clearly no problem in deciding when to sample. Usually, however, routine sampling programmes are intended to allow assessment of quality over an extended time period during which the quality may vary. Thus, the times at which samples are collected need to be chosen so that the samples represent adequately the quality parameter of interest. In addition, the number of samples must usually be minimised to reduce sampling and/or analytical effort. The problem is, therefore, to select the number of samples and the times at which they are taken so that information of the required accuracy is obtained with minimum effort. The choice of sampling frequency seems often to be made on the basis either of a subjective guess or allowing for the amount of resources available for sampling and analysis. These approaches may result in too few or too many samples being taken. The aim of this section is to outline an objective approach that will give a reasonable estimate of the frequency of sampling needed to achieve the objectives of the programme.

A solution to the problem of choosing an appropriate sampling frequency can be to carry out continuous monitoring of the parameter of interest. This approach may present difficulties in summarising the large quantities of data which are collected. If information is obtained, but only partly used, the apparent advantages over laboratory analysis can be illusory. In effect, sampling takes place from the data rather than from the body of water. The approach of continuous monitoring is often not feasible because suitable instrumentation is not available or is too costly. At present, most water analysis involves discrete samples which are taken from the sampling point to a laboratory. Thus, consideration of the frequency and time of sampling is necessary.

Sampling programmes are required for many reasons, but two main purposes may be identified: 'quality characterisation' and 'quality control'. The first is intended for characterising quality during a given time period without any short-term action being taken to change the quality on the basis of the measurements. Monitoring of this type is established as part of long-term monitoring programmes which seek to assess compliance with quality standards. The alternative purpose 'quality control' is used here to indicate that analytical data will be used to decide when short-term corrective action is required to ensure satisfactory quality. Such programmes include control of water treatment processes. This categorisation of sampling programmes is suggested for simplicity; the purposes of the two types are not mutually exclusive. Quality characterisation and control are discussed in Sections 4.4.2 and 4.4.3, respectively. Figures 8 and 9 give sequential presentations of the factors to be considered when selecting time and frequency of sampling for quality characterisation and quality control sampling programmes, respectively.

Whatever the approach adopted for choosing sampling frequencies, data should be regularly reviewed to decide whether or not changes in the frequencies are necessary. There is often a tendency not to change frequencies once they have been chosen and this can result in inadequate sample numbers or needless work.

Temporal variations also occur in the compositions of sediments and in the natures and numbers of biological species living in or on sediments. Thus, the sampling frequencies for sediment examination are also important, and similar principles to those in Sections 4.4.2 and 4.4.3 apply. It should be noted that biological sampling is often carried out to obtain information on water quality over a period of time before sampling and not only at the time of sampling.

4.4.2 Quality characterisation

4.4.2.1 Need for statistical considerations

Figure 10 shows two hypothetical records of the true concentrations of a determinand over a period of time. The results which might have been obtained from a series of discrete samples are also shown. Figure 10a illustrates the case of random variation of concentration. Figure 10b represents the case where cyclic fluctuations are also present. If the purpose of monitoring is to determine the average value over a period of time, it is evident that results from the series of discrete samples provide only an estimate of the true mean. This estimate, like all estimated parameters, is subject to error. It can also be inferred from the figures that the errors associated with the estimates will tend to decrease as the number of samples increases and as the true variability of the determinand decreases. Thus, in choosing the times and frequency of sampling the aim should be to provide an estimate of the quantity of interest of adequate accuracy. For example, monitoring objectives might require an estimate of the annual average concentration of a determinand which is within 10% of the true value. The simple statistical approach described below is intended to assist in meeting such an objective. It is based on a more detailed account given by Montgomery and Hart (18). Note that if the objectives do not include the magnitude of the tolerable error, a statistically based choice of required sampling frequency is impossible.

To simplify this discussion, only the estimation of mean concentration is considered; the approach applies equally to other estimates, for example, the estimation of percentiles of frequency distributions (18). If the variations of quality were purely random, the times of sampling would be unimportant. It would then be necessary only to choose the number of samples required to give adequately small confidence limits on the mean result; this is considered in Section 4.4.2.3. Many determinands may also show trends or cyclic variations during the period of interest. Consequently, the times at which sampling is carried out must be considered in addition to the number of samples. This is discussed in Section 4.4.2.2. It will be seen that estimates of the magnitude of the variabilities of the determinands are a requirement for rational decisions.

4.4.2.2 Time of sampling

Regular cyclic variations of quality may affect water systems. Daily fluctuations are common, but cycles of shorter or longer periods may also occur. Examples are regular variations corresponding to the cycle of discharges from industrial processes and tidal variations in estuarine and marine waters. When cyclic variations are present, important bias may be introduced into estimates of quality unless sampling times are chosen carefully. The importance of cyclic variations depends on their persistence and on their amplitude in relation to the random variations of quality. If the cyclic variations are not persistent or if the amplitude is appreciably smaller than any random variations, it will usually be adequate to sample at regular intervals as indicated in Section 4.4.2.3.

The choice of sampling time is important when large cyclic variations are present. For example, if the quality throughout the whole of the cycle is of interest, the times of sample collection must be chosen so that different parts of the cycle are sampled with equal emphasis. Alternatively, if the greatest concentration is of interest, samples should be taken at the corresponding peak of each cycle. The way in which the effect of cyclic variation may be accounted for is discussed in Sections 4.4.2.3 to 4.4.2.5.

It may also be possible to reduce the amount of sampling and analysis by concentrating on particular times. This relies on the use of prior knowledge or acceptance of assumptions. For example, in determining the likely worst effect of a polluting discharge on the quality of a river, it may be adequate to sample only in late summer at a time of low river flow. In this case the assumption is that the effect will be most marked at the time noted. Such

23

knowledge of the behaviour of contaminants and water systems is crucial in avoiding collecting samples at inappropriate times.

The time of sampling may also be governed by hydrodynamic factors. For example, in studying self-purification processes in rivers, it is sometimes necessary to measure the quality of the same portion of water at different distances downstream of a discharge. In such a case it will be necessary to determine specific sampling times (and locations) in order to monitor the progress of the discharge.

4.4.2.3   No important daily or weekly fluctuations

In this case, the variations of quality to be considered are those due to random, annual cycles and trends. The best ability (consistent with not having to make unwarranted assumptions concerning the time and nature of any changes) to detect annual cycle and trend variations is obtained when the samples are collected at approximately equal intervals of time during the period of interest. The total number of samples required can be estimated as described in Section 4.4.2.6. For example, if it were decided that 12 samples were required in a year, they should be taken at approximately monthly intervals. It is also suggested that not less than six samples per cycle be collected when it is required to characterise the cycle (13, 18, 49). The period between successive samples should ideally not be an integral number of days or weeks (in case there are unsuspected daily or weekly cycles—see Figure 10b).

4.4.2.4   Important daily variations

The total number of samples and their spacing in time should be fixed as described in Section 4.4.2.3. Three approaches to eliminating the effect of daily variations can be adopted.

i.   The samples should be collected at different times of day, the times being chosen so that each portion of the day is represented approximately equally in the complete set of samples. The total number of samples during the entire period of interest should not be less than 6. For example, if it were decided that at least 20 samples were required in a year, a suitable scheme for sample collection would be to collect samples on 24 days spaced approximately uniformly in time. On four of those days, samples would be collected at 0100 hours, on another four days at 0500 hours, on another four days at 0900 hours, etc.

ii.   The second option involves bulking samples collected on a given day. In the above example, the approach would be to collect at least six samples on each of the 20 sampling days. The samples on any one day should be evenly spaced in time throughout the 24 hours. All the samples for a given day would be mixed in appropriate proportions (see Section 4.5) to give one composite sample for analysis. This approach may make use of automatic sampling devices. Certain precautions are essential to ensure that the composite sample truly represents the average quality of the water of interest (see Section 4.5) and it is important to ensure that the concentration of the determinand of interest is adequately stable between sampling and analysis.

iii.   The third approach involves knowledge of the nature of the daily fluctuations. Samples might be collected at only one time of day. The average result is corrected by a predetermined factor to allow for the bias caused by the diurnal cycle. This approach assumes that the within-day variation of quality is known and does not change. The approach is not generally recommended unless checks are carried out from time to time to ensure that the assumptions are valid.

4.4.2.5   Important weekly variations

The approach is the same as in Section 4.4.2.3 so far as the total number of samples and their spacing throughout the period of interest are concerned. Two main approaches to correcting for the effect of weekly variations are available.

First, the samples are collected on different days of the week. The days are chosen so that each day of the week is equally represented in the entire set of samples. On this basis, the total number of samples must be a multiple of seven. For example, if it were decided that the total number of samples required in a year was not less than 20, 21 samples should be taken at approximately fortnightly intervals, three being collected on Mondays, three on Tuesdays, three on Wednesdays, etc.

The second approach would be to form 20 composite samples; each composite would be obtained by mixing samples collected on each of seven successive days (see Section 4.5). This approach has the disadvantage that greater effort is required for sample collection and that the stability of determinands may be difficult to maintain over the sampling period.

If both daily and weekly variations are present, the situation can become complicated and a combination of the suggestions in Sections 4.4.2.4 and the above paragraphs may be required.

If long-term trends are being sought, it is advisable to take samples consistently at a standard time, such as for example, 0930 on Mondays or at high tide on Fridays.

4.4.2.6 Number of samples

If the variations of quality occurring during the period of interest are essentially random, independent and follow a normal distribution the p% confidence limits on the mean result, $\bar{x}$, from the analysis of N separate samples are given by $\bar{x} \pm L$, where:

$$L = \frac{ts}{\sqrt{N}} \tag{1}$$

and

t =   Student's t, a factor whose value depends on N and p and is given in statistical tables, and

s =   standard deviation of the results. This standard deviation includes the variability of the quality of the water and also the additional variability introduced by the sampling and analytical processes.

Thus, if the tolerable uncertainty in the mean is $\pm U$,

$$N \geqslant (ts/U)^2 \tag{2}$$

For example, suppose it was required to estimate the mean annual concentration of ammonia with 95% confidence limits not exceeding 0.2 mg N/l and that prior information indicated that s = 0.5 mg N/l. How many samples should be analysed in a year? Approximate values of N for different values of s/U at the 90, 95 and 99% confidence levels can be quickly obtained from Figure 11 which shows that in this example N is between 25 and 30 (that is, approximately 30 samples should be collected and analysed). The values of s and U vary, in general, from one determinand to another, and the calculation of N should, therefore, be made for each determinand.

It should not be thought that the above approach will allow exact prediction of a suitable sampling frequency. The calculated number of samples may prove to be impractically large, or too small, to provide credibility. The calculations are based on several assumptions that may not be completely valid. Nevertheless, the statistical approach provides an objective means of estimating a reasonable value for the sampling frequency and is much preferred to vague or subjective approaches. More sophisticated statistical procedures are available, but their practical value in establishing measurement programmes can be limited by their requirement for detailed information on the variability of quality. The assumptions of the above approach are discussed below.

i.   An adequately reliable estimate of s must be available; this is discussed in Section 4.4.2.7.

ii.   It is assumed that the random variations follow the Normal distribution. Many determinands do not follow this distribution, but the effects of such departures will not usually be large, provided $N \geqslant 6$. When the distribution followed by a determinand is known, at least approximately, suitable modifications to the calculations can be made. For example, Montgomery and Hart (18) give a method of estimating N when variations follow a log Normal distribution. Plotting results on probability paper is useful in judging the type of distribution. Radiological and some bacteriological measurements, whose results are expressed as counts, often follow other distributions, for example, the Poisson distribution (50). Under certain conditions, the Poisson distribution is well enough approximated by the Normal distribution, but it is recommended that statistical advice should be obtained for counted measurements.

iii.   It is also assumed that the results obtained on successive samples are independent. This may not be true because many determinands are subject to serial correlation, especially if changes in the determinand of interest are small or the interval between samples is short. The effect of this damping effect, for a given value of N, is to make the value of L larger than that indicated by Equation 1. Moody (51) has discussed this point. The effect may be partially countered by collecting rather more samples than is indicated by Equation 2.

iv.   When a value of N has been decided, the periods between successive samples must be chosen. Strictly, the application of equations 1 and 2 requires that the sampling times be selected at random throughout the period of interest, and some authors commend this approach (52). However, others (18, 51, 53) have concluded that systematic sampling (that is, uniform spacing of samples in time) may lead to better precision in estimating mean concentration. Systematic sampling is simpler, easier to organise, and has better ability to detect trends in quality; it is, therefore, generally recommended (see Sections 4.4.2.2 to 4.4.2.5). A good description of the principles of random sampling for water examination has been published (12).

Similar calculations to those above can be made for other statistics (18), for example, the median and other percentiles. The approach can also be extended to more complex situations, for example, where it is required to choose a sampling frequency capable of allowing a trend of stated size to be detected within a given period (18).

When past records of quality are available, it is also useful to complement the above approach by an empirical procedure in which the past data are divided into subsets, corresponding to smaller frequencies of sampling. For example, if weekly results for several years were available, it would be useful to examine the statistical properties of the results that would have been obtained each year if the sampling frequency had been fortnightly, or monthly. Comparison of the means corresponding to the different frequencies gives a direct measure of the effect of reducing the frequency. Of course, no information on the effect of greater frequencies can be obtained. This approach has been used by many authors; see, for example, refs 18, 49, 54 and 55. An example of such an examination is shown in Figure 12.

In any statistical consideration of sampling frequency, conclusions can be reached only on the basis of past results. The factors causing random variations in quality may change with time, and this would clearly affect the required frequency. Analytical data should therefore, be reviewed regularly to decide whether or not sampling frequencies need to be changed.

4.4.2.7   Estimation of nature and magnitude of quality variations

For random variations, the estimates of the standard deviation, s, should be obtained from past results spread over the same period of time as that of interest. For example, if the routine programme is to estimate annual mean concentrations, the weighted average of several values of s for different years should be calculated. Early estimates of s may not be applicable to the current situation, and the values of s for different years should be examined for any trends present. The accuracy of the estimated value of s will improve as the number of available results increases, but reasonably reliable values for s will be obtained from 10 or more results.

When no (or very few) past results are available, two main approaches are possible. First, past results from similar water systems to that of interest can be used to obtain a tentative estimate of s. Second, a preliminary experimental investigation of the system of interest can be made. Both approaches are likely to give estimates that need subsequent revision, and it is desirable, therefore, to start the routine programme at a frequency, say, twice as great as that calculated from the preliminary estimate of s.

To estimate the magnitudes of any daily or weekly cycles, detailed experimental tests are necessary. For daily cycles, at least six (preferably more) samples should be collected at approximately equal time intervals during each of several days and all samples analysed individually. The results will then reveal whether or not a persistent cyclic variation is present. The times of sunrise and sunset should especially be taken into consideration when dissolved oxygen is of interest (for example photosynthesis). Similarly, for weekly cycles, samples should be taken at the same time of day on each day of the week, the seven samples obtained being analysed individually, and the whole test repeated for several other weeks.

The magnitudes of cyclic effects may be governed by factors that vary with time. Thus, if cycles are not found initially, special tests are desirable from time to time to check whether or not cyclic variations have developed. A number of more advanced statistical techniques are available for analysing past data in order to detect cyclic variations of different periods. These techniques are usually referred to as various forms of time-series analysis, for example, harmonic and spectral analyses. The use of such techniques is a powerful means of investigating the nature of the variability of quality, though extensive past data are required. Refs 43 and 56–62 provide details for those wishing to pursue this topic.

4.4.3   Quality control

In quality control applications it is usually necessary to control the concentrations of one or more determinands within given limits. The sampling frequency should, therefore, be chosen so that there is a tolerably small chance of important deviations from the control limits occurring between successive measurements of quality. Two main factors need consideration in fixing this frequency:

i.   the magnitude and duration of deviations that can be tolerated from the control limits; and

ii.   the probabilities of occurrence of deviations from the control limits.

It will often be difficult to define these two factors exactly, but this should not discourage attempts to form reasonable estimates so that at least an approximate value for the required sampling frequency can be deduced. Without some estimates, a rational approach to defining a finite sampling frequency is impossible. The use of continuous monitoring is the ideal approach for quality control applications, but discrete sampling is usually adequate. Detailed recommendations for the sampling frequency in the special case of bacteriological examination of potable water have been made in refs 63–67. In addition, it is advisable to base frequencies for bacteriological sampling of potable waters on past quality data for the source and distribution system, and the likelihood of contamination. Additional guidance for other determinands and types of water is given in refs 13, 14, 63 and 64.

Definition of factor (i) above is a management decision and not an analytical question. The decision should always be made or there will be no firm basis for control. The control requirement may simply be that no deviation outside the control limits is tolerable. Alternatively, it may often be more realistic to require that the tolerable magnitude of deviations be related to their duration. Other requirements are also possible, for example, that the average concentration over a stated period should lie within defined limits. Whatever the control policy, it should be explicitly defined.

The extent to which factor (ii) above should be taken into account in choosing a sampling frequency, depends on the importance of detecting deviations, and the extent to which the variability of the quality in the past can be used as an indication of variability in the future. If the past is not considered a useful indicator of the future, there appears to be no choice but to make the interval between successive samples rather shorter than the shortest period for which unacceptable quality can be tolerated. However, it is much more common that the past can be regarded as a reasonable indication of, at least, the immediate future. On this basis, the following approach is useful.

Past results should be analysed to determine the average concentration of a determinand and the nature and magnitude of its variability. The graphical analysis of results using probability paper can be very useful for this purpose, and has been described in refs 18 and

68. It is desirable to include as many results as possible, provided that they relate to the conditions of interest; useful conclusions can be reached, however, with twenty and sometimes even fewer results. Three main cases may be revealed by this examination and these are illustrated in Figure 13 (parts a to c).

$$\text{Case 1: } A < L, \ s/(L-A) \lll 1 \ \text{(Figure 13a)}$$

where   A is the average of results,
         L is the control limit, and
         s is the standard deviation of results.

In this case, the average and variability are such that there is an extremely small probability of the value obtained for the determinand exceeding the control limit. A small sampling frequency will usually suffice so long as the conditions likely to affect the determinand remain constant.

$$\text{Case 2: } A < L, \ s/(L-A) \approx 1 \ \text{(Figure 13b), and}$$

$$\text{Case 3: } A \approx L, \ s/(L-A) \approx 1 \ \text{(Figure 13c)}$$

In both these cases, there is an appreciable probability that the control limit will be exceeded from time to time. Quantitative characterisation of the variability of the determinand concentration is then desirable so that the probabilities of deviations of different magnitudes and duration can be assessed. For this purpose, it is strongly recommended that statistical advice be obtained whenever possible because estimation of an appropriate sampling frequency is not simple. A useful approach for this problem has been described by Itskovitch (69) for the situation where the concentrations of an impurity follow the Normal distribution whose means and standard deviations are constant in time. The rate at which the quality in a water system can change may help in choosing a sampling frequency (13, 70).

In defining a quality control programme, the effects of any cyclic variations and abnormal conditions (see Sections 4.4.2.2. to 4.4.2.5) should also be considered.

Ward and Vanderholm (71) have described an interesting approach in choosing a sampling frequency for the detection of accidental pollution of a river system.

4.4.4   Duration of each sampling occasion

Variations of quality during the time taken to collect a sample cannot be detected. The sample is, in effect, a composite of quality over the collection period. This is not normally an issue in water quality monitoring because changes in quality are slow in relation to the duration of sampling.

4.4.5   Methods of reducing sampling frequency

Collection of the number of samples indicated by statistical analysis may be impractical. A means of reducing this number, whilst still satisfying the programme objectives, must be sought. The use of on-line monitoring or composite samples may considered (see Section 4.5). Otherwise, further consideration of the objectives of the programme will be needed to determine the most suitable modifications. One approach is to relax the tolerable uncertainty in a parameter of interest. This will decrease the required value of N in Equation 2 (Section 4.4.2.6).

Many authors suggest that reduction of the number of sampling locations is preferable to reducing the sampling frequency. This is on the basis that spatial variation is often smaller or better understood than variation in time. Statistical analysis of past data may show that a determinand is sufficiently well correlated with another that determinations of one may be used as a guide to both. For example in a given water type, electrical conductivity might be used as an indicator of, say, hardness or chloride concentration. The value of a preliminary investigation and/or a review of past data cannot be over-emphasised.

The overall objectives should always be considered when attempts are made to reduce sample numbers. Economies are often made at the expense of reliance on questionable assumptions or a decrease in the reliability of the conclusions. Too great a reduction in sampling frequency will result in such large uncertainties that the programme becomes incapable of meeting any useful objectives. In such cases, it is better to employ the available effort more fruitfully on other work. For a statistical treatment see ref. 12.

4.5 Discrete and composite samples

The preceding sections have been concerned with the collection of discrete samples. The number of samples is chosen to assess quality during the period of interest. The number required can be so large that analysis is too costly. This problem may be addressed by the use of composite samples. A single complete sample is formed by mixing portions of the individual samples in appropriate proportions (Refs 18, 23, 72). Analysis of this composite sample indicates the average (or a weighted average) quality during the sampling period. The key point about composite samples is that the saving in numbers of samples analysed is gained at the expense of loss of discrimination. A composite sample cannot provide information on variations of quality which occur during the time over which the composite is obtained.

Composite samples can also be formed by continuous or intermittent collection of samples in one container over a given period. This approach has the advantage that a separate bulking operation is not needed. It can make it possible to use a greater sampling frequency to allow for variations in flow.

Composite samples may also be used if it is required to obtain the average quality of a non-homogeneous water body. Individual samples are collected at appropriate positions and then mixed in proportions relative to the volumes of waters they represent. This approach is subject to the same principles as bulking with respect to time, as discussed below.

Certain precautions must be observed if composite samples are to give useful information. The more important precautions are listed below.

i.   The concentration of determinands in individual samples must not change appreciably between collection and bulking; concentrations in the composite sample must not change appreciably before analysis (see Section 4.9.2).

ii.   Composite samples should not generally be used when the concentrations of determinands may be changed by reactions occurring as a result of bulking. For example, dissolved oxygen, pH, free carbon dioxide, dissolved metals and bacterial counts may all be changed by such reactions.

iii. The proportions in which the individual sub-samples are mixed should be governed by the information required. If the average concentration is of interest, the volume of a sub-sample used should be proportional to the portion of the total sampling period represented by that sample. It is often necessary to estimate the mass flow of a determinand; in this instance, the volumes taken of individual samples should be proportional to the corresponding flows at the times of sub-sampling.

iv.   The uncertainty of the estimate of average quality from a composite sample will generally be worse than the estimate obtained by analysing each of the individual samples. Thus, suppose σ_s represents the standard deviation of variations in true quality, and σ_a is the standard deviation of analysis. The standard deviation of the mean result from the analysis of n samples is:

$$\sqrt{\frac{\sigma_s^2}{n} + \frac{\sigma_a^2}{n}}$$

The standard deviation of the result from one analysis of a composite from n samples (equal volumes of each sample) is:

$$\sqrt{\frac{\sigma_s^2}{n} + \sigma_a^2}$$

However, provided σ_a^2 is small compared with σ_s^2/n, bulking will not degrade precision to an important extent.

4.6 Volume of sample

The volume of sample collected is usually unimportant provided it satisfies the requirements of analysis. Sample volume is usually specified in the analytical method. However the following points are relevant to sample collection.

i.   Discrete particles (for example micro-organisms) present at low densities can require a minimum sample volume to account for statistical variations. For example, if the water of interest contained 10 particles/litre, samples of 100 ml would not all contain 1 particle. The relative variability of the number of the particles in the sample decreases with increasing sample volume. Similar considerations apply to the area of a sediment sampled for benthos (see Section 4.8).

ii. Some determinands can be lost from the sample by adsorption to the container walls. The best solution to this problem is to control it by using an adequate method of sample preservation. However, if none is available, the use of larger sample containers (with a lower surface area to volume ratio) might be considered as a means of reducing adsorption losses.

iii. Sample volume can be critical when the concentration of determinand in the water being sampled changes rapidly with time. For instance, this can happen when sampling tap water for the determination of lead. On first opening the tap, the lead concentration may be relatively high, but then can decrease rapidly. The concentration in a sample will thus depend on the volume taken.

iv. Large volumes of sample (between 1 and 50 litres) may be required for the determination of trace constituents. Two approaches to sampling may be adopted. The first involves merely scaling up the way in which smaller samples are collected. This usually involves use of tubing and pumps. In this case, special precautions, including the use of field blanks (Section 4.9.2.1) may be needed to ensure adequate cleanliness of the equipment used. The alternative approach is to obtain a composite sample. This involves passing a stream of sample (continuous or intermittent) through a system (for example, an adsorbing column) that removes the determinand from the sample. The determinand is then subsequently recovered and measured. This technique is commonly used for removing organic compounds from large volumes of water using a variety of adsorbents. Care is needed to estimate the efficiency of collection and subsequent recovery of the determinand. Special checks on analytical error are also recommended because interfering materials may also be concentrated.

4.7 Sample collection techniques

Many techniques for special samples are illustrated in the chapters which follow. Others are illustrated in specialist companion volumes such as refs 73 and 74.

4.7.1 Manual sampling techniques

The choice of a correct technique for collecting samples is most important, otherwise markedly non-representative samples may be obtained. Two main aspects are involved: the sampling system and its method of operation.

4.7.1.1 Sampling systems

For many applications concerned with natural waters, no special sampling system is required. It is often sufficient simply to immerse a container in the water of interest so that it fills with water which may then be poured into appropriate sample containers. Alternatively, the sample containers may sometimes be directly immersed in the water, though it may be advisable in many cases to avoid the sampling of surface films. This can be done by opening the sample container underwater. Care must be taken not to contaminate the sample when using the sample container like this. Plastic gloves should be worn if appropriate, and if the water is flowing, the sample should be taken upstream of the sampler's position, with the open neck of the sample container also facing into the direction of flow. If there is no flow, the sampler may be able to move forwards while taking a sample in front, but care would then need to be taken to avoid disturbing sediments, etc. Care must also be taken to ensure that neither the collecting containers nor the sample containers possess materials that may cause contamination of samples.

When it is required to sample from depths which prevent the use of such simple techniques, special containers are available for lowering into the water and obtaining a sealed sample from a chosen depth. Many such devices have been used, and a number are described in detail in references 23 and 75–82. A useful review of such equipment for bacteriological examination of waters is given in reference 82. Two main types of depth samplers can be distinguished.

The first consists essentially of a tube with tight fitting lids at both ends. The tube is lowered on a cable into the water with both lids open; when the desired depth has been reached, the lids are closed. To ensure that the sample retained in the tube represents as closely as possible the water of interest, it is desirable to use samplers with no impediment to the flow of water through the tube while it is being lowered through the water.

The second type consists of a sealed container filled with air (or another gas if desired) which is lowered on a cable to the required depth. The means of sealing is then released so that the container fills with water as the gas is displaced (see ref. 83, Figure 1). See also Chapter 6.

The sampling device should be robust so as to withstand rough handling, and, if used to sample at great depth, to withstand high pressures. If the sampling device is to be used for bacteriological samples, it should be capable of being sterilised and should be constructed of an inert material that does not exert a bacteriostatic or bactericidal effect.

When sampling from treatment plant and distribution systems and for certain applications for natural waters, a pipe or tube is inserted into the water of interest so that a stream of sample can be obtained. Such sampling systems have been described in detail (77, 84) and Mancy and Weber (85) have discussed certain aspects for industrial waste-waters. Sampling systems for natural waters such as rivers must be carefully selected and installed to avoid blockage of the inlet by debris. It is usually necessary to protect the inlet by surrounding it with both a coarse and a fine mesh, and frequent inspection and removal of accumulated debris may be required. Sampling systems in exposed locations, for example, river banks, may also need protection from vandalism and environmental effects such as temperature. When pumps are required to deliver a stream of sample, submersible rather than suction type pumps should be used when dissolved gases are of interest. Suction may also cause increased concentrations of suspended solids. Contamination from pump components may also be a problem when trace metals are of interest. For such applications, peristaltic pumps using plastic tubing can be very useful. The need for pumps can also cause problems of installation when water levels fluctuate appreciably, for example, as in some estuaries and rivers. Mounting the pump on a floating platform has often been used to counteract this difficulty. Problems and errors may be caused by the growth of bacteria and/or algae in the tubing from the pump. These and related problems have been discussed by many authors (see, for example, refs 77, 85 and 86).

4.7.1.2   Iso-kinetic sampling

The concentrations of determinands in the water entering the sampling system should be the same as those in the water being sampled. There is usually no problem in ensuring this, except when the determinands consist of undissolved materials with densities appreciably different from that of water. Such materials tend not to follow the streamlines of the water as it enters the sampling system, and their concentration may, therefore, be changed (87). To prevent this effect when sampling from a flowing stream of water, the rate of sampling should ideally be adjusted so that the velocity of water in the inlet of the sampling system is the same as that of the water being sampled, that is, iso-kinetic sampling. The importance of deviation from iso-kinetic sampling depends on several factors, but when undissolved materials are of interest, it is desirable to attempt to achieve approximately iso-kinetic sampling. For a similar reason, the inlet of the sampling system should face into the water flow when undissolved materials are of interest.

4.7.1.3   Effect of sampling system on concentrations of determinands

Ideally, the concentrations of determinands in the sample should not change in passage through the sampling system. However, the determinand may deposit within the sampling system, or may also undergo chemical and/or biological reactions. In addition, the determinand may be released into the sample stream either from material adsorbed on walls or from the materials of the sampling system itself. All these effects can be of great importance for sampling systems consisting either of a simple container or a flow system.

Certain general precautions are useful in minimising such effects, and in considering these aspects, it is emphasised that a sampling system suitable for certain determinands is not necessarily suitable for others. Each determinand should be considered individually.

It is useful to minimise the contact time between the sample and the sampling system. When sampling lines are used, they should, therefore, be kept as short as possible, and a high linear velocity of sample maintained through them (subject to the need for iso-kinetic sampling if required).

The materials used for sampling systems should be such that no important contamination of the sample occurs. Plastics are often suitable, particularly when trace amounts of metals are to be determined, though other applications may require metallic samplers, for example, for waters of high temperature and/or pressure or when small concentrations of organic compounds are to be measured. Stainless steel is often suitable for such requirements and glass, though fragile, can be technically useful. Whatever the sampling system, it should be checked experimentally that it causes neither important contamination of samples nor any other type of bias.

The sampling system should be kept adequately clean, particularly with regard to undissolved materials and biological films. Opaque sample lines will prevent algal growth, and regular flushing of the sampling system with a biocide can also be useful. Residual biocide should be well flushed from the system to avoid possible contamination. Simple design of sampling systems will help to ensure cleanliness; for example, smooth surfaces and the absence of flow disturbances are all likely to be advantageous.

4.7.1.4   Collection of samples

It is very important that the procedure to be used for collecting samples be carefully prescribed and followed. Contamination of the sample from the environment around the outlet of a sampling line can be of great importance when small concentrations of determinands are to be measured. The site should always be inspected so that possible sources of contamination can be eliminated and contamination from the hands of the sampler should also be considered. Particular care is often needed to prevent contamination of bottle caps or stoppers while the bottles are being filled. Detailed recommendations for sampling for bacteriological analyses are given in refs 67, 78 and 82, and for biological analyses in ref. 19.

When sampling from a boat or ship, consideration must be given to possible contamination from the hydrowire and from the ship or sampling platform.

Contamination may also arise from the exhaust gases and air stream from helicopters.

Before collecting a sample from a tap, valve or sampling line, it is desirable to allow the water to run to waste for a few minutes, except when there is special interest in the quality during the first draw. This reduces the possibility of contamination of the sample by materials that have been deposited in the sampling lines. The flow conditions during sample collection should be standardised and kept constant until the required volume has been obtained; opening taps and valves during the sampling period should be avoided.

Many authors recommend that sample containers be rinsed two or three times with sample before finally filling the container. This is a useful practice, but cannot always be adopted, for example when the sample must be collected into a container with a preserving reagent (see Section 5.4.3) or when the sample contains materials that may be adsorbed on the walls of the container, for example, suspended solids, metals, oils and greases. In such cases, the containers must be adequately clean and free of water when they are taken to the sampling locations.

Extreme weather conditions may cause problems. It is essential to ensure that any sampling devices and other equipment are working efficiently. Collection of samples for dissolved oxygen from ice-covered lakes must also be made with great care to prevent contamination of samples by air; sample bottles should also be completely filled and securely sealed so that oxygen is not lost from the sample as it warms up. Water from freshly melted ice should be avoided.

4.7.1.5   Sampling of seeps, drips and puddles

Sampling wall or rock face seeps and ceiling drips can be facilitated by the use of a spout, or wick, stuck to the surface and leading into a collecting bottle. Puddles can be sampled using syringes or scoops (depending on the volatility of substances present).

4.7.2   Automatic sampling techniques

Automatic samplers can be invaluable for many purposes, for example preparing composite samples, or studying variations in quality and obtaining samples at inaccessible locations. It is essential, however, to ensure that sample instability does not lead to errors as a result of the longer storage time of samples associated with automatic samplers. Preserving reagents may be added to the sample containers to ease this problem. Alternatively, the containers can be installed in a refrigerated compartment, when suitable preserving reagents are not generally feasible, for example, as with biochemical oxygen demand.

Care is essential to guard against blockage of intakes by algae or sediments especially if the sampler is left in position permanently.

Portions of the water of interest are collected at fixed time intervals, each portion being of the same volume. The portions may be collected as required into one container or separate containers. Such equipment usually provides a choice of factors such as the number of samples in a given period, the duration of that period, the time during which each sample is collected and the volume of each sample. These samplers are useful when concentration rather than mass of a determinand is of interest, or when variations in flow rate of the water being sampled are negligible.

When the mass of a determinand is of interest and flow rate varies appreciably, two approaches are possible. In the first, the automatic sampler is arranged to provide equal volume samples at a frequency directly proportional to flow-rate. In the second, the volume of sample collected at equal intervals of time is directly proportional to the flow. Both types may arrange for each portion of sample to be collected into one container or into separate containers.

Many different designs of sampler have been described, and two review papers (72 and 88) may be consulted for more details and information is also given in refs 25, 85 and 89–91.

4.8   Sampling sediments

Analysis of sediments is an important component in studies of water quality. In addition, the biological species living on or in the sediments are frequently of interest in characterising water quality. As with water bodies, sediments may not be homogeneous. Thus, the choice of sampling location and position may be critical. If the information required on sediments is to assist the study and control of water quality, the locations and positions of interest for that quality will usually define the points at which sediments are to be sampled. Checks on the distribution of determinands at different depths may also be required.

It may be necessary to fix the sampling position so that comparative samples may be taken at other times. For most rivers, lakes and reservoirs, sampling positions can be fixed by reference to features on banks. On uncovered estuaries and coastal shores, sampling positions may similarly be related to an easily recognisable static object. When sampling from boats in these situations, instrumental methods for position fixing should be considered (see Chapter 6 and refs 48 and 73).

Two main objectives may be identified. Firstly, the primary purpose is to obtain a representative sample of the biological population of the sediment. Secondly, a sample of the sediment itself is required. Which of these objectives applies will govern the type of sampling device to be used.

The aim of the present section is to indicate the types of sampling devices available, the considerations involved in selecting from among them, and to provide references to more comprehensive descriptions of such devices.

In shallow waters or when sediments are exposed, hand sampling may be adequate. In other circumstances, some specific form of sampling device will be required. As stated above, the precise purpose of sampling will affect the choice of device, and this is also affected by the nature of the bottom and sediment and the particular position on or in the sediment of interest. For example, a rocky bottom may prevent the use of certain types of dredge samplers, while the need to sample sediments in depth may dictate the use of a core sampler. Four main types of sampling device can be used and they are summarised below. More detailed descriptions are given in refs 19, 73, 78, 82, and 92–94.

4.8.1 Dredge samplers

These usually consist of a hollow vessel, open at one end and closed at the other. The vessel is lowered to the bottom on a cable and then dragged along with the open end leading, the material from the bottom being retained in the closed end. When the area of interest has been covered, the dredge is brought back to the surface for collection of the sample. A mixture of bottom sediments is collected over an area and at varying depths. It is possible that sediment particles will be washed out of the open dredge as it is brought up through the water. Dredges are best suited for collecting samples of coarse sediments, particularly gravels and shells. Strengthened dredges can be used to obtain samples of rock deposits.

4.8.2 Grab samplers

These consist of a vessel with a set of jaws that is lowered on a cable to the desired position on the bottom. The jaws are closed so that a sample of bottom material is taken and retained within the vessel which is then returned to the surface.

The majority of grabs are constructed to collect a fixed area of sea bed, typically 0.1 m². They are large and heavy, and consequently require proper handling and hauling facilities. Lowering is usually by wire held away from the side of the boat by a boom which allows the grab to drop vertically through the water. Boat movement due to wind and wave action and strong currents can cause problems.

Grabs are best suited to sampling coarse silts and fine gravels, but penetration into compacted sands is usually poor. Pebbles and shells can prevent the jaws from closing which results in loss of sample as the grab is returned to the surface.

4.8.3 Core samplers

These consist simply of a tube which is pushed into the sediment to the desired depth. On retraction of the sampler, a core of sediment is obtained in the tube, various arrangements being used to ensure that the core is retained as the sampler is brought back to the surface. Core samplers may be either free falling or powered. They are best suited to collecting samples of fine deposits. Once back on the surface, the core can be extruded and cut into suitable lengths for subsequent analysis.

4.8.4 Artificial substrate samplers

These samplers are used in the biological field and consist of a number of units (for example, a series of plates) on which organisms may grow. The samplers are placed on the bottom at the point of interest and can be retrieved for examination when desired, thus overcoming many of the problems encountered in direct sampling. Such samplers also have disadvantages, mainly that they differ from the natural environment. Their use has been recently reviewed and compared with other sampling techniques (19, 95).

4.9 Quality assurance in sampling

Attention to the quality and effectiveness of sampling procedures is essential if data of adequate accuracy are to be obtained. The key issues of quality assurance in sampling are outlined in this section.

4.9.1 Quality assurance measures

The approach to quality assurance in sampling involves the establishment of a suitable 'Quality System'. This term is used to describe an organised, documented and systematic approach to the task in hand (96, 97). A quality system for sampling will include the following.

i.   Establishment of the documentation needed for adequate definition of the task. This includes definition of clear aims and appropriate accuracy requirements.

ii.   Selection and documentation of appropriate methods of sampling. In ensuring the effectiveness of sampling, the greatest emphasis should be placed on the choice of procedures at the outset. Subsequent activity is then placed on a firm footing.

iii. Identification of the staff who are responsible for sampling and who are authorised to take samples. This must include a documented approach to training. Sampling sites must also be clearly identified.

iv.   Establishment of a system of audit and review of the sampling process. This will cover aspects of documentation and should extend to quality control procedures.

v.   Maintenance of a system of records to support sampling activity. This covers recording of information relating to individual samples as well as related activities such as the servicing of sampling equipment.

4.9.2 Quality control measures

The steps taken to measure and control sampling errors—quality control—have three main objectives:

i.   to provide a means of detecting important sampling errors and hence a way of rejecting invalid or misleading data;

ii.   to act as a demonstration that sampling errors have been controlled adequately; and

iii. to indicate the variability introduced by the process of taking a sample and thereby to give a guide to this component of measurement uncertainty.

The following quality control measures should be put into practice wherever possible.

4.9.2.1 Field blank samples

These are samples of deionised water (or other relevant, determinand-free matrix) which are taken to the sampling site and treated, as far as is possible, in the same way as real samples. A field blank sample should be put into the container used to collect the sample. It should then be transferred to one of the containers used to transport the sample. It should be subjected to the same preparatory steps as real samples (for example filtration, storage and preservation) and analysed in the same way. The exact procedure (which should be documented) to be followed will vary with the approach to sampling. The guiding principle is that the field blank should be exposed to as many of the sources of error which affect real samples. Field blanks are an invaluable check on sources of sample contamination.

4.9.2.2 Field check samples

These are devised as a check on the stability of samples. In some situations a check sample of known determinand concentration can be prepared. This is treated in the same way as a real sample—see the previous section. Such a sample may be prepared by dividing a real sample into two (at the sampling site) and making a known addition to one portion. The recovery of the known addition is a check on some sources of sample instability. It can be used to provide evidence that undue loss of determinand, perhaps by adsorption to containers or by decomposition, is adequately controlled.

4.9.2.3 Container checks

Before sampling containers are used routinely, extensive checks that they do not introduce important contamination are recommended.

4.9.2.4 Duplicate samples

Collection and analysis of duplicate samples provides a guide to the random error associated with sample collection and therefore a way of assessing the uncertainty associated with measurement.

Note that duplicate samples can provide information on two distinct types of variability. In the first case, duplicate samples may be taken from a homogeneous sample matrix. The difference between these duplicate samples is a measure of the variability introduced by the process of sampling itself, compounded by variability from the analytical procedure used to produce the data.

$$\sigma_d^2 = \sigma_{sa}^2 + \sigma_a^2$$

where σ_d is the standard deviation observed in the duplicate measurements, σ_{sa} is the standard deviation of sampling and σ_a is the standard deviation of analysis.

The second case is one in which collection of true duplicate samples is impossible or impractical. The collection of duplicate grab samples of sediment from the sea bed, or of identical samples from a fast changing stream of effluent, are examples of this. Repeated sampling produces samples which are subject to an additional source of variation (σ_m)— that which represents the true variation in quality of the matrix.

$$\sigma_d^2 = \sigma_m^2 + \sigma_{sa}^2 + \sigma_a^2$$

The variation or inhomogeneity of the matrix of interest is often the dominant source of random error. It is not the purpose of routine quality control to examine this source of error. Matrix inhomogeneity should be assessed at the sampling programme design stage, as a means of determining the numbers of samples which should be taken and their spatial distribution.

5 Sample containers, and sample storage and preservation

5.1 Introduction

It is important to take steps to ensure that the determinand concentration in a sample does not change significantly in the period between sample collection and analysis.

The aim of this chapter is to address the way in which samples are treated after collection. This includes selection of container type, conditions of sample storage and any preservation or pretreatment procedures. Table 1 summarises appropriate sample containers and storage conditions for a number of determinands. This information has been obtained principally from Working Groups of the Standing Committee of Analysts. Information from the scientific literature and relevant references are given.

5.2 Sample containers

5.2.1 Factors affecting choice of sample containers

Sample containers may have important effects on sample stability. Sample bottles and other sampling equipment can contaminate and/or deplete the sample of both organic and inorganic substances.

When selecting sample containers the following points should be considered.

i.   The material of the containers may cause contamination of samples, for example, sodium and silica can be leached from glass and organic substances can be leached from plastics.

ii.   Determinands may be adsorbed on the walls of containers, for example, trace metals by ion-exchange processes on glass surfaces and adsorption of organic substances by plastics.

iii.   Constituents of the sample may react with the container wall, for example, fluoride may react with glass.

iv.   Certain volatile determinands, for example radon and mercury, can diffuse through the walls of the bottles (98).

Polyethylene or glass bottles are most commonly used; both are often equally satisfactory. Other plastic materials (for example, polypropylene, PET, polycarbonate) may also meet requirements. The ability to seal the bottles tightly with stoppers or caps is important. Glass bottles have the advantages that the condition of their internal surface is more readily apparent and they can be cleaned vigorously, and can be sterilised by heating. The advantages of plastic bottles are that they tend to be cheaper and less fragile than glass. Biological activity in samples can be reduced in opaque sample bottles.

The effects of sample instability often become more important as the concentrations of determinands become smaller. When determining small concentrations of many determinands, the choice of appropriate sample containers becomes more important.

Similar considerations need to be given to bottle stoppers or caps, both to the material of the top itself and to any insert or liner. Polytetrafluoroethylene (PTFE) sleeves and inserts are sometimes used with stoppers and caps respectively. As an added precaution, bottles are sometimes transported inside closed bags or containers.

5.2.2   Contamination by sample containers

Discussions of contamination effects are available (99, 100). In controlling contamination effects, the following points should be noted.

i.   It is not necessarily only the major components of container materials that cause contamination. For example, it has been reported that iron, manganese, zinc and lead may be leached from glass, and lithium and copper from polyethylene.

ii.   The need to clean bottles before use should be assessed (101). Experimental tests should be made on bottles to determine whether contamination of samples occurs. Such tests can be made by placing high purity water in each of the bottles, storing them in the same way as samples and analysing the contents of each bottle at the beginning and end of an appropriate test period.

iii.   The nature and magnitude of contamination effects may depend on the manufacturer or batch of a particular type of container.

iv.   The extent of contamination may depend on the sample. It is desirable, therefore, to check the effects for different types of sample. For example, the pH of a weakly buffered water may be significantly affected by storage in a soft-glass bottle, while no important error would occur for a hard, well buffered water. Borosilicate glass bottles are preferable to soft glass because of their greater resistance to attack by aqueous solutions.

5.2.3   Adsorption of determinands by containers

Adsorption of determinands to container walls can be an important source of error. Trace metals are particularly susceptible, but other determinands, for example, detergents, pesticides, and phosphate (102), may also be affected. The degree of adsorption depends on many factors including the nature and concentration of impurities in the sample, the material and history of the container, and the temperature. The addition of preserving reagents can prevent adsorption. Studies of adsorption effects are given in refs 81, 103 and 104.

Where adsorption may be important, samples should be taken directly into the sample bottle without pre-rinsing. The whole sample must be analysed, and steps should be taken to recover adsorbed determinands from the container walls. For determinands such as oils, greases and pesticides, it may be impossible to prevent adsorption onto the surface of the sample container. Therefore, it is necessary to reserve sample containers solely for that particular determinand so that the adsorbed material can be removed from the container (for example, by solvent extraction) as part of the analytical procedure.

A summary of the properties of many materials used for trace analysis is given in refs 105 and 106. Further guidance on the selection of sample containers and their cleaning can be found in ISO 5667/2 and 5667/3 (101).

5.3   Sample transportation

The transportation of samples should be arranged with regard to their stability. Facilities for refrigeration or freezing of samples during transport may also be necessary. The use of mobile laboratories or on-site analysis for unstable determinands, (for example, bacteria, biochemical oxygen demand) should be considered.

5.4   Sample preservation and storage

Marked changes in the composition of samples, sometimes over a short period of time can occur if appropriate steps are not taken. The sample analysed may then be quite unrepresentative of the water body at the time of sampling. Examples of processes involved are given in Ref (101).

As well as being dependent on the chemical, physical and biological characteristics of the sample, the extent of such processes is also influenced by conditions of temperature, illumination and agitation under which the sample is handled.

The principal techniques which have been recommended for sample preservation are outlined in Table 1. Table 2 provides information on specific preservation techniques. Different categories of determinands and their respective preservation techniques are discussed briefly below.

5.4.1   Special cases

5.4.1.1   Nutrients

Storage-preservation tests show that for some determinands/matrices there are no reliable preservation techniques. Analysis as soon as possible after sampling is recommended. If this is not possible, freezing the sample in a polypropylene bottle (without any acidification) is one approach. Short term storage at 4°C may also be adequate.

The use of mercury(II) chloride and phenylmercury(II) acetate as preservatives is no longer recommended. This is primarily with the aim of reducing discharges of mercury to the environment. It is also important to decrease the likelihood that organomercury compounds might be produced.

5.4.1.2   Metals

When analysing for trace metals and organometallics other than mercury and its derivatives, the storage bottles should be made of low or medium density polyethylene or PTFE. Other plastic materials may also prove to be satisfactory.

To minimise adsorption losses during storage (except when speciation is to be determined), samples should be acidified to a pH of between 1.5 and 2.0 with high purity nitric or hydrochloric acid. Acidification should be carried out after filtration if only dissolved metals are of interest. Bottles should be stored in sealed plastic bags for low level (sub microgramme per litre) metal determinations.

5.4.1.3   Mercury

The storage and cleaning procedures given below refer to sampling for mercury determination at trace levels, for example in seawater or rain. Less elaborate approaches may be satisfactory if concentrations of greater than 1 µg/l are of interest.

For mercury, plastic bottles are unsuitable because they are permeable to mercury vapour. Borosilicate glass bottles with glass stoppers or screw caps containing PTFE inserts are therefore recommended.

The bottles can be cleaned by first soaking in 2% v/v detergent solution for 24 hours, thoroughly rinsing with ultrapure water, soaking for 24 hours in 10% v/v nitric acid (analytical reagent grade) and thoroughly rinsing with ultrapure water. Bottles should then be transferred to a fume cupboard and soaked in 2% v/v hydrochloric acid containing 1% m/v of a solution containing 1% potassium bromate and 0.28% potassium bromide; after 24 hours, the bottles are treated with 4 ml of a 20% m/v hydroxylammonium chloride solution to reduce residual bromine and again thoroughly rinsed with ultrapure water, then filled with 0.6% nitric acid and stored in plastic bags prior to use. The bottles should not be allowed to dry out. Bottles should be emptied before use. It is essential to keep the sample in an oxidised state. For samples high in organic matter, an oxidising mixture of 1% nitric acid/0.05% potassium dichromate may be used as a preservative (111–113). Alternatively, for clean waters of low mercury concentration acidification with 0.6% v/v nitric acid (114–116) or bromine chloride, prepared from potassium bromate-bromide and hydrochloric acid as described above may be preferred as preservative.

5.4.1.4 Silver

For silver, the main problems in its storage are the readiness with which it forms insoluble compounds, and its ease of adsorption on to a wide variety of surfaces. For these reasons, various precautions are taken. For full details see ref. 117.

5.4.1.5 Total suspended solids

If the concentration of total suspended solids is to be determined, separate suspended solids samples are often taken and filtered using pre-weighed filters. If this cannot be carried out, care should be taken that bulk samples are thoroughly mixed before subsamples are taken for suspended solids determinations.

5.4.1.6 Organotins

For organotin determinations, water samples should be stored in a cool room and extracted within 48 hours of collection. Extracts have been held at -20°C for several months with no measurable breakdown of tributyltin (TBT). TBT hydrides revert to TBT chlorides on storage. In the hydride derivatisation technique for organotin speciation, additional sodium borohydride must be added to those extracts which have previously been stored. Before use, all glassware should be soaked in 10% detergent for 8 hours, then rinsed with tap water and soaked for a further 8 hours in concentrated hydrochloric acid (analytical reagent grade). Finally, glassware should be rinsed in double distilled water and dried in an oven at 50°C. Prior to use, glassware is rinsed with redistilled dichloromethane.

Full details of these procedures may be found in Waldock et al. (118).

5.4.1.7 Volatiles

Sample containers should be filled completely without undue aeration, and containers which minimise losses of determinand by adsorption to, or diffusion through the container walls should be used.

5.4.1.8 Sediments

Samples should be stored in a manner appropriate to the determinand of interest. Samples for mercury analysis should be stored in all-glass wide-mouthed jars while samples for most other metals can be stored in plastic jars or bags. If organic compounds such as PCBs are to be determined, storage should be in pentane-washed wide-mouthed glass jars with a layer of aluminium foil isolating the sample jar from any waxed lid liner. All the above samples should be stored at -20°C.

5.4.1.9 Biological and microbiological determinands

The methods of sampling and sample preservation are so dependent on sample type, sample site, determinand and analytical method used that a detailed summary is not desirable. In some instances specific sampling booklets in this series will be available (119), in others the sampling information is contained in the method booklet itself (67). See also the general note on biological sampling in Chapter 13.

5.4.1.10 Hazards from sewage sludge

Samples of sewage sludge and of soil rich in sludge are liable to ferment. Sample bottles should not be tightly stoppered. If samples must be stored, they should be kept at 4°C in darkness. Alternatively, biological activity should be arrested by the use of an appropriate inhibitor. Chloroform will be suitable in most circumstances, added to a concentration of 5–10 mg/l, but it should not be used when compounds such as chlorinated hydrocarbons are also to be determined on the same sample. When handling a stored sample, gloves, face and eye protection and appropriate body protection should be worn. Flammable gases may be evolved and appropriate precautions should be taken to minimise risk of fire or explosion.

Sludge and soil may contain harmful organisms and scrupulous cleanliness is essential.

5.4.2 Special storage conditions

5.4.2.1 Refrigeration

The storage of samples (waters, sediments and sludges) in the dark at low temperatures (normally about 4°C) is a widely employed method of sample preservation. The sample should be refrigerated as soon as possible after collection. Refrigeration is recommended as a minimum precaution when the stability of determinands is unknown.

5.4.2.2 Freezing

Freezing of samples in polyethylene bottles and storage at temperatures of -20°C has been suggested for several determinands and different types of water. Analysis of the thawed sample must be commenced before any changes in composition can occur, and repeated freezing and thawing of the sample should be avoided. Freezing has been recommended for the storage of sea water (120) or fresh water (80, 121) samples for periods of up to several weeks for the determination of certain parameters. Other investigators (109, 122–127) have however reported different findings. Rupture of cells of biota on freezing is a disadvantage of this technique as it can lead to errors. Dissolved gases can also be lost.

The advantages of refrigeration and freezing as methods of sample preservation are that the introduction of additional reagents is avoided and disturbance of the original speciation of many substances is minimised.

5.4.3 Addition of preserving reagents

Satisfactory stability of many determinands can often be achieved by the addition of a chemical reagent to the sample immediately on collection, or by the addition of the reagent to the empty container before collection of the sample.

When preserving reagents are used, they may interfere with the analytical method. Thus, both the preserving reagent and the analytical method should be considered together and tests made to check their compatibility. The preservative may also affect the chemical or physical forms of materials. For example, acidification of samples can lead to dissolution of colloidal and particulate metals.

Concentrated solutions of preserving reagents should be used so that only small volumes need to be added to the sample. Corrections for the dilution of the sample by the preserving reagent will then be small or negligible.

Acidification of samples has been found satisfactory when trace metals are to be determined (54, 78–81, 114, 115, 128–133). The minimum acidity required for stability depends on the metal to be determined, but the addition of sufficient nitric or hydrochloric acid to give a concentration of 0.05 to 0.1 M in the sample is recommended widely.

Many papers have been published on comparison of preservations; useful discussions of this topic appear in refs 110, 123, and 134–143.

In addition to preservatives suitable for a number of determinands, special preserving reagents for specific determinands may often be necessary, for example, copper sulphate and phosphoric acid for phenolic compounds (78, 128, 132), sodium hydroxide for phenolic compounds (128) and cyanide (128, 129, 132), and zinc acetate for sulphide (128, 129). See also specific methods in this series.

This section has been primarily concerned with chemical analysis of samples, but it is stressed that many biological and bacteriological species may show rapid changes in number between sampling and analysis. It is, therefore, important to take all possible steps to ensure that examination of samples begins as soon as possible after collection. The detailed recommendations given in the methods for biological and bacteriological examination should be consulted together with the recommendations given in Report 71 (67) and ISO 5667/3 (101).

5.5 Filtration

In most water samples there is a gradation from true solution, through colloidal solution, to finely divided suspensions, to suspended solids and finally to sediments. Filtration provides an operational distinction between 'soluble' and 'insoluble' species. Limitations of this definition, together with discussions on criteria for an 'ideal' filtering medium are reported by Riley (144) and Grasshoff (145). Filters with pore sizes of 0.4, 0.45 and 1 μm are commonly used, while 0.1 μm filters are only used occasionally (80, 103, 146). Conventionally, filters of 0.4 or 0.45 μm pore size are employed in marine work. Analysts should report what size filter pore has been used. The effective cut-off in particle size for a filter of specified pore diameter changes with clogging of pores, which depends on the volume filtered and the particulate load. Cellulose-ester membrane and glass-fibre filters will, under many conditions, retain particles much smaller than specified by pore size (147).

The suitability of a variety of filtration equipment has been investigated by Brewers (148). These fall into 2 basic categories: (i) on-line, and (ii) off-line. In on-line systems, the unit is connected directly to the water sampler which is pressurised to drive the sample through the filter to the storage bottle. The obvious advantage of such systems is minimal sample handling. In many cases, off-line systems, in which the sample is manually transferred from the sampler, may be more convenient and can prove perfectly adequate provided sufficient care is taken to minimise contamination. Apparatus for on-site filtration has been described in refs 80, 103, 146. The suitability of filtration apparatus should always be demonstrated by a contemporaneous field blank.

It is recommended that filtration is carried out as soon after collection as possible, otherwise a redistribution between dissolved and particulate phases can occur (149).

5.5.1 Filtration for trace metals and other inorganic determinands

For metals other than mercury, the most commonly used filters are cellulose acetate/nitrate or polycarbonate (0.4 μm). Polycarbonate filters give good size discrimination and are less prone to adsorption losses by virtue of their lower surface area (150), but they cannot tolerate high solids loadings. For mercury determination, glass fibre filters (nominal pore size 0.7 μm) are preferred.

Filter unit design should be such that no metal parts come into contact with the sample, and ideally should be of all plastic construction. Commercially available polycarbonate pressure filtration systems, designed to filter 250 ml samples through 47 mm diameter membranes, are suitable. Filter units should be cleaned prior to use by soaking for 24 hours in 2% v/v detergent solution, thoroughly rinsing with ultrapure water, soaking for a further 24 hours in 10% v/v nitric acid and finally rinsing thoroughly with ultrapure water (80, 151, 152). Sealing rings in some units, can deteriorate on prolonged exposure to strong acid and these should therefore be removed and soaked overnight in 2% v/v nitric acid. After cleaning, units should be stored prior to use in clean plastic bags. For many applications, filters can be adequately cleaned in the filter unit by passage of a filter reservoir volume of 1% v/v hydrochloric acid followed by 2 volumes of ultrapure water. Alternatively, they may be acid soaked for a more prolonged period, thoroughly rinsed and stored in acid cleaned plastic petri dishes. In cases where the number of samples to be processed is limited, it may be convenient to prepare one unit, loaded with a cleaned filter, for each sample, thus greatly reducing the extent of field manipulation.

Filtration is normally carried out under pressure (5–10 psi). However, when this is impractical, vacuum filter units can be operated with a hand pump. If possible, it is advisable to first filter a portion of the sample, rinse the collection and/or storage vessel with it, and discard this portion, then filter a further portion for retention. If units are to be repeatedly used during a survey, thorough rinsing with deionised water between samples should be adequate, unless filters are to be acid cleaned in the unit.

5.5.2 Filtration for organic determinands

Glass fibre filters, with nominal pore sizes of 0.7 and 1.2 μm respectively, are usually selected in preference to 0.45 μm membrane filters for organic determinands. These offer comparatively rapid filtration rates and can be readily prepared to give low blanks (either by ignition at 425°C, or by solvent extraction).

Membrane filters (pore size 0.45 μm) constructed from cellulose yield adequately low blanks (after pentane extraction) for hydrocarbon determinations. Contamination from membrane filters prior to dissolved organic carbon determination has been reported (153–155).

It is essential that 'blank' extracts of the selected pre-cleaned filters are analysed to ensure negligible contamination in quantification of the determinands. All surfaces of the filtration apparatus which come into contact with the water samples should be inert and constructed of glass, stainless steel or PTFE. Other plastics should be avoided. A suitable system consists of a stainless steel pressure vessel to filter under nitrogen top pressure (0.3–3 bar) through a filter unit of stainless steel and PTFE construction (142-mm diameter). The apparatus should be thoroughly cleaned prior to use (detergent soaked, rinsed in distilled water, dried and solvent rinsed) and solvent (for example pentane) rinsed between sequential samples. Filtration systems should be used in 'clean' locations so that potential contamination (including atmospheric) is minimised.

Finally, a highly critical approach to the selection and use of sample containers and storage conditions is urged. Tests of the efficiency of the selected procedures should be made on samples when there is doubt about the stability of one or more determinands. Bottles should be tested for contamination and adsorption by re-analysis of pre-analysed typical samples which have stored in them for longer than the normal storage time. Cleaning procedures should also be evaluated for efficiency. Although it is often suggested that bottles be reserved for a particular determinand, care, especially in cleaning for re-use, is essential so that there is no carry over from a former high concentration sample to a subsequent low concentration sample.

5.6 Use of Tables 1 and 2

Consult Table 1 for each determinand of interest. This table lists suitable bottle types, summarises preservation and storage conditions and special points of interest.

Consult Table 2 which gives greater detail on some of the preservation techniques. This table also lists restrictions, and gives essential variations of the technique which may be applicable. This information serves as a cross check on the first table.

With few exceptions, the information in the first table is given for samples taken for single determinand analysis. However, most samples now taken are for multiple determinand analyses. For such samples, note the bottle types, preservation and special points given in Table 1 for each determinand of interest and note any incompatibilities which occur. Similarly with the detail in Table 2.

Table 1 Summary of preservation methods and sample containers, listed alphabetically by determinand

Determinand	Container Material	Preservation (if so indicated—for details see Table 2)	Special Points
	A—amber coloured or light proof glass.	Note the volume of preservative used per litre of sample so that correction can be made if necessary.	Always read this column before taking action.
	B—borosilicate glass.	Where the sampling procedure is elaborate, it may be summarised in this column to ensure a correct analysis.	Important requirements which need to be considered at the time of sampling are recorded in this column.
	S—determinand free soda glass.		If handling samples rich in sewage sludge, first read Section 5.4.1.10.
	P—polyethylene, polypropylene, polycarbonate, or polyethylene-terephthalate.		
	N—borosilicate glass must not be used.		
Absorbable organic halogens (AOX)	B	Fill bottles to leave no air space. Transport and store at 2–4°C. Analyse as soon as possible.	Do not freeze. If it is impossible to transport cold, do not allow the sample to warm above the temperature at which taken.
Acidity	B or P	Fill bottle to leave no air space. Transport and store at 2–4°C. Analyse as soon as possible.	Do not freeze. If it is impossible to transport cold, do not allow the sample to warm above the temperature at which taken.
Acrylates	B	Fill bottle to leave no air space. Transport and store at 2–4°C. Analyse as soon as possible.	Do not freeze. If it is impossible to transport cold, do not allow the sample to warm above the temperature at which taken. For accurate results the analysis should be started the same day.
Alkali metals	P	No particular preservation required.	
Alkalinity	B or P	Fill bottle to leave no air space. Transport and store at 2–4°C. Analyse as soon as possible. For sludge samples see also Section 5.4.1.10.	Do not freeze. If it is impossible to transport cold, do not allow the sample to warm above the temperature at which taken.
Algae	AB	See specific methods booklet for details.	

Determinand	Container Material	Preservation (if so indicated—for details see Table 2)	Special Points
Alpha activity—see Radiation			
Aluminium	P	Acidify—see Table 2 for details.	If distinction between soluble and insoluble is necessary, filter on site before acidification.
Americium—as for Radium			
Ammonia (total)	B or P	Acidify—see Table 2 for details. Store at 2–4°C.	Do not use nitric acid. See also free and combined ammonia.
			If amides, hexamethylene-tetramine and similar compounds are present which are readily hydrolysed to ammonia by acids, do not stabilise.
Ammonia (free)	B or P	Fill bottle to leave no air space. Transport and store at 2–4°C. Analyse as soon as possible. For sludge samples see also Section 5.4.1.10.	Analyse as quickly as possible. Storage must be minimal at 4°C in the dark.
Ammonia (combined)	B or P	Fill bottle to leave no air space. Transport and store at 2–4°C. Analyse as soon as possible. For sludge samples see also Section 5.4.1.10.	Do not freeze. If it is impossible to transport cold, do not allow the sample to warm above the temperature at which taken.
Anions by chromatography	P	Fill bottle to leave no air space. Transport and store at 2–4°C. Analyse as soon as possible. Record time of sampling.	Do not freeze. If it is impossible to transport cold, do not allow the sample to warm above the temperature at which taken. For accurate results analysis should be started the same day.
Arsenic	B or P	Acidify—see Table 2 for details.	
Antimony	B or P	Acidify—see Table 2 for details.	
Barium	P	Acidify—see Table 2 for details.	Do not use sulphuric or phosphoric acids.
Beryllium	P	Acidify—see Table 2 for details.	Do not use organic acids. Dust must not be inhaled.
Beta activity—see Radiation			

44

Determinand	Bottle	Preservation and storage	Special precautions
Biochemical oxygen demand	AB	Fill bottle to leave no air space. Transport and store at 2–4°C. Analyse as soon as possible. If rich in sludge see the precautions given in Section 5.4.1.10 but do not add preservatives such as chloroform.	Do not freeze. If it is impossible to transport cold, do not allow the sample to warm above the temperature at which taken. For accurate results analysis should be started the same day.
Biota	B	See specific methods booklets for details.	Do not freeze.
Boron	S or P, N	No particular preservation required.	
Bromide	B or P	Store at 2–4°C out of direct sunlight.	Do not freeze.
Cadmium	P	Acidify—see Table 2 for details.	
Calcium	P	Acidify—see Table 2 for details.	Do not use sulphuric or phosphoric acids.
Carbamates	B	Fill bottle to leave no air space. Transport and store at 2–4°C. Analyse as soon as possible. Record time of sampling.	Do not freeze. If it is impossible to transport cold, do not allow the sample to warm above the temperature at which taken. For accurate results analysis should be started the same day.
Carbonate, Bicarbonate	P	Fill bottle to leave no air space. Transport and store at 2–4°C. Analyse as soon as possible. For sludge samples see also Section 5.4.1.10.	Do not freeze. If it is impossible to transport cold, do not allow the sample to warm above the temperature at which taken.
Carbon tetrachloride	B	Fill bottle to leave no air space. Transport and store at 2–4°C. Analyse as soon as possible.	Do not freeze. If it is impossible to transport cold, do not allow the sample to warm above the temperature at which taken.
Carbon (total organic)	B	Fill bottle to leave no air space. Transport and store at 2–4°C. Analyse as soon as possible.	Do not freeze. If it is impossible to transport cold, do not allow the sample to warm above the temperature at which taken.
Carbon dioxide (free)	B	Fill bottle to leave no air space. Transport and store at 2–4°C. Analyse as soon as possible. For sludge samples see also Section 5.4.1.10.	Do not aerate while taking or shake when handling. If under pressure see Section 11.7.2 before sampling.
Cations by chromatography	P	Acidify—see Table 2 for details.	Avoid use of unsuitable acids (see Table 2).

Determinand	Container Material	Preservation (if so indicated—for details see Table 2)	Special Points
Chemical oxygen demand	B	Filter if necessary. If a test portion gives no effervescence, acidify to pH 1–2 with sulphuric acid. If there is effervescence do not acidify the sample itself. In either case store at 2–4°C in the dark. For sludge samples see Section 5.4.1.10, but do not add chloroform.	
Chloride	B or P	No particular preservation required.	
Chlorinated hydrocarbons	B	Fill bottle to leave no air space. Transport and store at 2–4°C. Analyse as soon as possible.	Do not freeze. If it is impossible to transport cold, do not allow the sample to warm above the temperature at which taken.
Chlorine (combined)	B	Fill bottle to leave no air space. Transport and store at within 2°C of the temperature at which taken. Analyse as soon as possible.	
Chlorine (free)	B	Fill bottle to leave no air space. Transport and store at within 2°C of the temperature at which taken. Analyse as soon as possible.	If any delay in analysis is likely, the time at which the sample is taken should be noted as deterioration can be rapid. Do not aerate while taking or shake when handling.
Chlorine (total organic)	B	Fill bottle to leave no air space. Transport and store at 2–4°C. Analyse as soon as possible.	Do not freeze. If it is impossible to transport cold, do not allow the sample to warm above the temperature at which taken.
Chlorine dioxide	B	Fill bottle to leave no air space. Transport and store at within 2°C of the temperature at which taken. Analyse as soon as possible.	
Chloroform	B	Fill bottle to leave no air space. Transport and store at 2–4°C. Analyse as soon as possible. If free chlorine is present add a crystal of sodium thiosulphate.	Do not freeze. If it is impossible to transport cold, do not allow the sample to warm above the temperature at which taken.
Chlorophyll	AB or AP	Store in the dark at 3–10°C.	If samples cannot be analysed at once, measure the volume, filter (<0.45μm) and freeze the plant material. Colourless filtrates may be discarded.

Determinand	Container	Preservation and storage	Notes
Chromium	P	Acidify—see Table 2 for details.	If speciation is required do not use hydrochloric acid or oxidising acids. If distinction between soluble and insoluble is necessary, filter on site prior to acidification.
Cobalt	P	Acidify—see Table 2 for details.	If distinction between soluble and insoluble is necessary, filter on site prior to acidification.
Colour	B or S	Store in a cool dark place.	If the sample is filtered, the filter used must not absorb colour while removing coloured particles. See the two booklets on this method.
Conductivity (electrical)	P	Fill bottle to leave no air space. Transport and store at 2–4°C. Analyse as soon as possible.	Do not freeze. If it is impossible to transport cold, do not allow the sample to warm above the temperature at which taken.
Copper	P	Acidify—see Table 2 for details.	If distinction between soluble and insoluble is necessary, filter on site prior to acidification.
Cyanide	B, S or P	Add NaOH to pH 12. Store in the dark at 2–4°C. If oxidising agents are present it may be useful to add ascorbic acid. Analyse as soon as possible. If speciation is important take a second sample without sodium hydroxide, ascorbic acid or any other pre-treatment.	Aerate the samples as little as possible during filling. Toxicity of liquid and vapour may be a hazard—take precautions.
Detergents—amphoteric, anionic, cationic, non-ionic	B, S or P	Fill bottle to leave no air space. Transport and store at 2–4°C. Analyse as soon as possible.	Do not freeze. If it is impossible to transport cold, do not allow the sample to warm above the temperature at which taken.
Disinfecting agents	B	Fill bottle to leave no air space. Transport and store at within 2°C of the temperature at which taken. Analyse as soon as possible.	If any delay in analysis is likely, the time at which the sample is taken should be noted as deterioration can be rapid. Do not aerate while taking or shake when handling.
Dissolved oxygen	AB	Fill bottle to leave no air space. Analyse on site or fix sample by adding manganese and alkaline iodide-azide reagents, then store in the dark at 10–20°C for not more than 24 hours. See also specific method booklet.	
Dithiocarbamates	B	Fill bottle to leave no air space. Transport and store at 2–4°C. Analyse as soon as possible. This is especially important if the sample is acidic.	Do not freeze. If it is impossible to transport cold, do not allow the sample to warm above the temperature at which taken.

Determinand	Container Material	Preservation (if so indicated—for details see Table 2)	Special Points
Electrical conductivity	P	Fill bottle to leave no air space. Transport and store at 2–4°C. Analyse as soon as possible.	Do not freeze. If it is impossible to transport cold, do not allow the sample to warm above the temperature at which taken.
Fluoride	B or P	No particular preservation required.	Do not use glass containers if acidic.
Formaldehyde	B	Fill bottle to leave no air space. Transport and store at 2–4°C. Analyse as soon as possible. Stopper tightly.	Do not freeze. If it is impossible to transport cold, do not allow the sample to warm above the temperature at which taken. Do not use plastic screw caps on bottles.
Free carbon dioxide—see Carbon dioxide (free)			
Gallium	P	Acidify—see Table 2 for details.	If distinction between soluble and insoluble is necessary, filter on site prior to acidification.
Gamma radiation—see Radiation			
Gases—hydrocarbon	B or S	Fill bottle to leave no air space. Transport and store at 2–4°C. Analyse as soon as possible. For sludge samples see also Section 5.4.1.10.	Do not freeze. If it is impossible to transport cold, do not allow the sample to warm above the temperature at which taken.
Germanium	P	Acidify, preferably with hydrochloric acid—see Table 2 for details.	If distinction between soluble and insoluble is necessary, filter on site prior to acidification.
Greases and oils	B or S	Fill bottle to leave no air space. Transport and store at 2–4°C. Analyse as soon as possible. Surface films and slicks can cause problems. For sludge samples see also Section 5.4.1.10.	Do not freeze. If it is impossible to transport cold, do not allow the sample to warm above the temperature at which taken.
Hafnium	P	Acidify—see Table 2 for details.	If distinction between soluble and insoluble is necessary, filter on site prior to acidification.
Hardness (total by EDTA)	P	Acidify—see Table 2 for details.	If temporary hardness is required, treat as for Alkalinity.

Determinand	Container	Preservation/Storage	Freezing
Herbicides	B	Fill bottle to leave no air space. Transport and store at 2–4°C. Analyse as soon as possible. Aerate as little as possible during sampling. A few acidic herbicides such as 2,4-D may be stabilised by acidification to below pH 2.	Do not freeze. If it is impossible to transport cold, do not allow the sample to warm above the temperature at which taken.
Hexamethylene-tetramine	AB or AS	Ensure that the sample is made alkaline to pH 8 or higher. Cool to 2–4°C. Keep in the dark and analyse as soon as possible.	Do not freeze. If it is impossible to transport cold, do not allow the sample to warm above the temperature at which taken.
Hydrocarbons	B or S	Aerate the sample as little as possible during filling. Fill bottle to leave no air space. Transport and store at 2–4°C. Analyse as soon as possible. Surface films and slicks can cause problems.	Do not freeze. If it is impossible to transport cold, do not allow the sample to warm above the temperature at which taken.
Hydrogen peroxide	B, S or P	Cool to 2–4°C. Do not agitate. Analyse as soon as possible.	Do not freeze. If it is impossible to transport cold, do not allow the sample to warm above the temperature at which taken.
Hydroxylamine and hydrazines	B or S	Fill bottle to leave no air space. Transport and store at 2–4°C. Analyse as soon as possible.	Do not freeze. If it is impossible to transport cold, do not allow the sample to warm above the temperature at which taken.
Iodate	B or S	Store at 2–4°C out of direct sunlight.	Reducing agent stabilisers such as ascorbic acid must not be used.
Iodine	B	Store at 2–4°C out of direct sunlight. Adding alkali to bring the pH above 11 can be useful.	
For Radioiodine see under that entry			
Iron	P	If distinction between soluble and insoluble is necessary, filter immediately. Acidify—see Table 2 for details. Store in a cool dark place (<10°C) and analyse as soon as possible.	Do not freeze. If it is impossible to transport cold, do not allow the sample to warm above the temperature at which taken. Do not use nitric acid, unless only total iron is required.
Kjeldahl nitrogen—see Nitrogen (Kjeldahl)			

Determinand	Container Material	Preservation (if so indicated—for details see Table 2)	Special Points
Lanthanides	P	Acidify—see Table 2 for details.	If distinction between soluble and insoluble is necessary, filter on site prior to acidification.
Lead	P	Acidify—see Table 2 for details.	If distinction between soluble and insoluble is necessary, filter on site prior to acidification.
Lithium	P	No special precautions required.	Check bottles before use.
Macro-invertebrates	B or S	See specific methods booklets for details. Store in the dark at 2–4°C.	If sample material is to be preserved add strong formaldehyde solution to give a concentration of about 1% (v/v).
Macrophytes	B or S	See specific methods booklets for details.	
Magnesium	P	Acidify—see Table 2 for details.	If distinction between soluble and insoluble is necessary, filter on site prior to acidification.
Manganese	P	If distinction between soluble and insoluble is necessary, filter immediately. Acidify—see Table 2 for details.	Do not freeze. If it is impossible to transport cold, do not allow the sample to warm above the temperature at which taken. Do not use nitric acid, unless only total manganese is required.
Mercury	B	Store in a cool dark place (<10°C) and analyse as soon as possible. Two procedures are in common use. Either acidify with nitric acid (d_{20} 1.42) to a pH of 1 ± 0.1 and add sufficient strong (40–50 g/l) potassium dichromate solution to maintain an excess of dichromate until analysis starts, or for filtered samples, dissolve 10 g potassium bromate and 2.8 g potassium bromide in 1 litre of water. Add 10 ml of this solution and 20 ml of 10 mol/l hydrochloric acid per litre of sample. For unfiltered samples add 20 ml of 4.5 mol/l sulphuric acid or 10 ml of nitric acid (d_{20} 1.42) per litre of sample.	

Determinand	Bottle	Preservation	Notes
Metals (total)	P	Acidify—see Table 2 for details.	Contamination of samples by metals such as zinc, leached from plastic bottles, is known. If in doubt check bottles by storing a stabilised blank sample and then analysing it. Discard unsuitable bottles.
Metals (total filtrable)	P	Filter the sample as soon as possible after collection. If this cannot be done immediately, store a known volume at $4 \pm 1°C$ in the dark. Every effort should be made to filter the sample within 12–15 hours, but the delay should be noted. Acidify the filtrate—see Table 2 for details.	For information on choice and use of filters and filtration equipment see Section 5.5. See also Metals (total), above.
Metals (by inductively coupled plasma spectrometry)	P	Acidify—see Table 2 for details.	If distinction between soluble and insoluble is necessary, filter on site prior to acidification. See also the two preceding entries.
Metals (by inductively coupled plasma mass spectrometry)	P	Acidify to below pH 2.5, or if algal or bacterial growth is likely, to below pH 1.5. Nitric acid is usually used, but if there is a risk of oxidation, sulphuric acid may be substituted. However, if there is a risk of precipitating insoluble sulphates, another alternative acid may be used. Hydrochloric, perchloric and other halogen containing acids must not be used as these form noble gas compounds (such as $ArOCl$) in the plasma).	If distinction between soluble and insoluble is necessary, filter on site prior to acidification. See also the entries for Metals (total) and Metals (filtrable) above.
Methanol	B	No special treatment required. Do not use nitric acid, nitrites or oxidants if other determinands are to be sought in the same sample.	Do not freeze. If it is impossible to transport cold, do not allow the sample to warm above the temperature at which taken. Do not use plastic screw caps on bottles.
Microbiological parameters	B, S or P	See the specific methods booklets for details.	Separate samples are taken for these determinands.
		Keep samples cool and in the dark. Analyse for viable populations as soon as possible.	It is most important not to allow the sample to freeze.
		Do not fill sample bottles completely, to allow mixing before analysis.	Great care must be taken not to contaminate the sample.
		When sampling for viable populations in waters which have been disinfected, neutralise any remaining disinfectant at the time of taking. Bottles may be pre-dosed with neutraliser before sterilisation, or sterile neutraliser may be added on site if more convenient. If neutraliser has been pre-dosed, do not rinse the bottle with the sample. For more details see ref. 67.	Sample bottles should be sterile. Plastic bottles are only suitable if they can be sterilised by autoclaving (e.g. polypropylene, polycarbonate) or can be obtained pre-sterilised by gamma irradiation or other process.

51

Determinand	Container Material	Preservation (if so indicated—for details see Table 2)	Special Points
Molybdenum		Samples for microscopic analysis only may be fixed with formaldehyde if this is compatible with the staining system used. If appropriate to the method, large volume samples may be pre-concentrated on site by suitable filtration, and the filter transported to the laboratory for analysis.	
Neptunium—as for Radium			
Nickel	P	Acidify—see Table 2 for details.	
Niobium	P	Acidify—see Table 2 for details.	
	P	Acidify—see Table 2 for details.	If a precipitate forms, filter and dissolve by alkali fusion.
Nitrogen (ammoniacal)	B or P	If amides, hexamethylene-tetramine and similar compounds are present which are readily hydrolysed to ammonia by acids, do not stabilise. Analyse as soon as possible with minimum storage at 2–4°C in the dark. Otherwise, if both free and combined ammoniacal nitrogen are required, fill the bottle to leave no air space. Store at within 2°C of the temperature at which taken. If only total ammoniacal nitrogen is required, add hydrochloric or sulphuric acid to give a pH of <2. Store at 2–4°C. Sewage and other samples likely to ferment should only be loosely stoppered to prevent bursting, and be stored in easily-cleaned metal boxes. Formaldehyde solution may be added to sterilise.	Do not freeze. If it is impossible to transport cold, do not allow the sample to warm above the temperature at which taken.
Nitrogen (hydroxylamine and hydrazines)—see Hydroxylamine and Hydrazines.			
Nitrogen (Kjeldahl)	B or P	Unless free ammonia is also required, acidify to below pH 2. Store at 2–4°C in the dark and analyse as soon as possible. For sludge samples see also Section 5.4.1.10.	Do not freeze. If it is impossible to transport cold, do not allow the sample to warm above the temperature at which taken.

Determinand	Bottle	Treatment and storage	Notes
Nitrogen (nitrate, nitrite)	B or P	Fill bottle to leave no air space. Transport and store at 2–4°C. Analyse as soon as possible. If storage is unavoidable add alkali to give a pH value of 12. For sewage samples see the advice given under Nitrogen (ammoniacal).	Do not freeze. If it is impossible to transport cold, do not allow the sample to warm above the temperature at which taken.
Nitrogen (organic)	B or P	Fill bottle to leave no air space. Transport and store at 2–4°C. Analyse as soon as possible. For sludge samples see also Section 5.4.1.10.	Do not freeze. If it is impossible to transport cold, do not allow the sample to warm above the temperature at which taken.
Nitrogen (oxidised, total)	B or P	See Nitrogen (nitrate, nitrite).	
Nitrogen (total)	B or S	Acidify with hydrochloric or sulphuric acid to below pH 2. Fill bottle to leave no air space. Transport and store at 2–4°C. For sludge samples see also Section 5.4.1.10.	Do not freeze. If it is impossible to transport cold, do not allow the sample to warm above the temperature at which taken.
Nitrogenous herbicides and pesticides	B, S or P	Fill bottle to leave no air space. Transport and store at 2–4°C. Analyse as soon as possible.	Do not freeze. If it is impossible to transport cold, do not allow the sample to warm above the temperature at which taken.
Nutrients—anions	B or P	Fill bottle to leave no air space. Transport and store at 2–4°C. Analyse as soon as possible.	Do not freeze. If it is impossible to transport cold, do not allow the sample to warm above the temperature at which taken.
Odour	AB or AS	Fill bottle to leave no air space. Transport and store at 2–4°C. Aerate the sample as little as possible.	Do not freeze. If it is impossible to transport cold, do not allow the sample to warm above the temperature at which taken. Note the water temperature at time of sampling, and record with the sample data.
Oils and Greases—see Greases and oils			
Organic carbon (total)—see Carbon (total organic)			
Organic chlorine (total)—see Chlorine (total organic)			
Organic compounds (not listed separately)	B or S	Fill bottle to leave no air space. Transport and store at 2–4°C. Analyse as soon as possible.	Do not freeze. If it is impossible to transport cold, do not allow the sample to warm above the temperature at which taken.

Determinand	Container Material	Preservation (if so indicated—for details see Table 2)	Special Points
Organochlorine pesticides	B	Either fill the bottle to leave no air space and store at 2–4°C in the dark, or add the extraction solvent used in the method, fill the bottle completely, noting the volume, stopper, shake well and store in a spark-proof refrigerator at 2–4°C. In either case analyse as soon as possible.	Do not freeze. If it is impossible to transport cold, do not allow the sample to warm above the temperature at which taken.
Organochlorine solvents (see also volatile substances)	B	Fill bottle to leave no air space. Transport and store at 2–4°C. Analyse as soon as possible.	Do not freeze. If it is impossible to transport cold, do not allow the sample to warm above the temperature at which taken.
Organometallics	B	For total metal determinations acidify to about pH 2 with acetic acid. If speciation is required freeze in a plastic bottle surrounded by a sealed plastic bag. In either case analyse as soon as possible.	If it is impossible to transport cold, do no allow the sample to warm above the temperature at which taken.
Organonitrogen pesticides	B, S or P	Fill bottle to leave no air space. Transport and store at 2–4°C. Analyse as soon as possible.	Do not freeze. If it is impossible to transport cold, do not allow the sample to warm above the temperature at which taken.
Organophosphorus pesticides	B	Either fill the bottle to leave no air space and store at 2–4°C in the dark, or add the extraction solvent used in the method, fill the bottle completely, noting the volume, stopper, shake well and store in a spark-proof refrigerator at 2–4°C. In either case analyse as soon as possible.	Do not freeze. If it is impossible to transport cold, do not allow the sample to warm above the temperature at which taken.
Organotin compounds	B or S	For total tin determinations acidify to about pH 2 with acetic acid. If speciation is required freeze in a plastic bottle surrounded by a sealed plastic bag. In either case analyse as soon as possible.	Contamination by tin contained in the glass is well known. Acid leach bottles before use, then evaluate by storing blank water in them which is subsequently analysed. Reject any bottles which are unacceptable. Precautions are necessary to prevent loss of sample should bottles burst when samples are frozen.

Oxygen demand (biochemical)—see Biochemical oxygen demand

54

Determinand		Preservation and storage
Oxygen demand (chemical)—see Chemical oxygen demand		
Oxygen Demand (total)	AB	Fill bottle to leave no air space. Transport and store at 2–4°C out of direct sunlight. Do not freeze. If it is impossible to transport cold, do not allow the sample to warm above the temperature at which taken.
Oxygen (dissolved)—see Dissolved oxygen		
Ozone	B	Keep at ambient temperature and analyse as soon as possible after sampling.
Permanganate index or value	B	Acidify to below pH 1.5 with sulphuric acid. If there is a reaction on acidification, re-sample and do not acidify. Store at 2–4°C in the dark.
Permethrins	B	Fill bottle to leave no air space. Transport and store at 2–4°C. Analyse as soon as possible. Do not freeze. If it is impossible to transport cold, do not allow the sample to warm above the temperature at which taken.
Pesticides (general)	B	Fill bottle to leave no air space. Transport and store at 2–4°C. Analyse as soon as possible. Do not freeze. If it is impossible to transport cold, do not allow the sample to warm above the temperature at which taken.
Pesticides (organochlorine)—see Organochlorine pesticides		
Pesticides (organonitrogen)—see Organonitrogen pesticides		
Pesticides (organophosphorus)—see Organophosphorus pesticides		
Phenols	AB, AS	Acidify to about pH 2 with sulphuric acid. Store at 2–4°C in the dark and analyse as soon as possible. Do not freeze. If it is impossible to transport cold, do not allow the sample to warm above the temperature at which taken.

55

Determinand	Container Material	Preservation (if so indicated—for details see Table 2)	Special Points
Phosphates, phosphonates and phosphorus (total)	P or B	If necessary, filter at once and treat as liquid and solid samples. If biota are present avoid rupturing cells as this will release determinand into the filtrate. Do not stabilise. Store at 2–4°C in the dark and analyse as soon as possible after sampling.	Phosphate is readily adsorbed onto plastic surfaces, so good quality borosilicate glass containers are to be preferred. They should first be conditioned by cleaning and standing overnight filled with sulphuric acid (d_{20} 1.84), then emptying and rinsing several times with water. Store filled with water in a cool dark place. With reasonable care this acid hardening treatment need only be repeated occasionally. Do not allow glassware to come into contact with detergents or alkaline liquids. The use of plastic containers in the higher concentration ranges may be acceptable. Some losses may occur, but they will be small in relation to the phosphate present. Low density polyethylene or nylon bottles are suitable, but high density polyethylene or polypropylene bottles are not. The plastic bottles may be treated with iodine to prevent the adsorption of phosphorus compounds. The procedure is described in ref. 156.
pH values	B or P	Do not aerate while sampling. Fill the bottle completely and transport without shaking. Keep at ambient temperature and analyse as soon as possible, preferably on site. For sludge samples see also Section 5.4.1.10.	Loss or pick-up of carbon dioxide can markedly affect the pH value.
Plankton	AB	See the specific methods booklets for details.	
Platinum	B or S	Acidify—see Table 2 for details.	
Plutonium—as for Radium			
Polycyclic aromatic hydrocarbons (PAH)	AB	Store at 2–4°C out of direct sunlight. Watch for surface films and suspended solids. Sample solids separately if present, as these often contain the determinands.	If the water has been disinfected, thiosulphate should be added to prevent additional formation of chlorinated PAH.
Potassium	P	No special conditions needed.	Can be found in sediments.

Determinand		Sampling and storage	Notes
Pyrethrins	B	Fill bottle to leave no air space. Transport and store at 2–4°C. Analyse as soon as possible.	Do not freeze. If it is impossible to transport cold, do not allow the sample to warm above the temperature at which taken.
Radiation (alpha)	P	If distinction between soluble and insoluble is necessary, filter through a 0.45 µm filter as soon as possible. If liquid, add 20 ± 1 ml of 50% (v/v) nitric acid (d_{20} 1.42) per litre of sample. Store at 2–4°C in the dark, and analyse as soon as possible.	Safety precautions and containment are dependent on the activity of the sample. Radioactive dust must no be inhaled or left on the body or clothing. Note the time and date when the sample was taken.
Radiation (beta)	P	If distinction between soluble and insoluble is necessary, filter through a 0.45 µm filter as soon as possible. If liquid, add 20 ± 1 ml of 50% (v/v) nitric acid (d_{20} 1.42) per litre of sample. Store at 2–4°C in the dark, and analyse as soon as possible.	Safety precautions and containment are dependent on the activity of the sample. Radioactive dust must not be inhaled or left on the body or clothing. Note the time and date when the sample was taken.
Radiation (gamma)	P	If suspended matter is present and a separate measurement of its activity is required, or the solids are not readily dissolved, filter the sample and treat as two separate samples. Alternatively, if it is possible to homogenise the sample, and only a total measurement is required, homogenise before any subdivision or analytical operation is made. If liquid, add quantitatively to the sample a known amount of carrier solution. Typical carrier solutions are listed in ref. 157. For samples containing metals, the solution is usually acidified to below pH 2. The acid used must not volatilise the elements of interest.	The maximum storage time before analysis depends on the half life of the radionuclides of interest, the shorter the half life, the sooner the analysis must be carried out. Safety precautions and containment are dependent on the activity of the sample. Radioactive dust must not be inhaled or left on the body or clothing. Note the time and date when the sample was taken. Special requirements are necessary for radon isotopes (see separate entry). Do not pre-concentrate unless the analysis specifically requires this.
Radioiodine	P	Adjust to pH 11.0 ± 0.1 with sodium hydroxide solution. Add 20.0 ± 0.1 mg of non-radioactive sodium iodide per litre of sample. Add 2–4 ml of commercial sodium hypochlorite solution per litre of sample.	Safety precautions and containment are dependent on the activity of the sample. Radioactive dust must not be inhaled or left on the body or clothing. Note the date and time when the sample was taken. Samples must not be acidic when the iodide is added. This is especially important if a joint sample is taken for alpha and beta activity measurement. If necessary take an extra sample.

Determinand	Container Material	Preservation (if so indicated—for details see Table 2)	Special Points
			If acidic, free iodine would be evolved and the activity lost to the atmosphere. Use of ammonia causes problems due to various aminohalogen compounds.
Radiostrontium—see Strontium			
Radium	B or P	If the sample is to be determined by radon ingrowth, proceed as for radon below. Otherwise acidify to below pH 2 with nitric acid.	Note the date and time when the sample was taken.
			Analyse within 2 months.
			Safety precautions and containment depend on the activity of the sample. Radioactive dust must not be inhaled or left on the body or clothing.
Radon	B	A borosilicate glass bottle is fitted with a stopper carrying inlet and exit tubes such that the stopper can be inserted leaving no ullage or void.	Note the date and time when the sample is taken. Also note the temperature of the sample.
		Fill bottles without bubbling or splashing. If possible fill and stopper under the surface of the liquid.	Analyse as soon as possible, and within 48 hours.
			Plastics can be porous to radon.
		Transport and store at a temperature slightly below that at which taken. Do not freeze.	Good housekeeping is essential. Periodically check storage area for any increase in background due to radon (or thoron or actinon) or aerosol leakage. If this occurs, find the cause, rectify and decontaminate.
		If solid matter is present it may contain occluded radon, but do not attempt to dissolve until the analysis has started and all simple dissolved radon has been outgassed.	
Salinity	B	Fill bottle to leave no air space. Transport and store at 2–4°C. Analyse as soon as possible.	Do not use soda glass bottles. Do not freeze. If it is impossible to transport cold, do not allow the sample to warm above the temperature at which taken.
Scandium	P	Acidify—see Table 2 for details.	If distinction between soluble and insoluble is necessary, filter on site prior to acidification.
Selenium	P	Acidify—see Table 2 for details.	If selenides are present, treat as for sulphide below.

Determinand	Container	Preservation and storage	Remarks
Silicates	P, N	Do not stabilise. Store at 2–4°C and analyse as soon as possible.	If the sample tends to precipitate or deposit a gel, either filter, or make alkaline to above pH 11, depending on the nature of the solid and its filterability.
Silver	AB	Preservation is highly dependent on the method of analysis used. If cyanogen iodide or similar reagent is added to the sample, no special preservative addition should be made. Otherwise, an addition of nitric acid to give a final concentration of 0.1–0.3 mol/l has been suggested. For specific details see ref. 117. Alternatively, add thiosulphate to a nearly neutral solution, and then add alkali to achieve a pH value of greater than 7.	
Sodium	P	No special storage conditions needed.	Can be found in sediments.
Solids (dissolved)	B or P	Filter to remove insoluble matter. No special conditions needed.	
Solids (settleable, suspended, total)	B, S or P	Add no preservative. Take a large enough sample to be representative. When emptying, do not leave material in the bottle. Sticky particles may need policing out of the bottle.	
Sparingly soluble salts	P	If possible, maintain at sampling temperature to avoid crystallisation. If this is impossible note the temperature and volume. Prior to analysis, redissolve any crystals which have formed, adding water if necessary. Note the new volume and correct the results back to the original volume (and temperature).	If re-solution proves too difficult, dilute the sample quantitatively to prevent further crystallisation, filter and treat as two samples.
Speciation studies	P	If necessary, filter at once and treat as liquid and solid samples. Unless there are special reasons, samples are not stabilised. Fill bottle to leave no air space. Transport and store at 2–4°C. Analyse as soon as possible. If the compounds likely to be present are known, see also the requisite entries in this table.	If the sample is filtered, the filter should not adsorb or decompose the sample.

Determinand	Container Material	Preservation (if so indicated—for details see Table 2)	Special Points
Strontium	P	If soluble and insoluble values are required, filter. Acidify with nitric acid. If radiostrontium is to be determined, add 50.0 ± 0.5 mg non-radioactive strontium per litre of sample as a carrier.	Do not use sulphuric or phosphoric acids. If radiostrontium is being determined safety precautions and containment are dependent on the activity of the sample. Radioactive dust must not be inhaled, or left on the body or clothing.
Sulphate	B or P	The preservation technique is highly sample dependent. For clean and potable waters no preservation is required, and samples are normally stable. For other waters, if sulphide, sulphite or other thioacids are present, fill the bottle to leave no air space. Transport and store at 2–4°C. Analyse as soon as possible. If there is risk of biological action (either reducing sulphate or oxidising other sulphur-containing anions), store in the dark and start analysis as soon as possible. If sulphate is the only thioacid present, but biological action is probable, hydrogen peroxide may be used to stabilise the sample. The same procedure may be used if total sulphur as sulphate is the determinand.	
Sulphide	B or P	Unless the sample is to be analysed by chromatography, fix at the sampling site by adding zinc acetate, then making alkaline with sodium hydroxide. Stabilisation cannot be used if analysis is by chromatography of ions. Acidic samples may be made faintly alkaline provided no metals are precipitated or anions decomposed or converted to another form. Analyse as quickly as possible with fume extraction. For complex mixtures of thioacids, do not stabilise, fill the sample bottle completely, store at 2–4°C in the dark. If biological activity is likely, analyse at once.	Hydrogen sulphide may be present. It is toxic and temporarily paralyses the sense of smell, causing people to confuse foul air for fresh. Under some circumstances the characteristic rotten egg smell is masked. Do not work alone. Rescuers should use self-contained breathing apparatus. Note that sulphide, like cyanides, can occur as part of complex ions, e.g. thiomolybdates and thiophosphates.
Sulphide and sulphur dioxide	B or P	Fill bottle to leave no air space. Transport and store at 2–4°C. Analyse as soon as possible. If biological action is possible, keep in the dark. If other determinands are not affected, a small amount of formaldehyde may be added. If the sample smells of sulphur dioxide, add sodium hydroxide to give a pH value above 8.	Free sulphur dioxide may be preserved in the same way—alkali should be added to give a pH value above 8.

Determinand	Container	Preservation and storage	Notes
Sulphur (other compounds)	B	Fill bottle to leave no air space. Transport and store at 2–4°C. Analyse as soon as possible.	
Sulphur (total)	B or P	As for sulphate, adding hydrogen peroxide if necessary.	
Surfactants—see Detergents			
Tantalum	P	Acidify—see Table 2 for details.	If a precipitate forms, filter and dissolve by alkali fusion.
Taste	AB or AS	Fill bottle to leave no air space. Transport and store at 2–4°C. Analyse as soon as possible.	Do not freeze. If it is impossible to transport cold, do not allow the sample to warm above the temperature at which taken. Record the water temperature at the time of sampling.
Tellurium	P	Acidify—see Table 2 for details.	If tellurides are present, treat as sulphide.
Tetrachloroethylene	B	Fill bottle to leave no air space. Transport and store at 2–4°C. Analyse as soon as possible.	Do not freeze.
Thallium	P	Acidify—see Table 2 for details.	Do not use hydrochloric acid. Thallium (I) halides are insoluble in water. Some three valent compounds, including the chloride, are volatile in steam.
Thiosulphate	B or S	Aerate the sample as little as possible during sampling. Adjust the pH value to between 7 and 8. Store at 2–4°C out of bright sunlight. If the concentration is high, a drop of chloroform is sometimes added as a stabiliser.	
Thiuram disulphides	B	Fill bottle to leave no air space. Transport and store at 2–4°C. Analyse as soon as possible. If the sample is acid, take care not to aerate when filling the bottle.	Do not freeze. If it is impossible to transport cold, do not allow the sample to warm above the temperature at which taken.
Tin	B	For total tin, acidify—see Table 2 for details. For organotin, see separate entry.	Concentrated nitric acid can oxidise two valent tin, and may sometimes precipitate tin (IV) oxide.
Titanium	P	Acidify—see Table 2 for details.	If precipitate forms, filter and dissolve by alkali fusion.
Total organic carbon—see Organic carbon (total)			
Total oxygen demand—see Oxygen demand (total)			

Determinand	Container Material	Preservation (if so indicated—for details see Table 2)	Special Points
Trichloroethylene	B	Fill bottle to leave no air space. Transport and store at 2–4°C. Analyse as soon as possible.	Do not freeze.
Trihalomethanes	B	Fill bottle to leave no air space. Transport and store at 2–4°C. Analyse as soon as possible.	Do not freeze.
Tritium	B	Avoid tritium contamination from local surroundings. No special preservation treatment is required.	Note the date and time of sampling. Analyse as soon as possible, and within one month. Some luminous items contain tritium.
Transuranic elements—see Radium			
Tungsten	P	Acidify—see Table 2 for details.	If a precipitate forms, filter and dissolve by alkali fusion.
Turbidity	B	Use no preservative. Store at 2–4°C. Analyse as soon as possible.	Do not freeze. If it is impossible to transport cold, do not allow the sample to warm above the temperature at which taken.
Uranium	P	Acidify—see Table 2 for details.	Dust must not be inhaled or left on body or clothing.
Ureas and phenylurea herbicides (urons)	B	Do not aerate when filling the bottle. Leave no air space. Transport and store at 2–4°C in the dark. Analyse as soon as possible.	Do not freeze. If it is impossible to transport cold, do not allow the sample to warm above the temperature at which taken.
Vanadium	P	Acidify—see Table 2 for details.	
Volatile substances	B	Do not aerate when filling the bottle. Leave no air space. Do not add a stabiliser. Transport and store at 2–4°C. Analyse as soon as possible.	Do not freeze. If it is impossible to transport cold, do not allow the sample to warm above the temperature at which taken.
Yttrium	P	Acidify—see Table 2 for details.	Do not freeze. If it is impossible to transport cold, do not allow the sample to warm above the temperature at which taken.
Zinc	P	Acidify—see Table 2 for details.	New sample bottles should be pre-tested before use by storage of a blank sample which is subsequently analysed.
Zirconium	P	Acidify—see Table 2 for details.	If a precipitate forms, filter and dissolve by alkali fusion.

Table 2 Information on three special techniques

Technique	Information	Restrictions
Acidification	Samples which are acidified are usually brought to a pH of less than 2 by addition of strong acid. The actual concentration of the acid used is dependent on safety. Thus concentrated sulphuric acid is almost never used, and concentrated (60%) nitric acid used only rarely. If algal growth is likely to be a problem, samples are brought to below pH 1. However, for some determinands there are more strict pH limitations. These are listed with the determinands in Table 1.	Samples for the determination of the following must not be acidified: amides, carbonates and bicarbonates, carbon dioxide, cyanides, herbicides (except some phenoxy organic acids), hexamethylene tetramine, nitrites, organic esters, phosphonates (if to be speciated), pesticides, soaps and surfactants (detergents), sulphides, sulphites, sulphur dioxide, selenides, tellurides, thiosulphates, samples where speciation is to be investigated, and samples for free ammonia.

Do not use hydrochloric acid for: antimony, bismuth, lead, mercury (I), silver and thallium (I).

Do not use sulphuric acid for: barium, calcium, lead, radium and strontium. Care is needed with silver.

Do not use nitric acid with some forms of tin, and metals liable to hydrolysis or oxidation.

Nitric acid is usually preferred for atomic absorption spectrometry, electrothermal atomisation atomic absorption spectrometry and emission methods as it has the least effect on flame intensity. Hydrochloric acid often has the greatest effect.

Perchloric acid can react violently with organic matter and reducing agents. Hydrofluoric acid reacts with glassware and should never be allowed to come in contact with skin. If it does, wash off immediately and seek medical attention. |
| Making alkaline | This is normally carried out by addition of sodium hydroxide solution. A pH of over 11 is often used, but lower pH is sometimes preferred. Other preservatives may be used in conjunction with alkali. See advice given with the determinand in Table 1. The most common anions when alkali is considered are: iodide (and radioiodine), nitrate and nitrite, simple cyanides, sulphide and occasionally sulphite. | Alkali cannot be used if most heavy metals are present in lower valence states. Consult a detailed chemical text if in doubt as there are some unusual exceptions, especially at pH 12. Anions also influence metal precipitation. Alkali cannot be used for nitrogenous and most organic compounds. It is not recommended if ions are to be separated by chromatography. It must not be used if alkali metals are to be determined, nor hydroxide, carbonate, bicarbonate and free carbon dioxide, and sulphur dioxide. |

63

Technique	Information	Restrictions
		Use of ammonia is not usually recommended even though it often has higher purity. It must not be used if iodine compounds or disinfecting agents are present. It forms insoluble compounds with some forms of mercury, and can form azides with silver.
Freezing	This should not be carried out in glass bottles. A sealed outer plastic bag is recommended in case plastic bottles rupture. Most solutions require homogenising after thawing, as many salts crystallise out on freezing.	This must not be used for any materials such as biota where the cell structure is to be kept intact. It must not be used for samples containing dissolved gases, volatile substances, or other materials liable to be lost from solution. It can affect the form of many polyanions, thus changing their reactivity.

6 Sampling marine and other saline and deep waters and related sediments

6.1 Introduction

6.1.1 Aim of this chapter

A number of alternative techniques for sampling in the marine environment have been developed. Whilst these may be sound from a scientific standpoint, they are not necessarily equivalent. The aim of this chapter is to provide advice and guidance on the establishment and operation of marine sampling programmes.

6.1.2 Topics considered

Many of the points discussed in earlier sections of this book apply to marine sampling. However, there are differences from sampling practice for other waters, due to salinity, tidal effects, mixing, etc. These need to be understood before embarking on a marine sampling programme. The difficulties experienced working in a marine or estuarine environment demand that precise objectives are established at the start of the programme. In common with all moving waters, especially those in which several different quality waters mix, and which are subject to evaporation and chemical changes, concentration patterns will arise which may change with time. For example, in poorly mixed estuaries where stratification can lead to differences between samples taken at varying depths, a single sample may yield misleading information. If it is desirable to have an adequate picture of water quality in a stretch of water, it is essential to have sufficient samples to allow for variations both across the water and with depth, and to know how this pattern may change with time. Given the low concentrations of many determinands in the marine environment, staff must be aware of the major problems caused by contamination.

6.1.3 Extension to other saline and aggressive waters

Waters of these types can be sampled using the strategy and techniques described in this supplement but even greater care and pre-planning than normal are required.

6.2 Strategies for sampling in estuaries and coastal waters

6.2.1 General

The strategy to be adopted for sampling estuarine and coastal waters depends on the purpose of the study. Typical objectives are listed in Table 3. A sampling strategy must be devised which will ensure that the objectives will be met. It is therefore advisable to consider a number of objectives, including future requirements, prior to the design of sampling programmes.

When planning, account must be taken of the fact that water moves in three dimensions and can vary widely in quality. Flow patterns are dependent not only on local shoreline and bottom configuration, but on currents and even distant storms. These patterns can vary with tide, season, weather and with changes in other conditions such as river flows.

Where spatial variations are to be studied, the main concern is the number and locations of the sampling stations. For studies of temporal variability, the timing and frequency of sampling is the primary consideration. The information summarised here is taken largely from accounts by Morris (158, 159) which should be consulted for more detailed background material.

Process-orientated studies often involve sequential measurements on a particular water body, which is tracked during its transit through the environment. Surveying and monitoring studies, on the other hand, usually involve measurements at fixed locations or at points determined by reference to a variable such as salinity.

In estuaries, the most obvious factor giving rise to variations at a given geographical location is the tidal movement of water and suspended material. However, variability also arises from other cyclic processes with a range of time scales, and from intermittent processes and long term changes. Variability on a scale shorter in time than that of the sampling will not be observed adequately, and the choice of the scales on which observations are made is thus a crucial factor in experimental design. Similarly, spatial intervals must be chosen so that features in distributions can be resolved adequately.

Wherever a quantitative conclusion is required, statistical considerations need to be incorporated at the survey design stage, to ensure that a demonstrable conclusion can be reached. Many variables influencing the final survey design are site specific. The extent to which some of them can be minimised will affect the number of samples required to meet the objectives. Therefore, for the planning of tidal water surveys to meet particular identified objectives, only general guidelines can be given.

For measurements at a specific geographical location, sampling under conditions of constant salinity can largely eliminate the variations due to tidal state and differences in river flow. This approach is complicated because:

i.   river inputs may change over the time period of interest so that the system is not at a steady state (though the detection of such changes may be the objective of the monitoring programme);

ii.   some dissolved constituents that show conservative, or at least quasi-conservative, behaviour under some conditions may behave non-conservatively under others. This applies particularly to constituents that are taken up by organisms at periods of high biological activity and there will often be a complex interaction between the intensity of such activity and the residence time in the estuary.

6.2.2   Sampling and spatial variability

Problems of spatial variability have to be considered for all measurement techniques. Continuous measurements may presently be made for only a few constituents by *in-situ* sensors or pumped shipboard continuous sampling systems. When continuous measurements can be made, the problems of spatial resolution arising with discrete sampling can be largely eliminated. It is still necessary, however, to consider the extent of spatial coverage that is necessary to attain the specified objectives with economy of effort.

The use of salinity distribution as a spatial reference frame gives a built-in compensation for the changes in the geographical location at which water of a particular salinity is found. Sampling points and depths will often be determined by reference to this distribution. Once the salinity distribution and its temporal variability are established, it may be convenient to adopt geographically fixed sampling points and depths. For some studies, particular geographical locations may be of specific interest in relation to the objectives of the study. The spatial intervals, whether measured as actual distances or as salinity differences, should be dependent on the distribution of the parameter of interest and the degree of resolution required.

A frequent requirement in estuaries is for longitudinal sampling of surface or near-surface waters. Sampling at unit intervals of salinity will often give adequate spatial resolution. For larger estuaries, attention to lateral variability may be necessary. This may also be the case for smaller estuaries as a result of specific features such as tributaries or waste inputs. Typical estuarine mixing patterns are shown in Figure 14. Most British estuaries are either well mixed or partially mixed. However, examination of variations with depth may be required in relation to bottom sources (for example, in dumping areas) and under conditions where the degree of stratification is sufficient to lead to the modification of bottom waters; this may be particularly important with respect to dissolved oxygen and constituents of biological importance. Obstructions to flow can result in different flow regimes along the various shores with a multiplication of concentration patterns. Reefs and bars can provide barriers to flow at depth and can drastically change vertical concentration profiles, especially in estuaries and straits. In coastal waters, very large differences exist between waters above and below the seasonal thermoclines that occur in many regions during the spring to autumn period.

In open and coastal waters, the constraints of a restricting shore line do not exist, though a nearby shore will affect the direction of water movement. Currents and tides can have a marked and complicated effect. Temperature and salinity differences can occur, both vertically and horizontally. Upwellings and very large eddies are well known even in the open ocean. The influence of large river inputs and of straits leading to large enclosed lagoons or seas can extend far out into open water.

6.2.3   Sampling and temporal variability

The processes that give rise to temporal variability in chemical and physical parameters in estuaries are summarised in Table 4. Many fluctuations in these parameters are cyclic, and in many cases, the amplitude and frequency of the cycles are predictable. Differentiation between a cyclic change, a longer-term trend, or an abrupt change, depends upon the timing and frequency of sampling relative to the cyclic period concerned. Further information is provided by Gunnarson (160) Wastler and Walter (161) and Ibanez (162).

6.2.4   Synoptic surveys

Spatial surveys should ideally be synoptic (ie the measurements should be made, or the samples collected, simultaneously at all locations) so that temporal variability does not prejudice the interpretation of the data. The effort required for a synoptic survey may be substantially reduced if fixed access points, such as bridges and jetties, are used. In practice, most surveys involve sequential sampling and should be carried out as rapidly as possible, ideally at a single tidal state. Where lengthy surveys are needed, the time should still be short relative to the replacement time for freshwater in the system; this may be a few days or less for estuaries of small to medium length. For parameters which change slowly, or for which a steady state assumption can be made, non-synoptic data can be adjusted to compensate for tidal variations, if these are significant. This adjustment involves calculating for each given sampling station, the position that the water body would have occupied at some reference state of the tide. As discussed by Head (163), these adjustments can often be made for coastal waters using published data on tidal streams, but for estuarine waters more complex calculations are necessary. The distribution obtained may not conform to the true synoptic distribution but gives a coherent picture suitable for purposes of comparison. Comparative pictures can also be obtained by sampling each location in the survey at the time of local high or low water.

6.3   Position fixing

6.3.1   General

The position fixing strategy adopted for any survey will depend upon numerous factors. Of primary importance will be:

i.   whether the survey is to be regularly undertaken or is a one-off investigation and with what precision the sample station must be located; and

ii.   the availability of suitable fixed marks, which may be influenced by the size or openness of the area to be sampled and their visibility from the sample station.

Other factors will include the type of boat and equipment made available.

The method of choice should be the simplest and most convenient which will provide adequate accuracy for the survey required. In an open area remote from any significant outfalls, position fixing to better than ± 50 m will be hard to justify unless a very precise correction for tidal state is going to be made. Conversely, in the immediate vicinity of an outfall giving rise to a surface effluent plume, a position fixing error of ± 2 m may make the difference between sampling or not sampling the effluent plume, which may or may not be visible. For more additional detailed information, especially on inshore navigation, the publications of the Royal Yachting Association are useful.

6.3.1.1   When good landmarks exist or can be established

For many estuarine surveys, the intersection of visible transects from landward features, bridges or buoys will provide easily and accurately located stations. An optical square (Section 6.3.2) will allow lines between features on opposite banks to be used. Buoys can be used, but have the potential disadvantage that they move around their mooring radius. The significance of such movement will be dependent upon the nature of the survey and accuracy required. In little used shallow or intertidal areas, it is often both practical and desirable to pre-place poles or marker buoys to facilitate easy station relocation.

6.3.1.2   When there are no good landmarks but high precision is not required

In more open waters, relatively remote from visible landward features, buoys may still be used, but electronic aids are more likely to be useful. Where ultimate accuracy is unnecessary, radar ranges and bearings or satellite systems should be adequate.

6.3.1.3 When greater accuracy is required

Often it is necessary to locate a sample station (such as a long sea outfall, a wreck or a dumping ground) exactly and return to it on subsequent occasions. Alternatively, sampling may need to be carried out on a predetermined grid which is not coincident with visible transect lines.

Several suitable techniques have been described by Hooper (164). In near shore situations, the use of double horizontal sextant angles can provide a very accurate system. The versatility of this technique has been enhanced by the recent availability of handheld microcomputers which can be programmed to give almost instantaneous position fixes from sextant angles and provide course and distance data to the next desired position. Several stations can be fixed by means of a series of single horizontal sextant angles along a transect line.

Electronic methods of position fixing are available which are capable of providing fixes to ± 1 m accuracy or better (164). Unless there is a suitable chain of transmitters already established in the area to be sampled, then the shore transmitters will have to be prepositioned for each survey. The overall accuracy obtained will be dependent upon the accuracy with which the transmitters are positioned. In some areas, the transmitters may have to be manned or guarded to prevent vandalism. Two basic systems, using radio interferometry or microwave range finding are widely used.

6.3.2 Use of the optical square

The optical square is very useful when sample stations can be fixed by transects from easily visible landmarks. It is a hand held device with 3 prisms which are set so as to give 3 images, one of an object straight ahead and the others of objects at 90 degrees to either side. The 3 images are formed one above the other so that alignment can be very rapidly checked. It is particularly useful in transect work, since it enables both end markers of a transect line to be viewed simultaneously, thus giving a check on any drifting off the line.

By reference to the appropriate Admiralty Chart or Ordnance Survey map (of the largest available scale) a suitable transect line can be defined between 2 markers which are obvious, both on the map and the site. For more detailed information see the section in ref 48.

6.3.3 Use of soundings

Soundings by echo sounder, or weighted line, can still be used as a confirmatory procedure especially when there are rapid changes in sea bed depth. The techniques are time consuming and prone to error, but can be used in the open ocean if sea mounts, canyons, shelf edges or trenches are being located.

6.4 Sampling techniques

The low concentrations of many of the determinands present in saline waters requires special sampling equipment in order to ensure that the samples returned to the laboratory are truly representative of the water mass sampled. In particular, special attention must be given to control of contamination.

The use of boats for sampling is a common cause of sample contamination. Sampling personnel and sample bottles are also well documented sources of contamination. To prevent contamination of samples, sampling devices and sample bottles, clean plastic gloves may be worn. They may also act as protection against skin contact with noxious samples.

The method of storage of the samples is also dependent upon the analyses which is to be carried out. Recommended procedures for the preservation of water samples are given in Chapter 5.

6.4.1 Water samples

Marine samples may have to be taken from below the water surface micro-layer, which contains elevated concentrations of many determinands (165, 166). This section describes suitable sampling techniques, first for the major components of seawater and secondly, for a variety of trace determinands which require additional precautions to be taken, or specific equipment.

6.4.1.1 Sample collection

It is prerequisite for all procedures that the equipment used is scrupulously clean. The next objective is to ensure that the sample is as representative as possible of the position from which it is taken. Once taken, the sample must be kept free from contamination.

6.4.1.2 General sampling procedures

Samples for determinands which are present in seawater at more than trace concentrations, may be taken using any of a variety of clean sampling devices.

Subsurface samples can be satisfactorily collected by simple (manual) submersion of the sample container. The top can then be opened and the container allowed to fill before recapping. Plastic gloves should be worn by operators, to avoid contamination of the sample which should be taken upstream or up-tide of the sampling platform and in open water. This can be achieved by taking the sample from a point ahead of the bows of the boat as it moves slowly into the wind.

Open mouthed vessels, such as buckets, may be used for sampling at, or immediately beneath, the surface. However, buckets cannot be recommended for subsurface sampling because of contamination by the surface layer, which may contain elevated concentrations of some compounds.

Samples from the surface micro-layer should be taken with special samplers. The surface micro-layer can only really be sampled in a qualitative manner. Various devices for sampling surface slicks and the surface micro-layer have been described in a report in this series (74) and elsewhere (167–171). The chemistry of the surface micro-layer has been reviewed by Liss (172).

The collection of samples from depth requires the use of closed pipe samplers or pumping equipment. Closed pipe samplers are tubes, fitted with valves or stoppers, which obtain samples from defined depths (either spot samples, or a series of samples), or depth-integrated composite samples. There are two types of design, air displacement and open-ended.

Air displacement samplers are lowered on a rope with orifices closed by stoppers or other means. At the appropriate depth these closures are released. Examples are shown in Figures 15–19. Water pressure and drag limit the depth at which these samplers will operate successfully.

Open-ended samplers are free-flushing as they are lowered through the water column. When in position, the sampler should be allowed to 'acclimatise' to its surroundings before the tubes are sealed. Some designs are lowered with shutters closed, preventing contamination with the surface micro-layer and water from different layers. Examples are shown in Figures 20–23.

Samples from very close to the seabed should be taken with special samplers made for this purpose (173, 174).

Pumping devices may be used to sample chemically stable determinands in either or both the particulate or dissolved phases, but are unsuitable for volatile compounds.

Peristaltic pumps, or centrifugal pumps with impellers unlikely to introduce contamination, may be used. Sampling tubes are lowered with the aid of a weighted hydrographic cable. The open end of the tube should be kept well away from the cable and the pump and the tube should be well flushed before the sample is taken. The device may be used for sampling from defined depths, not greater than 100 m, (either spot samples or a series of samples) or for obtaining depth-integrated or area integrated composite samples. For clean water, concentration procedures in which large volumes of water are pumped through an adsorbent cartridge or column are possible. The limitation to this is the blocking of the column or cartridge by suspended solids.

Automatic sampling devices are available, which allow the collection of discrete samples at regular predetermined time intervals. Such systems are often combined with on-site monitors, data loggers and telemetry links. Continuous monitoring probes are particularly useful for these applications.

6.4.1.3   General sampling procedures for organic compounds

Water samples are collected in 2.7 litre glass winchester bottles mounted in a weighted stainless steel frame which is deployed by means of a nylon rope (Figure 24). The bottle is sealed by means of a PTFE stopper which may be removed at the sampling depth by means of a second nylon rope. The stopper is spring-loaded so that the bottle may be resealed when full, being open therefore, only during sample collection and sealed during deployment and recovery.

The shallow water sampler illustrated in Figure 24 can be used to a depth of at least 50 m without imploding. The sampler is usually operated in the 1 to 10 m depth range.

In general, subsurface water samples (taken from 1 m depth) are analysed for organic determinands without filtration. However, in areas of high particulate loading, it may be desirable to carry out analyses of filtered water and suspended particulate material separately.

With water samples, after tightly stoppering each bottle, it is good practice to rinse the outside of the bottles and closure with clean water. This is to remove any saline water from the outside, which could dry and subsequently flake off into the sample when the bottle is opened. If sampling is carried out from a small boat, rinsing can be carried out after return to the laboratory. For many trace determinations, sample bottles can be kept and transported within a clean sealed polyethylene bag in order to keep the outside of the bottles clean. Note that polyethylene may contain plasticisers, such as dibutylphthalate, which can interfere with some trace organic analyses by co-elution.

6.4.1.4   Special precautions when sampling for hydrocarbons

Glass sample bottles are rigorously cleaned and thoroughly rinsed with pentane before use. The sampler (particularly the stopper) is cleaned with pentane at the start of each day's sampling, following any period of inactivity and periodically during sampling, or after use in areas of high hydrocarbon concentrations. For determinands not soluble in pentane, another appropriate solvent should be used in the initial cleaning. A general guide to sampling the water column for determination of oil content has already been prepared (74). See also refs. 175 and 176.

Ships use a variety of oil products, and wastes containing small quantities of oil are routinely discharged into the sea. In addition, losses of oil occur during normal operation, from leaks, spills and the use of lubricated machinery. In order that such contamination may be recognised, it is recommended that samples of fuel oil, bilge oil and any other oils and greases used on board a sampling vessel should be collected and returned to the laboratory for analysis. They should be analysed and the hydrocarbon profiles compared with those of the environmental samples, to identify any samples which have been contaminated. This is more of a problem with water samples than sediments, as the concentrations found in the former are usually so much lower and the opportunities for contamination during collection are greater.

6.4.1.5   Sampling procedure when determining trace metals

Wherever possible, sample handling should be carried out in a manner which minimises sample contamination.

When sampling surface water from a large vessel, samples can be taken using a 'Buoy' surface water sampler (177) deployed 2 to 3 m from the side of a stationary vessel. The water is pumped through PFA tubing directly into a PTFE pressure vessel, or into a borosilicate glass bottle when mercury is to be determined.

If surface sampling from a small boat, samples are taken using hand-held polyethylene bottles or, for mercury determinations, borosilicate glass bottles are used. The samples are taken over the bow of the boat while the boat is moving slowly into the wind, to prevent sampling contaminated water (178). The bottles are submerged with their lids on, then opened. Once filled, the lids are replaced before the bottles are removed from the water. The bottles are stored in clean polyethylene bags until filtration.

When sampling deep water, modified Go-Flo, bottles (General Oceanics), ie PTFE-coated with silicone rubber seals, are used. It is advantageous to replace the drainage tap with a special PTFE tap, especially if using pressure to transfer samples to filters. The bottles are deployed on a Kevlar hydro wire with a plastic coated weight and activated using PTFE coated messengers. Once the bottle is at the required depth, it is left to equilibrate for 2 to 3 minutes before the sample is taken. The samples are transferred directly into a PTFE pressure vessel, or glass bottle for mercury determination. The performance of Go-Flo samplers have been compared with others by Bewers and Windom (179).

6.4.2   Sampling sediments

Sediments are divided into two classes; those that have already settled to the bottom and those that are in the process of settling.

Settled sediments can also be divided into two groups, those always, or almost always, covered by water and those exposed for much of the tidal cycle. Settled sediment samples are usually taken using grabs or corers. If an exposed sediment becomes sufficiently firm it may also be sampled using shovels, as detailed for soil sampling in ref. 73. See also ref. 180. If suspended (settleable) sediment is to be sampled, the devices illustrated in Figures 25 and 26 may be used.

6.4.2.1   Techniques for sampling sediments

A range of devices may be used to obtain samples of the sea bed. Each has characteristics which suit it to certain sediment types and objectives. Each also has biases which should be taken into account when designing surveys or analysing results.

Surface sampling, for the assessment of spatial or temporal trends, is most readily achieved using a grab sampler. Widely used examples are the Day, Smith-McIntyre, van Veen and Shipek grabs. These devices are all described by Holme and McIntyre (181).

The Day, Smith-McIntyre and van Veen grabs have the following advantages:

i.   the tops of the grabs have lifting flaps, to allow access to the surface of the sediment for collection of relatively undisturbed sub-samples;

ii.   the jaws of the grab close tightly, to prevent loss of fine material when the grab is lifted from the sea bed; and

iii.   there is a facility for adding weights to the grabs to improve the depth of penetration.

All three grabs are suitable for sampling mud and sand. The van Veen grab can cause considerable disturbance to samples due to the action of the jaws which are not stabilised by a frame. However, it may be required for the finest muds where the other designs can become buried in the seabed. The Smith-McIntyre grab has the disadvantage that it is spring-loaded and can prove dangerous in poor weather conditions.

All three grabs described above are less effective when sampling gravel type sediments, as stones may prevent closure of the jaws and result in loss of material from the grab. A Shipek grab can be used in situations where this may occur. The Shipek grab suffers the disadvantages that it only collects a small sample and that due to its single jaw action, the sample tends to be disturbed, possibly with the loss of fines from the surface layer.

It must be noted that most grabs may not recover the surface sediment intact. The degree of surface disturbance depends not only on the grab design, but also on the mode of deployment. For example, vigorous deployment can cause disturbance both by the bow-wave of the grab and the impact of the device on the seabed. This should be avoided, the grab being lowered to the seabed as gently as possible. Where the grab is deployed from a winch, a length of clean rope is used between the grab and wire to prevent lubricants from contaminating the sample.

When sub-surface samples are required, it is essential to use a corer. Many corers are capable of collecting samples with minimal disturbance of the sediment surface and these may be used when undisturbed samples of surface sediment are required.

Large box corers such as the Reineck (182, 183) are suitable for most sampling applications requiring cores no longer than about 30 cm. These types of corer are good for collecting undisturbed sediment samples but suffer from the disadvantage that they are large and heavy and therefore difficult to use from small vessels or in bad weather. The Craib corer (184) is a smaller device particularly suited to the collection of intact sediment/ water interface samples and undisturbed surface samples. However, it only collects cores less than about 10 cm in length and is only effective in muds and fine sands. If cores are required from coarser material such as gravel, a vibro-corer should be used. In this case, the surface sediment is often highly disturbed. Further details of various corer designs may be found in standard texts such as Holme and McIntyre (181) and Bouma (185).

If samples are required for chemical analysis, it is essential that all surfaces that come into contact with the sediment sample are made of non-contaminating material. Similarly, when sub-sampling from grabs or corers it is important to use only utensils made from non-contaminating material. The exact nature of this material will depend on the determinand of interest, for example, PTFE or nylon utensils should be used if samples are to be analysed for metals. If organic compounds are to be analysed it is generally advisable to wash the sampling device and utensils with pentane before use and between each sample.

Samples should be stored in a manner appropriate to the determinand of interest. Samples for mercury analysis should be stored in all-glass wide-mouthed jars, while samples for most other metals can be stored in plastic jars or bags. If organic compounds such as PCBs are to be determined, storage should be in pentane-washed wide-mouthed glass jars with a layer of aluminium foil isolating the sample jar from the waxed lid liner. All the above samples should be kept at -20°C prior to analysis.

6.4.2.2   Separation of sediment samples into fractions

Great care is necessary to ensure that the original sample is truly representative and that the same is true for all sub-samples.

Some analysts analyse a representative portion of the whole sample, if necessary, crushing any coarse material and re-homogenizing the crushed sample prior to taking portions for analysis. Other analysts prefer to divide sediment samples by particle size. This is done by passing the dried sample through a nest of sieves of the desired mesh sizes with a pan under the finest sieve. For trace metal analysis, the most common size cut is made at 63 μm with a possible extra cut at 1-2 mm to separate gravel or fine stones.

For the preparation of samples for trace metal analyses, nylon sieves are used; for organic determinands metal sieves should be used. Equipment preparation and sample storage is as given in Section 6.4.2.1. If sieves are used, they should be inspected for cleanliness. Particles should not be prodded or brushed out. Sieves should be back washed with a strong jet of water and discarded if they have sagging or damaged screen material.

6.4.2.3   Interstitial water etc

High gravity centrifugation or high pressure squeezing presses are often used to separate solid from liquid, coupled with filtration to remove residual solid. Care must be taken to avoid changes in solubility with pressure, and to allow the sample to return to normal before analysis (168, 186 and 187).

Table 3 General guidelines for the operation of practical estuarine chemical investigation

Type of investigation	Timing of investigation	Positioning and spacing of sampling points	Frequency
(a) Water column sampling			
Survey—whole estuary	Non-exceptional conditions with respect to tides, river flow, weather, season, etc. Synoptic or pseudo-synoptic sampling.	At geographical sites fixed according to the salinity gradient, for example at 1 or 2 g/kg salinity intervals through entire range, including fresh water sampling. Closer spacing at selected sites if required, for example around major inputs. One, two or three dimensional sampling according to estuarine type and investigational aims.	Repeated as appropriate to cover normal range of environmental conditions. Opportunistic sampling of abnormal conditions.
Survey—regional, for example around point discharge	Non-exceptional conditions with respect to tides, river flow, weather, season, etc. Input must be representative, ie is the discharge regular or intermittent? Is it of constant composition? Synoptic sampling.	Siting dependent on volume and rate of input of discharge. Increased spacing with distance from discharge. Sampling throughout depth range even in vertically homogeneous estuaries. One or two horizontal dimensions as appropriate to size of estuary.	Hourly as minimum, or more frequently over a tidal cycle. Repeated as appropriate to cover normal range of environmental conditions and variability in discharge. Opportunistic sampling of abnormal conditions.
Survey—fixed site, for example mariculture establishment	Non-exceptional conditions with respect to tides, river flow, weather, season, etc.	Determined by scale of investigation area.	Hourly as minimum, or more frequently over a tidal cycle. Repeated as appropriate to cover normal range of environmental conditions and variability in discharge. Opportunistic sampling of abnormal conditions.
Fire-brigade, for example accidental toxic discharge	Incident related.	Determined by scale of incident.	As necessary throughout period of occurrence of abnormal conditions and effects.
Monitoring to test compliance with environmental quality standards	Likely to be (a) year round, (b) in conjunction with effluent sampling or (c) during period of stressful conditions, for example low river flow to estuary.	Likely to be within area affected by discharge, but outside defined "mixing zones".	At least several sampling occasions. Frequency may be reduced where justified by statistical analysis of results.
Monitoring to test for trends in contamination levels	May be long-term, or short-term in response to change in inputs.	Likely to be within area affected by discharge, but outside defined "mixing zones".	Annual programme for long-term studies will be designed to minimise effects of temporal variations and freshwater influences.

Type of investigation	Timing of investigation	Positioning and spacing of sampling points	Frequency
Specific investigations and modelling studies, for example quantification of geochemical processes, or modelling of proposed inputs	Defined by aims of investigation. Irrelevant temporal variations must be minimised by design.	Determined by aims of investigation. Will often be intensive and demanding.	Determined by aims of investigation. Will often be intensive over a relatively short period.
Long-term studies	Regular and repetitive over period of study. Additional investigations for extremes of environmental conditions and regions of special interest. Synoptic or pseudo-synoptic sampling.	Either geographically or salinity related for entire estuary or region as appropriate. Closer spacing at sites of special interest, e.g. major inputs. One, two or three dimensional sampling according to estuarine type and purpose of study.	Usually weekly to monthly. Greater frequency at specific times, e.g. during spring bloom.
(b) Sediment Sampling			
Survey—whole estuary or region	Defined if related to proposed schemes.	Regular grid throughout estuary or region. Finer grid at sites of special interest or accentuated variability. Grid size reduced until required definition obtained. Core sampling for historical record.	Single survey.
Monitoring	Defined by monitoring requirements. Regular and repetitive.	Defined by monitoring requirements. May be based on preliminary survey results.	Defined by monitoring requirements.

Table 4 Processes imparting temporal variations in estuarine water quality at a fixed geographical point (adapted from ref 159).

Time Scale	Variability	Process
Cyclic Fluctuations		
Seconds–minutes	Small-scale random oscillations about mean level or trend.	Turbulent eddying.
Minutes–hours	Variations about mean level or trend.	Eddying; incompletely mixed input; temporary isolation of water parcels in bays, sub-estuaries or over mud flats.
Hours	Regular interruptions to mean levels or trends regularly cyclic; 12 hour period usually with spring/neap amplitude oscillations.	Timed discharges; tidal advection and associated processes, for example sediment mobility.
Annual	Regular and cyclic.	Biological and climatic processes.
Intermittent Fluctuations		
Hours–annual	Irregular interruptions to mean levels or trends.	Irregular discharges; abnormal events.
Annual, more probable at certain times	Intermittent significant but reversible changes in physical, chemical or biological characteristics.	Climatic effects; exceptional conditions; biological instabilities.
Sporadic	Permanent discontinuity in physical or biological characteristics.	Change in exploitation, for example new discharges; rapid natural evolution, for example re-channelling; changes in bed bathometry; storm events.
Trends		
Annual and longer	Persistent year to year trend.	Change in exploitation; for example continuous increase or decrease in discharge; natural estuarine evolution; long term climatic change.

7.1 Introduction

This chapter is intended for those who sample rivers and streams, or who plan and supervise such sampling. It is intended to give guidance on river sampling and to be used in conjunction with the general guidance given in earlier chapters.

7.2 Sampling location and position

The general points made in Section 4.3 apply to choosing sampling locations in rivers and streams, but the specific points in the following sections should also be considered.

7.2.1 Factors affecting choice of sampling location

Many characteristics influence the behaviour of contaminants in river systems. An understanding of the nature of these characteristics is important when planning and carrying out river sampling programmes. Important factors include temperature, turbidity, depth, velocity, turbulence, slope, changes in direction and in cross-sections and the nature of the river bed. These factors are so interrelated that it is difficult to assign more or less importance to each one. In addition, chemical and biological processes may occur, for example photosynthesis, respiration and metabolic effects.

7.2.2 Mixing of effluents and streams

The physical characteristics of stream channels largely control distances required for mixture of effluents with stream flow.

Effluents mix in three directions in a stream:

i.   vertically;

ii.   laterally; and

iii.   longitudinally.

The distances in which effluents mix in these three directions must be considered in the selection of sampling locations and positions.

7.2.2.1 Vertical mixing

Vertical mixing, almost always, is the first of the three types to be complete in a stream. Shallow water and high velocities result in rapid vertical mixing but even in deep water with low velocities, vertical mixing is relatively rapid. Effluents discharged to most streams mix vertically, within one tenth of a kilometre or within a few tenths at most. Therefore, it is rare that a stream needs to be sampled at more than one depth.

7.2.2.2 Lateral mixing

Lateral mixing usually occurs after vertical mixing has occurred but before longitudinal mixing is complete. Differences in solids content and especially in temperature of effluents and stream water can cause the effluents to stratify and travel across the stream more rapidly on surface or bottom than they would if mixed vertically at the point of discharge. This phenomenon is most significant at very low velocities since even moderate turbulence quickly destroys stratification, causes vertical mixing and slows the lateral movement of the wastes.

Change in direction of stream flow is also effective in lateral mixing. This, combined with normal vertical mixing, can cause rapid and fairly complete lateral mixing. However, even when a stream passes through two approximately 90° reverse bends that are reasonably close together it cannot be assumed that lateral mixing of upstream effluents is complete.

Whereas turbulence may cause vertical mixing within a few tenths of a kilometre, the distance for lateral mixing generally is dependent on the occurrence of relatively sharp reverse bends. As a general rule (18) the distance for adequate lateral mixing is in kilometres rather than tenths. Frequently, a stream must be sampled at two or more points at one or more locations downstream from an effluent discharge or a tributary stream because of slow lateral mixing.

7.2.2.3   Longitudinal mixing

The effect of longitudinal mixing of an effluent with a stream is shown in Figure 27. Such mixing is caused by differences in times required for water to travel from the effluent discharge to the downstream sampling stations. The result is the smoothing out of the effects of an irregular effluent discharge.

Consideration of longitudinal mixing distances can be important in deciding frequency of sampling. More frequent sampling will be required to give representative results just below an irregular discharge than would be necessary some distance downstream, where mixing longitudinally has been completed.

7.2.3   Inhomogeneity of rivers.

Ideally, tests of heterogeneity would be made for each quality determinand at each of the proposed sampling locations. However, such a detailed investigation can often be impractical. When tests of homogeneity cannot be made at all sampling locations, the locations may be divided into various classes, and tests made at least in one location from each class. The classes are best decided from local experiences. If the locations tested initially were adequately homogeneous, other work could proceed but with the longer aim of checking all locations as soon as practicable.

Different determinands may show different degrees of heterogeneity. It is suggested that the following determinands (provided they are required for the routine programme) should be checked at each sampling location to be tested: pH, conductivity, chloride, ammonia, suspended solids, dissolved oxygen, colour, iron, chlorophyll, total organic carbon and biochemical oxygen demand. Other determinands should be included if they are of special interest, or are indicated by local circumstances.

Ideally, samples should be taken from many different points, but the following approach is suggested to restrict the amount of work involved. The portion of the cross-section through which a large proportion (say 90%) of the total flow passes is decided approximately. Within that portion, at least six samples should be taken (see Figure 28). Large rivers might require more lateral and vertical samples. To determine whether any apparent differences between samples are caused by non-homogeneous distribution or by analytical errors, a statistical analysis of the results is necessary. The basis of these statistical tests is the technique of "Analysis of Variance". This technique assumes that the variability within samples is the same. This assumption is reasonable for the tests of homogeneity of quality parameters in cross-sections of rivers. All such samples must be collected at as close to the same time as possible to avoid the effects of temporal variation.

Samples should be taken from at least three flows corresponding as closely as possible to the minimum, modal and maximum flows expected during the period of the tests. Factors other than flow may affect the degree of heterogeneity of certain parameters, for example climatic conditions may affect dissolved oxygen. Ideally, each one of these factors should be identified and investigated. It is suggested that consideration of such factors be deferred until the results from the tests are available.

7.2.4   Sampling position at a given location

When the desired location has been selected, the position at that location from which to sample must also be decided. For example, the location may be a bridge over a river downstream of an effluent discharge. The position(s) within the river cross section at that location then need to be chosen. This is discussed in Section 4.3.2.

7.2.5 Further specific points regarding river sampling locations and positions

Choice of sampling location of certain single sampling stations may be reasonably flexible. For example, a monitoring station for a base line record of water quality may be moved upstream or downstream several miles, to permit use of a convenient bridge or to allow an upstream effluent discharge or tributary to be well mixed laterally when the stream arrives at the station.

When selecting a series of sampling locations to establish a baseline record of water quality, it is desirable that the locations should be established at marked changes in physical characteristics of the stream channel. For example, a stream reach between two adjacent stations should not include both a long rapids section of swift shallow water with a rocky bottom and a long section of deep, slow-moving water with a muddy bottom. Stations at each end of the combined reach would yield data on certain rates of change such as re-aeration, that would be of an unrealistic average to two widely different rates. Much more would be learned of the actual natural purification characteristics of the stream by insertion of a third station within the reach between the rapids and the quiet water sections.

When the effects of a tributary or an effluent on the quality in a particular reach of the main stream are of interest, at least two locations are necessary, one just upstream of the confluence and the other sufficiently far downstream that lateral and vertical mixing are complete. It may be necessary to sample the tributaries and effluents just before they reach the main river and further upstream. In some cases, it may be desirable to project the concentration or load of some unstable constituent from the sampling station above the effluent discharge to the point of discharge. In such cases, it may be desirable to locate two or three stations above the effluent discharge to establish the rate at which the unstable constituent is changing. The time of travel between the stations should be sufficient to permit accurate measurement of the change in the constituent under consideration. The sampling location on a tributary should be as near the mouth as possible. Two or three stations on the tributary, to establish the rates of change of unstable constituents, may be desirable when projection of data on unstable constituents from the tributary station to the main stream is necessary. When sampling tributaries, care must be taken to avoid collecting water from the main stream that may flow into the mouth of the tributary on either the surface or bottom because of differences in density resulting from temperature, dissolved salts, or turbidity differences.

For detailed studies, more sampling positions downstream of an effluent discharge may be necessary. The number of intermediate points will depend on the rate of flow, the degree of pollution, the self-purification capacity of the river, the existence of sludge deposits, etc. and especially on the use to be made of the results; the more detailed the information needed, the more sampling points will have to be used.

Cross sectional mixing in a river usually proceeds more rapidly than longitudinal mixing and the distance downstream of an effluent or tributary at which to sample can sometimes be chosen with advantage. For example, if interest is centred on short-term variations in quality due to temporal variations, then this distance should be as small as possible, consistent with adequate cross sectional mixing. On the other hand, if the long-term average quality were of prime interest, it would be preferable to make the distance as large as possible so that the short-term variations are smoothed out by the longitudinal dispersion (Figure 27).

Care should be taken that particular local features of a river or stream do not affect the validity of samples. For example, weirs promote re-oxygenation, heavy growths of weeds or sewage fungus may affect a number of determinands, drainage ditches can be a source of heavy pollution during rainstorms, and inflow of ground water can cause changes in quality. In addition, the river quality may be affected by other discharges, adsorption on bottom deposits and re-suspension of settled material. Such factors should be considered during a preliminary reconnaissance.

A special problem in river sampling arises when non-conservative determinands (for example, biochemical oxygen demand, bacteria) disperse into a river because the rate at which the concentration of the determinand changes (as a result, for example, of biochemical degradation) may be more rapid than the process of dispersion. No recommendations can be given to overcome this problem, but it is as well to recognise it. Another example is the change in the chemical form of a determinand in an effluent or tributary, when mixing with a river, for example the precipitation of iron.

Generally, sampling at or near the surface, bottom, bank, stagnant areas and pools should be avoided. Particular care is needed not to disturb bottom sediments and to avoid non-representative films on the surface. It has been suggested that samples should, whenever possible, be collected from positions at least 30 cm above the bottom of a stream, and a similar distance below the surface will usually be satisfactory.

7.2.6 Biological sampling locations

These are highly dependent on the species being sampled. Only sample for species in a suitable habitat: conversely if it is essential to sample at a given location, only rely on species suited to that habitat. Consult specialist booklets in this series (refs 48, 73, 74, 119 and 189–196) and Chapter 13.

7.3 Sample collection techniques

In general, the sample collection techniques described in Section 4.7 are applicable to rivers and streams. Sample containers should be selected by referring to Chapter 5. Many of the techniques described in Chapter 6 are also appropriate, especially for sampling deep rivers from boats or other structures.

In many cases, samples can simply be taken by hand, either directly into the sample bottle, or by filling a bucket or other container, then decanting. The most important point is that the sampler should not contaminate the sample, or disturb the conditions at the sampling point, for example by re-suspending sediment material. In flowing water, the sample should be taken in an upstream direction to avoid such problems, and consideration should be given as to whether the surface layer is sampled or not.

7.4 Sediment sampling

Sediments are present on the bottom of all surface water bodies and can directly or indirectly affect water quality, for example impurities can be released from sediments, or oxygen may be consumed by them. Analysis of sediments is, therefore, of common importance in studying water quality. In addition, the biological species living on or in the sediments are frequently of interest in characterising water quality.

As with water bodies themselves, sediments often show heterogeneous distribution of determinands, so that sampling location and position are again of importance. If the information required on sediments is to assist the study and control of water quality, the locations and positions of interest for that quality will usually define the points at which sediments are to be sampled. However, the amounts of determinand in a given sediment can vary with depth. Therefore, depending on the determinands of interest, it may be necessary to check the distribution of determinands at different depths.

It may be necessary to fix the sampling position so that comparative samples may be taken at other times. For most rivers, sampling positions can be readily fixed by reference to features on the banks. When sampling from boats instrumental methods for position fixing should be used (see ref. 73 and Chapter 6).

Equipment and physical methods for taking samples of sediments are given in Chapter 6.

7.5 Measurement of time of travel in rivers

Time of travel is the time taken for a given mass of water to move between two defined points. This may be from a point of discharge to the next point of discharge or from a point of discharge to an abstraction point, etc. Information on the time of travel or river retention of substances in this mass of water is important for several reasons.

i. It provides information on the lateral mixing characteristics of a given stretch of river which assists in defining the most representative point on that river system from which to take a sample.

ii. It provides information on the longitudinal velocity profiles in the river, which can be used to calculate re-aeration rates to predict the assimilative capacity of a reach for biodegradable organic matter. The self-purification, or river recovery rate, may be presented as a mathematical model. Such models are very important as they assist in the prediction of oxygen sag curves, and the re-use capability of a river. Time of travel measurements may also be used to study the rates of change of other unstable constituents in rivers, for example the oxidation of ammonia, the decomposition of phenols and the decay of radionuclides.

iii. It provides information on mean flow velocities under a set of given discharge conditions in assessing the distance travelled from pollution source. This information may enable remedial action to be taken before the pollution arrives at a water abstraction point, or allow the water treatment processes to be varied to compensate for the effects of the pollution or to predict the time interval necessary for the abstraction to be stopped.

iv. It provides information on the selection of sampling locations and for deciding the length of a river reach to be studied. It can be used to estimate the subsequent downstream position of a mass of water in which some abnormal result was obtained at one or more sampling locations. This allows additional sampling to be carried out to confirm or revise any idea or conclusion based on the abnormal result.

7.5.1 Determination of time of travel

Time of travel can be determined by three principal methods, the use of surface floats (see ISO 748), the use of tracers (see ISO 555/1, ISO 555/11 and ISO 555/14) and the measurement of cross sectional areas. Details are given in ref. 197.

8 Sampling of lakes and reservoirs

8.1 Introduction

This chapter first considers the various types of lakes and reservoirs, in so far as type can influence sampling methods. Next, the hazards involved will be considered. This is followed by a discussion of sampling strategies and techniques.

8.2 Variations in the conformation of lakes and reservoirs affecting their sampling

8.2.1 Lakes and ponds

For sampling purposes, the important variables are the steepness and nature of the shoreline, and the profile and nature of the bottom. The criteria to be considered are whether the sample can be safely taken from the shore (directly or indirectly by lowering or reaching with a boom, or by wading), from a boat, or whether special means should be used. Consideration needs to be given to the stability of the banks, firmness of beaches, depth of water, the presence of sand-banks, rocks and islands and whether convenient boat landings are available.

8.2.2 Reservoirs

Reservoirs can be regarded as falling into three types:

i. artificial lakes made by damming a valley, excavating a hole, or enclosing land with a dyke;

ii. large roofed tanks or containers at or below ground level. These differ from underground lakes in that the walls are usually sheer and access is usually via a manhole in the roof;

iii. elevated water towers.

8.3 Hazards

The chief hazards are:

i.   from rock falls, bank collapses and quagmires;

ii.   falls into water causing drowning or hypothermia;

iii.   more rare are hazards due to harmful plants and animals, and dangerous effluents. Abandoned hazardous materials also occasionally cause problems.

When sampling underground, in deep wells or when in enclosed reservoirs, before entry, always check the quality of the air for sufficiency of oxygen, that the level of carbon dioxide is not too high and that toxic gases are absent. An access hatch or door must never be closed until it is certain that either everyone is out or that the door opens easily from the inside, those inside know how to open it and they can see how to do so with the door closed. Many of the open air safety requirements also apply underground.

Always check precautions and local conditions thoroughly before sampling. Use a check list based on the above information and local knowledge. Written handovers with copies and signatures of receipt are useful.

Be prepared for the unexpected. Always be sure that your programme is known to others and that good lines of communication exist if there should be an emergency, or in the event of difficulties. Rescuers must ensure that a message about the problem is sent and if feasible, has been received, before going to help. Portable radios save time if reception is good. If reception is poor, they can be an additional hazard.

In places where snow and frost are common on higher ground, lakes, especially deep ones, can remain at close to freezing even on a hot day. Conversely, after a period of very hot sunny weather, very shallow lakes with sandy bottoms can become hot enough at the surface to give mild scalds on long exposure.

Very acidic and highly alkaline lakes are known to exist. Some of these lakes are so rich in dissolved salts that, even though at temperatures well above 100°C, they do not steam. Some algae and other micro-organisms can grow in water hot enough to scald. Always check the temperature and pH of water. If wading or paddling, beware of corrosion of footwear, slipping and splashes.

In places where there can be oscillations between sub zero weather and milder weather causing partial thaws, some lakes tend to form layers of ice covered by water. Sometimes several such layers may form one above the other. These layers may carry weight and then suddenly break. Immersion in such water is dangerous, but an added risk is that of being trapped under the submerged ice or mineral layer. If such layers are suspected, never venture out from shore without having carefully probed the route well ahead. If possible, use other methods for obtaining the sample.

In sub zero weather, if anchoring a boat, remember that despite the maximum density effect at about 4°C, water above black, highly radiative rock can freeze from the bottom up and so loosen anchors. Tied shore moorings are preferable.

8.4   Strategies for sampling lakes and reservoirs

The simplest way to sample a lake or reservoir is to sample at the outlet. If the effect of mixing, residence or source on a determinand is also of interest, sample additionally at the various inlets. This may not always be so easy. Some lakes receive subsurface springs. These may sometimes be detected from infrared photographs taken during warm or cold weather (depending on the temperature of the spring). A few lakes have subterranean outlets, even if only by seepage through porous rock.

If lakes or reservoirs are sampled from the shore, ensure that the sample is sufficiently representative.

If a detailed study of a lake or reservoir is required, it will be necessary to know the profile of the bottom at least approximately. Samples are then taken at different depths from surface to bottom in a pattern across the lake. It is best to use a systematic scheme such as a three dimensional grid (see Figure 29). The pattern chosen should be based on the overall three dimensional shape of the lake and on its current flows, with attention given to relatively stagnant areas, underwater inputs and so on.

If there is doubt about the homogeneity or stratification of the lake or reservoir, it may save effort to carry out an initial survey using parameters which are measurable by probes or sensors such as temperature, conductivity, or dissolved oxygen, taking only a few actual water samples initially. Large bodies of water may experience mixing effects due to density changes on warming and cooling. Similar density effects can be caused by differences in salt content. Patterns may change with the wind.

Many lakes are influenced by seasonal variations in the rivers flowing into them and can vary in composition. However, the size of large lakes usually has a buffering effect on changes. Both evaporation and sunlight can change the chemical and biota composition of lakes and reservoirs, and depending on variations in depth and the surrounding landscape can sometimes cause quite large differences between one part and another. It is especially prudent to check for this where narrows and/or shallows inhibit mixing.

All this should be considered and checked when planning a long term study of the water quality in a lake or reservoir.

8.5   Sampling techniques

For information on sample bottles, special filling procedures, preservation and storage times see Chapter 5.

Unless special inlet and or outlet sampling points are provided, as at some reservoirs, for surface samples, sample by filling the bottle directly, or by scoop or ladle, or by a pump, depending on the determinand. For subsurface sampling use the techniques described in Chapter 6.

Most reservoirs have specially built outlets which may have variable draw off points at predetermined depths. If the output needs to be sampled, these can often be fitted with conventional sampling taps. If the outlet is a river, stream or spillway, these may be sampled in the same way as rivers and streams.

Some reservoirs have piped or conduit inlets which can likewise be sampled by conventional sampling taps. Other reservoirs and most lakes are fed by streams or rivers. Inlet samples should again be taken as for rivers and streams of the appropriate depth. Submerged inlets and outlets which are not accessible up or down stream need to be sampled as for deep water, but with additional care due to the current. Pumps may also be used. Equipment used must not contaminate the sample. If sampling from a sampling line, always flush out more than the volume of the line before filling the sample bottle.

Some water towers have only a single inlet/outlet pipe and care should be taken that water is flowing in the direction that requires sampling. For sampling of sediments, see the techniques described in Chapter 6, and also ref 73.

9   Sampling and monitoring of groundwater quality

9.1   Introduction

A good knowledge of the hydrogeology and local groundwater flow regime is important when planning a sampling programme, to enable the sensible interpretation of resultant analyses. Samples should preferably be collected from dedicated monitoring boreholes which are only open to limited vertical sections of the aquifer. Results from these boreholes enable quality changes with depth to be investigated, whereas a borehole penetrating the full thickness of the aquifer will only give an integrated sample.

Groundwater quality measurement typically requires the use of a sampling device and the collection, storage and subsequent analysis of that sample for selected determinands. Within this procedure sampling can be the single largest source of error. Modern analytical techniques therefore demand properly planned and well executed sampling programmes to obtain samples which represent specific groundwater flow paths that accurately reflect the quality of the groundwater under investigation (198). Sampling may relate to a study of ambient groundwater quality, or to a dynamic pollution problem caused by a diffuse or a local source.

Groundwater may be analysed for a wide variety of reasons:

i.   to determine the suitability of groundwater as a source of drinking water;

ii.   to determine the suitability of groundwater as a source for non potable uses;

iii.   to identify and monitor the movement of a pollutant caused by potentially hazardous surface and subsurface activities, such as landfill sites, industry (including extractive industries) and agriculture;

iv.   to monitor groundwater pollution in the vicinity of sources of groundwater used for potable, or other supply purposes, in order to protect the integrity of these supplies and maintain their continued use;

v.   to develop an understanding of regional groundwater quality variations as an aid to understanding the groundwater regime and to achieve optimal groundwater resource management;

vi.   to assess the impact of changes in land use on groundwater quality;

vii.   to calibrate and validate groundwater quality models developed for pollution control and resource management; and/or

viii. to determine flow paths and rates of groundwater movement using injected tracers.

The evaluation of the inorganic and organic constituents of groundwaters provides a valuable tool with which to solve hydrogeological problems. The hydrogeologist, however, must previously have determined as much as possible about the prevailing groundwater regimes using classical hydrogeological techniques, before optimum sampling locations can be selected and the appropriate method and procedure of sampling devised.

The techniques available for groundwater sampling in both the saturated and unsaturated zone are many and varied. This chapter aims to describe those techniques and their advantages and disadvantages. The information will assist in selecting the optimum equipment and procedures for the prevailing conditions and the required determinands. References to informative works are cited and include a selection of previously published guides to groundwater sampling, as well as papers describing particular techniques and innovative procedures.

9.2   Design of monitoring programmes

Routine monitoring of groundwater quality is most often carried out to determine deterioration with time. These data are expensive to collect, particularly if boreholes have to be drilled, so care must be taken to ensure the data are useful and representative of the aquifer being monitored.

Wilkinson and Edworthy (199) identified four major reasons why groundwater monitoring systems yield inadequate data:

i.   the objectives of the monitoring programme are not properly defined;

ii.   the monitoring systems are installed without sufficient hydrogeological knowledge of the area;

iii.   insufficient planning of sample collection, handling, storage and analysis of samples; and

iv.   data are poorly archived.

Despite these inadequacies, data are often used for long term predictions of water quality and as the basis for decisions on major capital expenditure. Careful planning of a groundwater monitoring system is therefore vital in order to gather useful, unambiguous data on which sound decisions can be made (200). Groundwater monitoring systems can be very cost effective and lead to better aquifer management. This is particularly so now that aquifers are being put under increasing stress from abstraction, waste disposal, mining activities and diffuse and point source pollution.

Planning new groundwater sampling and monitoring programmes, or revision of existing programmes, should preferably be organised to incorporate current quality assurance (QA) practices.

Guidelines have been compiled and specifications for quality assurance of all aspects of groundwater investigations. These guidelines are discussed by Van Ec and MacMillion (201) who stress that programmes of QA should be devised prior to a study to ensure collection of scientifically and, if necessary, legally sound data. They also point out that the development of excessively rigorous QA standards may have undesirable effects such as cost increase in excess of benefits.

Groundwater quality monitoring can have different objectives and these should be clearly defined and documented. The two main areas of interest are surveillance of potable water supplies and monitoring of pollution, either diffuse or point source.

Groundwater quality is variable, not only spatially in three dimensions but also with time. The latter variations can be cyclic on an annual basis or over much shorter periods related to recharge events. Areal variations are usually gradual but the hydraulic characteristics of an aquifer can result in considerable variability with depth, controlled by high permeability layers or fissure-flow zones (202). These variations can occur in an aquifer in its natural state but the system is further complicated by pumping, artificial recharge or pollution.

If the system is to monitor an aquifer regionally, the optimum number and distribution of sampling points must be determined, to ensure that sufficient good quality data are collected to meet the objectives. Similarly, if a local source of pollution is to be monitored, then the selection of sampling points both areally and with depth is vital.

The optimum number of monitoring wells and the frequency with which they are sampled can be evaluated statistically (203, 204). The latter paper investigates the relationship between the number of sampling points, their spatial configuration and the sampling frequency in order to derive an optimal sampling programme.

Monitoring existing water supply boreholes will provide data on changes in water quality that have occurred but will not give warning of a pollutant moving towards the borehole. Additionally, pumping boreholes provide a bulk sample for the thickness of aquifer penetrated and do not give an indication of water quality from different production zones.

Once the objectives of any groundwater quality monitoring programme have been clearly defined, the next essential step is to obtain an understanding of the hydrogeological regime of the region or area of interest. This can usually be obtained from existing data or by comparison with a similar area, but may involve an investigative programme of logging existing boreholes or even drilling. Without knowledge of the groundwater flow regime, groundwater quality monitoring can be either misleading or financially wasteful due to monitoring in the wrong place or at the wrong depth.

On a site specific scale, a knowledge of the well design and hydraulics is vital so that the origin of the water sample is known. For example, a borehole may penetrate two aquifers where, because of different piezometric heads, water from the first is flowing into the second. A depth sample will only give the water quality of the first aquifer. Only by isolating the second aquifer using a packer system or other suitable device, can a representative sample be obtained.

Similarly, the location of monitoring boreholes must be selected with due regard to the regional and local groundwater flow regimes. For example, if a water supply borehole shows signs of pollution, then the regional groundwater flow regime, modified by local pumping, will indicate the most likely source of the contamination. The nature and extent of the pollution plume can then be investigated using the minimum number of boreholes.

Boreholes that are specifically designed for monitoring offer several advantages over non-dedicated boreholes. The single screen borehole allows head measurements and samples to be drawn from a single horizon. Clusters of single screen boreholes provide information from different horizons at the same location. The extra cost of installing and monitoring clusters is justified by the increased value of the data so obtained. These data include information on differential head with depth and variations in water quality from one horizon to the next.

Long screen boreholes only provide a general picture, but short single screen boreholes offer the essential details. Reconnaissance work has to be carried out using existing boreholes. The preliminary data so obtained must then be used to design a monitoring system with cluster groups placed strategically within each aquifer. It is desirable to maintain some of the original long screen monitoring boreholes, although the data they will yield will need to be reviewed with time (see Figure 30).

9.3   Monitoring for specific objectives

The main decisions to be made relate to the number of sampling points, the frequency of sampling and the determinands to be monitored at each sampling point.

A policy of frequently sampling each borehole and other available sample points for a wide range of determinands is obviously not going to be cost-effective and operation of a monitoring system needs to be regarded in two stages (199).

Firstly, a period of initial assessment, where frequent sampling of available sources for a wide range of determinands identifies seasonal fluctuations and key determinands which can act as indicators later in the programme. The second stage of the programme entails long-term surveillance when sampling frequency and number of determinands are reduced to optimise costs, but still meet the objectives of the sampling programme. For example, once the general hydrogeochemistry of an area has been defined it may be sufficient to measure chloride levels quarterly to monitor saline intrusion.

These criteria can be applied even to existing monitoring programmes which have been in operation for many years. The programmes may require review to reassess the objectives, evaluate the current sampling points for suitability of location and horizon from which water is collected. An assessment of the frequency of sampling and the range of determinands monitored may result in financial savings. Objectives of regional monitoring programmes will change with time in a dynamic groundwater system with changing demands in supply, waste disposal and the water quality deterioration due to pollution.

Poor archiving and accessibility of data was identified by Wilkinson and Edworthy (199) as one of the main areas of inadequacy in groundwater quality monitoring programmes. Often the data gathered on a specific project are not archived effectively and the data are lost or inadequately recorded for future use. Historic data are very valuable when studying temporal changes in water quality.

Handling and storage of data should therefore be included in the original planning of the monitoring and quality assurance programmes. The data archiving system should be designed to be readily accessible.

Currently, data storage systems should be computer based to facilitate handling of large volumes of data. These systems should be compatible with data handling packages capable of assimilating and plotting the data to facilitate presentation and compilation of reports. However, if data are required for legal or official purposes or long term storage, provision of hard copy may be necessary to protect the data.

9.3.1   Potable water supply surveillance

Monitoring water quality from a public supply borehole is primarily to ensure that the consumer is provided with a "wholesome" supply, that meets the relevant water quality standards. This is achieved by frequent monitoring of selected determinands at the source prior to treatment so that rapid action can be taken if one or more determinands should change to an unacceptable level. Only a few indicators such as pH, colour and microbiological determinands are monitored in this way, with a more extensive analysis being carried out at longer intervals. This latter data set can be used to monitor the long-term changes, provided the sampling interval is suitably selected.

9.3.2 Pollution monitoring

Pollution of groundwater bodies can be classified into two main groups.

i.   Diffuse pollution where the water quality deteriorates over an area or region. This type of pollution includes the leaching of nitrates and other agrochemicals and the effects of acid rain. Also included in this group are the pollution effects of a large number of point sources, particularly in urban areas, which result in general pollution over a wider area.

ii.   Point source pollution relates to the local pollution caused by waste disposal practices or accidental spillage. Line source pollution is included in this group and relates to the effects of motorways and railway lines.

The design of water quality sampling regimes, to investigate and monitor these different types of pollution, using different determinands requires very different approaches.

9.3.3 Diffuse source

Diffuse pollution of groundwater in the UK and Europe has received a great deal of attention in the last two decades because of the concern about nitrate pollution. Nitrate-rich fertiliser has been leached to varying degrees through the unsaturated zone to major aquifers, particularly in the unconfined areas of recharge (73, 205, 206).

In general, the problem has been defined as pulses of nitrate moving slowly through the unsaturated zone over a period of 10 to 40 years, depending on the thickness and hydraulic characteristics of the rock. Once the nitrate reaches the water table, it moves relatively rapidly with the groundwater flow, either on a natural gradient or one modified by pumping. Pesticides are thought to move in a similar manner.

Monitoring this type of pollution poses special problems. If the problem is approached wholly by surveillance of water quality from supply wells, then, when the increase in level of determinand is recorded, the pulse of pollutant has already reached the water table. Any subsequent increase in concentration is then liable to be rapid and levels may quickly exceed the statutory limits. Little time is then available for remedial action and the source may even have to be removed from supply.

Early warning monitoring networks are required in both the saturated and unsaturated zones. In the latter zone, the methods described in Section 9.5.2 can be used to sample a point repeatedly, or water quality profiles can be derived from pore-water extracted from cores. Once a 'pulse' of pollutant has been identified in a profile through the unsaturated zone, its movement is best monitored by subsequent sampling at the same site in a rolling drilling programme.

Regional monitoring of the saturated zone is best achieved in purpose drilled monitoring boreholes. The purpose of the monitoring programme must be clearly defined and sample point locations and depths identified to ensure representative samples are collected. In an area where diffuse pollution is thought to be moving vertically towards the water table, then monitoring the zone of fluctuation will identify the initial arrival at the zone of saturation. Similarly, when monitoring the lateral movement of a pollutant, sample depths must be selected in zones of preferential flow.

A system to enable even earlier warning requires the monitoring of the unsaturated zone at sufficient sites to be able to model the likely input of pollutant in an area. Although the pollution is diffuse, it is also variable with such factors as rate of application, nature of soil and rock, precipitation, thickness of unsaturated zone, type of crop grown and natural attenuation. All these factors influence the amount of pollutant eventually leached to the groundwater. The design of a monitoring network would therefore require these factors to be taken into account in deciding on the minimum number of sampling sites to achieve the objective of quantifying the future pollution problem.

The selection of determinands to be monitored, relates to the type of pollution under investigation. Leached nitrate from whatever source is relatively easy to measure, as the levels of interest are of the order of tens of milligrams per litre. The concentrations of the nitrogen species and a selection of major ions can be determined from a few millilitres of sample which can usually be obtained by centrifugation of rock from the unsaturated zone.

Much greater difficulty is attached to sampling for pesticides as the recommended limits and the concentrations likely to be encountered are about four orders of magnitude lower than those of nitrate. A much larger volume of water, usually a minimum of two litres, is required for analysis. In addition, a wide range of chemical compounds are employed and could potentially be present, together with their breakdown products. Pesticide analysis is expensive, so a few compounds should be targeted for analysis. Selection should be based on records of pesticide application in the area under investigation, together with an assessment of which compounds are most likely to leach to groundwater, based on their properties of solubility and persistence and their methods of application.

Water for pesticide analysis is best gathered using an *in-situ* tensiometer which will collect an integrated sample over a period of time (see Figure 31). If the nature of the rock precludes the use of tensiometers then coring and extraction of pore-water by centrifugation is possible. Currently, no wholly satisfactory method for sampling the unsaturated zone for agrochemicals exists. Probably the most effective method of providing early warning of agrochemical pollution is a network of piezometers that monitor the water table in the zone of fluctuation at a suitable time interval.

9.3.4   Point source

Point source pollution of groundwater bodies can originate from a multitude of sources, most commonly landfill sites, from which leachates originate and percolate into the aquifer. The nature of the leachate and its potential to pollute the aquifer depends on the landfill site, its geological setting, the types of waste and the effectiveness of management.

Slurry dams containing waste from mining or industrial processes are another type of point-source pollution, as are accidental spillages and illegal dumping of oils, fuels and chemicals. Particularly serious problems can arise where natural storm-water drainage from roads, railways or airport runways is designed to flow into underground sumps. This practice can directly recharge an aquifer and if accidental spillage occurs at the site of the soakaway serious pollution of the aquifer may result.

Pollution associated with major lines of transport is referred to as line source. Other linear structures, such as pipelines, are potential line sources of pollution, but leakages are more likely to be restricted to point sources along the length. Asphalt and vehicles can also contribute to line source pollution.

Each case of point source pollution is an individual event and although similarities between events will occur, the approach made to determine the nature and extent of the pollution requires flexibility. Monitoring of point source pollution events needs to be tackled in a systematic manner.

i.   Evaluation of existing data

The location of the site in relation to the geological, hydrological and hydrogeological environment needs to be assessed. The historical record of inputs and operation of the site or nature of the spillage requires investigation, to form a preliminary model of the likely chemical and physical nature of the pollutant.

An understanding of the transport of the contaminant originating from a point source is required and this is discussed in detail by Freeze and Cherry (207). Dispersion processes can be both physical and chemical and the relative importance of these effects will determine the shape of the pollutant plume. Input of the pollutant may be continuous and still active or the source of pollution may have been removed or the input may be cyclic. The resultant pollution plumes will vary greatly and may be found a considerable distance down gradient with no sign of contamination adjacent to the site. The density of the pollutant plume can also affect its shape and demands careful selection of the depth of sampling points. Inhomogeneities in aquifers, particularly fissured aquifers and complex alluvial aquifers with sand and clay lenses, will further complicate the shape of pollution plumes both areally and with depth.

ii.   Preliminary monitoring network

The preliminary model is liable to have many unknowns such as detailed local geology, hydraulic properties of the aquifer and groundwater flow regimes. These need to be determined by drilling and testing, but the operation should be carried out in conjunction with installation of a network of monitoring wells to identify the nature and extent of the pollution plume. Because of the expense of drilling and installation of monitoring wells, the selection of sites, both up gradient and down gradient of the point source, should be carefully made. The three dimensional nature of the system must be taken into account by completing monitoring wells at different depths.

iii.   Monitoring network

Utilising the results of the first two stages, the preliminary model is revised and further gaps in the understanding of the system identified. These gaps should be filled by drilling further monitoring wells for inclusion in the monitoring network in conjunction with the design of the sampling strategy. As described in Section 9.1 this will involve an initially intensive programme to identify indicator parameters, which can be monitored at frequent intervals, supplemented by more comprehensive sampling at suitable intervals.

These three basic stages of an investigation should enable the pollution from a point source to be identified and its nature, extent and rate of movement quantified. This information can then be used as a basis for predictions of detrimental effects likely to be inflicted on the environment and water supply and assist in the decision as to what remedial action should be taken.

9.3.5   Research investigations

The three main areas of groundwater quality sampling and monitoring are regional assessment, monitoring the quality of pumped public supply systems and monitoring pollution. Other specialised investigations, dependent on accurate measurement of groundwater quality, are also carried out but the principles described in the previous sections apply.

Monitoring the extent and movement of induced saline intrusion, requires an understanding of the hydrogeological regime with the additional complication of fluids of differing densities. The use of tracers to determine the direction, path and rate of groundwater movement not only requires accurate sampling but more importantly, a knowledge of the hydraulic regime and a good understanding of what is being sampled.

9.4   General safety precautions

Safety at wells, boreholes and drilling sites, in trenches, chambers, mines and other areas is dependent on knowledge of potential hazards as much as common sense. If in any doubt seek information and ensure care is taken and that work is carried out in pairs (208).

Physical dangers may arise from collapse around or into old excavations, wells or boreholes due to failure of structural supports and formation wash-outs. Physical dangers are also present at all drilling sites at all times, and instructions from the drilling rig operator must be obeyed promptly. Toe protector footwear and hard hats are mandatory on drilling and borehole test sites. Additional protective clothing is desirable particularly if toxic or radioactive groundwaters are to be sampled. In the latter case, advice should be taken from qualified health personnel, before and during sampling.

A particular hazard can arise from the occurrence of gas which can collect in wells, well-head sumps and enclosed basements. This is commonly gas that is deficient in oxygen and consists of nitrogen mixed with carbon dioxide. Other gases encountered underground are methane and hydrogen sulphide: the latter two are explosive. Carbon dioxide is a component of foul air but it is also found in most rocks, particularly limestones, or where acids have been used, for example to improve permeability. If the atmospheric pressure falls, a well may begin to discharge carbon dioxide (or foul air) and this can collect at a well-head, or in sumps if ventilation is poor.

Carbon monoxide and petrol and diesel vapours can collect in wells, sumps and basements when internal combustion engines are operated nearby. Fumes can accumulate from spills of petrol and diesel.

Hydrogen sulphide has a characteristic smell of rotten eggs but the sense of smell rapidly declines in the presence of this gas; very small amounts cause death quickly.

Methane is associated with carbonaceous strata and landfill sites. It is lighter than air and therefore, accumulates near the roofs of closed chambers or adits. High concentrations lead to suffocation. It is explosive at low concentrations. Other hydrocarbons have also been reported and cause explosions when ignited by drills or pumps. High pressure oil and gas, hot water and superheated steam have also been encountered. Knowledge of the local geology and past history of the site can often forewarn of risks such as these.

Wells, well-head sumps, basements that contain a well or borehole, and sampling or inspection pits should never be entered without first testing for gas. Tests must be continuously carried out while working in such environments. This must include tests below the working level. A naked light must never be used if explosive gases are suspected. The detector should not be lowered on a nylon line because of a risk of generating static electricity in an explosive atmosphere. Where there may be highly volatile hydrocarbons, any operations of drilling or sampling must be carried out in a safe manner. All machinery must be fitted with flame traps and spark arresters and there should be no arcing to the atmosphere from any switch gear. Hydrocarbon detectors and alarms should be used and the need for having adequate fire fighting equipment available should be surveyed.

If it is necessary to enter a well it must only be done when at least two other people are present. A proper safety harness must be worn, connected to a lifting system or mechanism by which an individual can be recovered. If possible, analyse the air for oxygen content, carbon dioxide and any toxic, flammable or irrespirable gases likely to be present. Consider whether there is a risk of a sudden gas or liquid blow out into the chamber, hole, or pit. If in doubt, wear a self contained breathing apparatus. High concentrations of toxic gases can render a person unconscious before a face mask can be put on if not immediately accessible. Gas masks are no protection against lack of oxygen or large concentrations of toxic gases.

9.5   Sampling techniques

9.5.1   Saturated zone sampling

The saturated zone of an aquifer is that part where all interconnected pore spaces, fractures and other voids contain groundwater at a pressure equal to, or greater than, atmospheric pressure. The groundwater can move freely within the rock in the direction of the prevailing hydraulic gradient. In an unconfined aquifer, the upper surface of the saturated zone is the water table, at which surface, the pressure of the groundwater is equal to that of the atmosphere. Where an aquifer lies beneath an impermeable (or confining) layer such as a clay, the aquifer is confined and the water pressure at this boundary is termed the confining or piezometric head; the head is described by the potentiometric surface or the level to which water will rise in a borehole penetrating the confining layer.

9.5.1.1   Sources of problems

Natural groundwater chemistry is the result of interactions between water and the soil and rock through which the water has passed and in which the water is contained. Groundwater derives largely from meteoric water infiltrating the ground and passing vertically through the unsaturated zone to the saturated zone to the aquifer. There may also be some connate water present. Infiltrating water attains a horizontal flow component only when it arrives at the saturated zone. Full chemical equilibrium between water and rock only occurs in slow moving groundwaters.

Recharging water may contain pollutants derived from near surface, domestic, industrial and agricultural sources which may be regional or local in nature. A pollutant may be highly soluble, or relatively immiscible, lighter or heavier than water and will behave in the saturated zone according to its physical and chemical characteristics. This behaviour may encourage concentration layering which can be further accentuated by differential flow rates associated with vertical inhomogeneity of aquifers, such as coarser grained, more permeable layers or open fractures.

In an unconfined aquifer, recharging waters tend to remain at shallow depths and older and more mineralised waters tend to occur at greater depth. This trend continues as groundwater flows into the confined parts of an aquifer, accompanied by characteristic changes associated with the decreasing availability of oxygen away from the recharge zone (209).

Vertical mixing of groundwaters occurs with time and provides additional problems in groundwater sampling and interpretation. Layered sequences of permeable and impermeable strata may create a series of semi-confined aquifers, one above the other, each with a different piezometric head. This gives rise to vertical flux and the potential for upward or downward flow with consequent mixing wherever the confining layers are relatively permeable.

In some places, the different waters may react. Thus if descending surface water carrying humic materials meets ascending water containing metals such as iron or aluminium, impermeable layers may be formed in otherwise permeable rock. Alternative leaching by ascending sodium carbonate waters and descending acidic waters containing dissolved carbon dioxide can form layered trace element zones (210–214). The ascending mineralised waters are usually surface waters from higher regions which have leached rocks elsewhere.

Where concentration layering occurs, production boreholes withdraw a 'cocktail,' of groundwaters according to the relative transmissivity of each layer, the pumping rate, the design of the borehole, the depth to the pump intake and the period of pumping. This cocktail results from the mixing of groundwaters from different depths and the mix will vary with pumping period and pumping rate (215). Pumping a borehole in an unlayered aquifer draws water from further afield as pumping proceeds and this too can result in changes in water quality.

Additional problems derive from the borehole construction. In general, percussion and air-hammer drilling techniques provide a cleaner borehole than rotary methods but in all cases comprehensive well-development and purging are essential before collecting samples.

9.5.1.2   Limitation of common sampling methods

Groundwater is commonly obtained from boreholes and wells as pumped samples or grab samples. Pumped samples are taken from as near to the well-head as possible, and well-head sampling taps are often provided for this purpose. These samples are drawn from the aquifer penetrated by the borehole and represent a mixture of undefined proportions which may vary with pumping rate, pumping depth and period.

Depth samples are obtained by lowering a grab device into a borehole to a selected depth where the sample is trapped and withdrawn. This allows vertical variations in water quality to be measured, but samples may suffer contamination from well construction materials or cross contamination due to vertical flow in the borehole from one horizon to another. A range of grab samplers is available for collecting waters from unpumped wells and boreholes and these are discussed more fully in Section 9.5.1.4.

There is often a need to purge stagnant water in the borehole before sampling. However, there may be a conflicting need to monitor standing water columns as certain determinands require that the natural environment of the groundwater be retained so that degassing and loss of volatile substances are restricted. To this end, special techniques have been devised but they are all restricted in scope and applicability.

Direct suction pumping from the surface can only be used to a maximum well depth of approximately 10 m as the hydraulic head in the pump inlet cannot exceed atmospheric pressure. For lifting water from greater depths, immersed or down-hole pumps, or pressure air lifts, or containers on wire or chain must be used. Suction pumping also has the disadvantage of partially degassing samples.

9.5.1.3 Production borehole samples

Pumped borehole samples derive from mixed and ill-defined origins. However, long term pumping provides valuable bulk samples of groundwater from production boreholes (216). Permeability stratification in an aquifer promotes abstraction from higher transmissivity layers. However, fissure flow along joints, bedding planes or other discontinuities allows less permeable horizons to drain slowly over a wide area into fissures and can result in rapid flow to the borehole. Differential piezometric pressures within strata penetrated by the borehole may also favour abstraction from selective horizons and the location of the pump inlet will prejudice the near field rather than the vertically more distant levels.

The pumping rate and the time since pumping began will also influence the producing zones of an aquifer system. As pumping commences, the water standing in the borehole adjacent to the pump inlet is drawn first, then water in the aquifer near the borehole will begin to move forward, and with time, water from further afield will arrive at the pump inlet. In a layered aquifer, the relative dynamic stress on each permeable horizon will change with time and the volumetric ratio of the water derived from each source horizon will vary. In an unconfined aquifer, dewatering will commence around the borehole and as the cone of depression expands a greater proportion of the water will be drawn from further afield and from deeper in the aquifer.

Borehole construction and design will greatly influence the hydraulic regime around a production borehole. Adequate hydraulic continuity must be available between borehole and aquifer or borehole and intended sampling zone; only if the borehole design is properly recorded can the sampling regime be adequately described. The risk of cross flow from other permeable horizons, which are not intended to be sampled, is commonly considerable.

In summary, the zone sampled in a production borehole and hence the ultimate analysis of the sample, depends on the following factors:

i. groundwater regime,

ii. depth to pump inlet,

iii. pumping rate,

iv. time since pumping started,

v. borehole design.

It is, therefore, essential that the local hydrogeology, groundwater flow patterns and construction of the borehole to be sampled are reasonably well understood before undertaking any detailed hydrochemical investigations based on pumped samples.

Care must be taken with the interpretation of analyses derived from pumped samples. Anomalous data should be identified to separate short term effects from long term trends. A standardised sampling procedure is desirable to ensure that the sample mix derived from the aquifer system is reasonably consistent.

Mixed samples drawn from a pumped borehole may be of value on a regional scale (216) but are often insufficient for the investigation of groundwater pollution (217). Samples will not provide information regarding the progress of a pollution plume, as this may be concentrated in one small horizon or along one bedding plane or joint and dilution with unpolluted water from other horizons may render the pollutant undetectable. The zones of adverse quality cannot be identified from this type of sample.

Pumped samples are liable to contamination by the very process of pumping from a borehole and discharging at surface. An airlift pump is least desirable as it produces a water and air mix which may destroy the stability of the sample. Submersible and turbine pumps, although better, effect a pressure release at the surface which encourages outgassing from the sample and possible uptake of oxygen from the atmosphere. The turbulent effect of the pump may increase the water temperature by up to 10°C and this in turn may affect the stability of the sample.

9.5.1.4 Grab sampling in unpumped boreholes

A variety of depth sampling devices are available to suit different conditions and requirements (40). The traditional depth sampler is the grab sampler, which may consist of a simple bailer or some triggered valve device, designed to entrap a sample at a given depth in a borehole (Figure 32). The depth sampler enables a small volume of borehole water to be lifted to the surface. However, it offers very little control because the sample is derived from the borehole column and not the aquifer and the volumes removed are too small to have any purging effect on the borehole. The borehole column may be stagnant or it may be flowing over certain interconnected sections of aquifer, under differential head and the depth sample may not represent groundwater from the depth at which it is acquired. In the case of a stagnant water column, interaction between the borehole casing and the atmosphere and the presence of bacteria which may act as a catalyst to ion exchange, may produce a water which bears little resemblance to the true groundwater (218).

9.5.1.5 Improved sampling methods

Improved sampling techniques are required to provide more meaningful data. Some techniques require purpose built monitoring boreholes; the benefit of the data so acquired must however be balanced against the increased cost.

9.5.1.6 Purpose designed boreholes

Narrow monitoring boreholes of nominal 50–100 mm diameter are widely used for pollution studies. However, cleaning such boreholes may be difficult and special sampling and pumping equipment is required. Monitoring boreholes should ideally be not less than 100 mm completed diameter and may alternatively be completed to 150 mm or 200 mm nominal diameter. This ensures that proper cleaning and completion of the new monitoring borehole can be undertaken. The casing and borehole screen should be manufactured from material that will not react with the determinands to be sampled. Materials commonly in use (219) and their advantages and disadvantages are listed in Table 5.

The use of drilling fluids should be reduced to a sensible minimum and preference should be given to air or water circulation (220). The use of drilling muds for rotary drilling is not recommended for the construction of monitoring boreholes and salt-weighted muds should not be used. Bentonite, for example, may chemically interfere with the ground-water and adsorb certain ions and exchange others. Biodegradable polymers tend to leave an organic residue and affect microbiology, and the use of cement in borehole completions may increase the pH of groundwater. A full record should be maintained of all fluids used during drilling and completion. The advantages and disadvantages of each drilling method are summarised in Table 6.

Cleansing of drilling equipment and completion materials is recommended before use in monitoring boreholes and is best undertaken by steam cleaning. Decontamination solutions include sodium bicarbonate (water softener), trisodium phosphate (detergent) and calcium hypochlorite (disinfectant).

Borehole development and cleaning are essential. Walker (221) showed that drilling fluid additives could be detected in one borehole two years after drilling was finished. The effects of bentonite on water samples and of organic residues from polymeric muds decline with time, but may remain detectable for the first 90 days and may interfere with analyses thereafter. Air may also be introduced into groundwater via the borehole and this may locally affect the groundwater chemistry.

Borehole design depends on the location and number of horizons needing to be monitored. Several screened lengths in a single string can be inserted into a borehole, but the risk of cross contamination between screened lengths and cross-flow behind the casing, as well as the need to use packers to isolate the sampling zones renders this system least desirable. One alternative is to place nests of monitoring boreholes in a single drilled borehole with a hydraulic seal placed between each zone (Figure 33). The best method is to place carefully structured monitoring boreholes to strategic depths with a short length of screen open to the zone of interest. These can either be placed singly or in clusters, to monitor different depths at selected locations (Figure 30). Further details are available in refs 222 and 223, but single completion boreholes are preferable to nests because of the danger of cross contamination between sampling zones.

The selection of locations for monitoring boreholes and the depths to proposed sampling points depends on a good understanding of the prevailing groundwater regime. Monitoring point source pollution requires prediction of groundwater flow paths and velocities and pollution transport. Monitoring boreholes, therefore, need careful siting and design to fulfil their role.

9.5.1.7 Controlled grab sampling and specialised equipment

A variety of bailer samplers are available, and these and other sampling devices are summarised in Table 7 (from ref. 224). They include ball-valve type bailers (Figure 34), the bladder pump (Figure 35), suction lift (Figure 36), gas lift pump (Figure 37) or peristaltic pump (225). Care should always be taken to avoid cross contamination between boreholes via the sampling equipment.

The bladder pump provides efficient well purging and enables representative samples to be collected over a range of conditions. Grab samplers may include the conventional bailer, dual-check valve bailer and syringe pump: they are unsuitable for well purging and require careful handling. The peristaltic pump is suitable for depths down to 6 m only; a loss of determinand may arise with it for some organic compounds.

There are a number of innovative sampling devices described in the literature which satisfy the peculiar requirements of particular determinands. For example, Gillham (226) and Pankow *et al* (227) describe a remotely operated syringe for obtaining samples for organic analysis and Emenhiser and Singh (228) and Edge and Cordry (229) describe a number of other techniques. A foot valve on a length of tubing forms an inertial pump when the tube is rapidly moved up and down. The inertial pump has been successfully used up to a head of 50 m (230).

Depth samples, taken from the column of water within a borehole, represent groundwaters whose origin can only be crudely defined by means of borehole geophysics and a thorough knowledge of the prevailing groundwater regimes. Flow meter, conductivity and temperature logging (in conjunction with calliper and electric logs in uncased boreholes) carried out, both when the borehole is pumped or static, enables the most likely sources of groundwaters to be located.

Flow meter logs measure the velocity of water in the borehole column; conductivity logs define the specific electrical conductance of the water column and temperature logs show variations in groundwater temperature within the borehole. The calliper log measures the borehole diameter at any given depth and helps to identify cracks, joints and other areas of weakness that may intersect the borehole. Electric logs indicate certain physical properties of the rock and groundwater adjacent to the borehole. Upward or downward flow may occur naturally between zones of different heads and depth samples may be located at influent zones in order to identify discrete groundwater types entering the borehole.

9.5.1.8 Packer sampling

The use of borehole packers, enables discrete zones of particular hydraulic significance to be isolated for sampling. A packer comprises two inflatable seals which are lowered to straddle a particular zone of interest within a borehole and inflated to isolate that zone hydraulically. This provides a greater degree of control over the sample source than is allowed using depth samplers. Packers may either be located temporarily whilst a particular sample or suite of samples is collected or they may be permanently installed (Figure 38).

A variety of commercially available internal casing packer systems is available. These may be lowered, inflated, deflated and raised to enable samples to be collected from discrete zones. External casing packer assemblies may be used on a permanent basis to isolate specific zones in a borehole (Figure 31). A special tool is necessary to open and close access ports to each zone (231).

9.5.1.9 Pore water extraction from cores

Pore water may be recovered from cores to obtain a precise log of groundwater chemistry with depth. However, care must be taken to avoid contamination of the pore water by fluids used in the drilling process. Air flush or percussion coring methods of drilling are preferable.

Lithium chloride (LiCl) tracer may be added to the drilling fluid to check on fluid invasion. Edmunds and Bath (284) demonstrated core invasion in English Chalk to a depth of 1.0 to 1.5 cm, but in Permo-Triassic sandstones of Cumbria it was greater. The use of a tracer in drilling fluids is always desirable and sub-sampling of the inner axial part of the core provides least contaminated material.

Rotary coring devices include conventional core barrels and thin wall tube samplers (Figure 39). The hollow-stem auger is suitable for sampling shallow depths in unconsolidated material and dry percussion driven samplers such as U100's (100 mm diameter tubes) can be used in unconsolidated sediment and in consolidated chalk.

Extraction of pore water should be rapid and preferably carried out on-site, otherwise fractionation, denitrification and TOC degradation of the interstitial water may occur. Core samples may be stored in thin walled sample tubes with the ends sealed, or they may be extruded from the core barrel or tube and suitably coated.

Pore water extraction is generally undertaken by centrifugation. Either the water is allowed to drain freely through a porous plate supporting the sample and collected in a cup at the bottom of the centrifuge tube or an excess of dense immiscible liquid (for example chlorinated solvent) is added to the sample and the displaced water collected after it has floated to the top (232). Centrifugation may be carried out in an inert atmosphere if required. In the case of mud rocks, squeezing in a triaxial cell to extract pore water may be effective.

The representativeness of centrifuge extracted pore waters was tested by Kinniburgh and Miles (232), who demonstrated that little analytical variation was observed between samples which were subject to centrifugation for a range of times and speeds. Work (233) has shown that for mud rocks and clays, centrifugation and solvent extraction are not as satisfactory as squeezing.

Sampling for organic compounds may be carried out by solvent extraction or headspace methods. The solvent extraction technique requires solvent to be mixed with crushed core samples and removed by centrifugation. The headspace technique is the removal of volatile vapours from crushed core samples. This is done by incubating the sample at 70°C to drive vapour into a confined headspace from which vapour samples can be collected.

9.5.1.10 *In-situ* sampling

A number of *in-situ* sampling devices are available for permanent installation in a borehole which may then be backfilled with inert permeable material incorporating bentonite seals between sampling zones (234, 235). The Water Research Centre *in-situ* sampler uses compressed inert gas to lift the sample to surface (Figure 40). The device may clog with sediment and bacterial colonies may develop in time. The main advantages of gas driven samplers are cost, and they require minimal purging; disadvantages are that sampling of large volumes is time consuming, it is not suitable for immiscible pollutants and the sampler cannot be retrieved or replaced. Nitrogen is commonly used as the inert gas to drive the systems. Detailed profiles of water quality can be obtained using a multi-level sampler which utilises dialysis cells, which equilibrate with groundwater in discrete zones (236).

9.5.1.11 *In-situ* measurements

Measurements of certain parameters can be carried out within the borehole column. They may be carried out by normal geophysical logging techniques or by a probe permanently installed in rising mains or monitoring boreholes. In addition to conductivity and temperature logs, sondes are available to make point measurements of dissolved oxygen,

Eh and pH within the borehole column and work has been carried out on the measurement of nitrate, ammonium and chloride (237). Development work is hindered by the need to work at high pressures with remote interrogation of the probe.

In-situ measurements of certain volatile organic compounds, notably chlorinated hydrocarbons, can be undertaken with down-hole sorption cartridges. The cartridges utilise adsorption media, such as activated carbon or resins, from which contaminants can be eluted in the laboratory, once they are recovered from the borehole (227).

9.5.2   Unsaturated zone sampling

The unsaturated zone holds large volumes of water under surface tension in the porous matrix, which also contains varying proportions of gas. In the case of chalk, the pore sizes are so small that the matrix is virtually saturated. Below the zone of influence of plant roots, the movements of this water will be predominantly downwards. This is the water which will recharge the aquifer in the future and its quality will affect the quality of the groundwater once it reaches the saturated zone. Monitoring of the unsaturated zone, therefore, provides an early warning of incipient groundwater contamination from diffuse or point-sources.

British aquifers, notably chalk, have relatively thick unsaturated zones (more than 20 m and in certain cases up to 50 m) and surface derived pollutants can remain in this zone for several decades. For the most part, the soils developed over the outcropping aquifer are thin, highly permeable and well aerated and they allow rapid infiltration of excess rainfall to the unsaturated zone.

9.5.2.1   Pore water sampling

The methods and procedures used for sampling pore water in the saturated core generally apply in the unsaturated zone. Unconsolidated sediments are best obtained with a hollow stemmed continuous flight auger, or an undisturbed percussion core sampler, with the borehole wall supported by drive pipe above each sample interval.

The advantages and disadvantages of the direct pore water sampling methods are summarised by Wilson (238). Core samples can be obtained by the undisturbed (100 mm diameter) core sampler dry tube (U100) to minimise contamination.

9.5.2.2   Suction sampling from tensiometers

The use of a porous ceramic cup placed under vacuum for collecting water in the unsaturated zone (Figure 41) was first described by Wagner (239). A porous cup mounted on the end of a piezometer tube and placed under vacuum will slowly suck water, percolating through the unsaturated zone, into the cup. The water may be periodically raised to the surface under suction. Only small volumes can be obtained in this way.

The validity of the samples derived from suction tensiometers was described by Hansen and Harris (240), who found a 60% range in sample concentration derived from eight different samplers in a small uniform plot. Sample bias may occur due to sorption, leaching, diffusion and the drainable soil water concentration. The sampling technique and sampler design should be standardised within any one project. The ceramic cup should be buried in silica sand to provide an adequate hydraulic contact wherever coarse-grade material is present.

Shallow sampling (for example in the soil zone) may also be carried out using pan lysimeters. These are small collection trays driven horizontally from the sides of a trench to intercept percolating water (241). This technique induces less bias to the water samples than do suction tensiometers but is confined to the depth of a trench.

9.5.3   Spring sampling

Springs offer a useful source of groundwater which discharge naturally from an aquifer. Perennial springs are likely to represent effluent from deeper, larger aquifers, whereas seasonal springs may drain superficial gravels, or, in the case of chalk and other fissured aquifers, represent temporary discharge at higher elevations than normal, due to seasonal or short-term recharge. For the most part, the flow paths of water leading to a spring are not known and the source represents a mixture of groundwaters whose origin can only be described in general terms. Care should be taken to check if field drains contribute to a source. Nevertheless, spring sources provide a valuable means of collecting 'bulk,' groundwater samples.

Spring samples should be obtained directly from the spring orifice to avoid contamination at the surface from, for example, sediment and vegetation. Contact between water and air will probably have modified any reducing characteristics of groundwater before it appears at the surface, but tubing can be pushed into small sources to draw the least affected spring water. Such springs often have a slick or deposit of metal oxide (often brown or yellow) around them. Sample bottles should be completely full of inert gas which is vented off as the bottle is filled, or alternatively filled with an inert liquid which is drained out into another bottle.

Underwater springs exist and these can be sampled by insertion of tubing, the sample flow into the bottle being regulated so that excess water escapes round the tubing and supernatant water is not drawn into the sample. It may not be possible to avoid including standing water which has soaked into the ground around the spring and been drawn up with it from below the surface.

9.5.4 Sampling wells

Large bore wells are exceedingly easy to contaminate. Great care is necessary not to contaminate them more than they already are. They are usually sampled by dipping. The procedure is detailed in Chapter 11. Pumping can also be used. If it is necessary to sample for segregation in the water layer, procedures for pump sampling stratified boreholes, or sampling deep marine waters can be used. See earlier in this chapter and also Chapter 6.

9.5.5 Sampling seeps and puddles

When sampling seeps from walls and/or ceilings, fixing a spout or wick to the wall or ceiling at a suitable point may facilitate filling of the sample bottle. If possible, use inert materials. Puddles can be sampled using scoops or if volatiles are not significant, a syringe may be used.

9.5.6 Sample size

Always ensure that sufficient sample is taken from boreholes, springs or wells, to more than satisfy the requirements of the analytical method.

Table 5 Well casing and screen materials, after Driscoll (222).

Type	Advantages	Disadvantages
Polyvinyl chloride (PVC) and acrylonitrile butadiene styrene (ABS)	Lightweight. Excellent chemical resistance to alcohols, aliphatic hydrocarbons and oils. Good chemical resistance to strong mineral acids, concentrated oxidising agents and strong alkalis. Readily available. Low price compared with stainless steel and PTFE.	Weaker, less rigid and more temperature sensitive than metallic materials. May adsorb some constituents from groundwater. May react with and leach some constituents from groundwater. Poor chemical resistance to ketones, esters and aromatic hydrocarbons.
Polypropylene	Lightweight. Excellent chemical resistance to mineral acids. Good to excellent chemical resistance to alkalis, alcohols, ketones and esters. Good chemical resistance to concentrated oxidising acids, aliphatic and aromatic hydrocarbons. Low price compared with stainless steel and PTFE.	Weaker, less rigid and more temperature sensitive than metallic materials. May react with and leach some constituents from groundwater. Poor machinability.
Polytetrafluoro-ethylene (PTFE)	Lightweight. High impact strength. Outstanding resistance to chemical attack.	Tensile strength and wear resistance low compared with other engineering plastics. Expensive relative to other plastics and stainless steel.
Kynar	Greater strength and water resistance than PTFE. Resistant to most chemicals and solvents. Lower price than PTFE.	Not readily available. Poor chemical resistance to ketones.
Mild steel	Strong, rigid. Temperature sensitivity not a problem. Readily available. Low price relative to stainless steel and PTFE.	Denser than plastics. May react with and leach some constituents in groundwater. Not as chemically resistant as stainless steel.
Stainless steel	High strength at a great range of temperatures. Excellent resistance to corrosion and oxidation. Readily available. Moderate price for casing.	Denser than plastics. May corrode and leach some chromium in highly acidic waters. Some varieties sensitive to chloride. May act as a catalyst in some organic reactions. Higher price than plastics.

97

Table 6 Comparison of drilling methods, after Foster and Gomes (200)

Method	Principle of operation	Advantages	Disadvantages
Drive point	Small-diameter casing with pointed tip and integral screen is mechanically driven to required depth.	Low cost, easy installation. Water samples can be collected during drilling. Good seal around solid casing in most formations.	No geological samples. Limited to loosely-consolidated formations. Screen easily clogged. Only metal casing and screen can be driven.
Cable tool percussion	Heavy string of drilling tools percussed into ground with temporary casing driven slightly ahead. Drill cuttings removed intermittently with bailer.	Suitable for all geological formations. Reasonable geological logging possible. Cross-contamination reduced by use of temporary casing.	Slow penetration rates, especially in hard rock formations.
Jetting	Hydraulic pressure erodes formation and permits penetration of drill rod. Drill cuttings brought to surface by return flow.	Low cost. Easy installation without specialised personnel.	Only feasible in limited range of formations due to penetration problems or formation caving. High pressure water supply needed, but even then depth limited to 45 m. Poor geological control.
Air hammer	Reciprocating air hammer connected to drilling bit advancing borehole by pulverising formation. Drill cuttings raised by return airflow.	Very fast penetration, especially in hard rock formations. Only small amounts of water added for temperature and dust control.	Expensive. Rig mobility restricted. Cross-contamination likely. Hazardous if toxic pollution encountered.
Augering (bucket, solid-stem, hollow-stem)	Unconsolidated formations are cut by rotation of augers of various types and sizes. Cuttings are brought to the surface by rotary action of auger.	Low cost and fairly simple operation, not needing specialised personnel. Rapid setting-up time and moderate penetration rates in some formations. No drilling fluid needed, especially if core sampling taken intermittently.	Depth limited to about 40 m in favourable conditions above groundwater table. Not suitable for rock or gravel formations. Smearing of borehole walls makes development difficult. Cross-contamination of water samples very likely.

Method			
Hydraulic rotary	Rotating drilling bit penetrates formation and cuttings brought to the surface by drilling fluid (mud/water/air) which can be recirculated after settlement of cuttings.	Rapid penetration in most geological formations. Practically unlimited depth capacity depending on rig size. Core sampling can readily be undertaken.	Expensive and requires skilled operator and many accessories. Contamination of samples by drilling fluid and from higher levels in borehole. Geological control can be poor if no core sampling undertaken. Use of drilling mud has numerous advantages, but presents borehole development problems.
Reverse rotary	Similar to hydraulic rotary, except that drilling fluid is always water, which circulates down the borehole outside, and rises inside the drill stem (the reverse to the standard rotary method).	Produces a very clean, well-developed borehole, suitable for all geological formations to considerable depths. Split-spoon core samples can be taken intermittently during drilling.	Large water supply needed, especially for boreholes in deep permeable formations. Expensive, and requires skilled operator and many accessories. Minimum borehole diameter about 45 mm. Cross-contamination of water samples very likely. Poor geological control.

Table 7 Summary of sampling devices and their applications, after Pohlmann and Hess (224)

Well and Sample Data / Groundwater Parameters

Sampling devices	Approximate maximum sampling depth (m)	Minimum well diameter (mm)	Sample delivery (ls^{-1})	Inorganic							Organic				Radioactive		Biological
				EC	pH	Redox	Major ions	Trace metals	Nitrate, fluoride	Dissolved gases	Non-volatile	Volatile	TOC	TOX	Radium	Gross alpha and beta	Coliform bacteria
Grab:																	
Bottom sealed bailer	no limit	12	variable	•			•	•	•		•				•		•
Top and bottom valve bailer	no limit	12	variable	•	•	•	•	•	•		•	•	•	•	•		•
Syringe sampler	no limit	38	0.05–1	•	•	•	•	•	•		•				•	•	•
Positive Displacement (Submersible):																	
Bladder pump	120	38	0–0.15	•	•	•	•	•	•	•	•	•	•	•	•	•	•
Helical rotor	48	50	0–0.08		•	•	•	•	•	•	•	•	•	•	•	•	
Piston pump (gas driven)	150	38	0–0.04	•				•	•		•				•	•	
Centrifugal	variable	75	variable	•			•		•						•	•	
Suction Lift:																	
Peristaltic	8	12	0–0.02	•			•		•		•				•		•
Gas Contact:																	
Gas-lift variable	25	variable															
Gas-driven	45	25	0–0.01	•			•		•		•				•		
In-situ:																	
Pneumatic	no limit	n/a	0–0.01	•	•	•	•	•	•		•				•	•	•

NOTE: • Indicates that the device is generally suitable for the application.
 A blank indicates that the device may be unsuitable, or is currently untested for the application.

<table>
<tr><td>

10 Sampling of precipitation

</td><td>

10.1 Introduction

Precipitation occurs in various forms, the most common of which in Britain is rain, but with significant amounts as snow, frost, hail, dew and mist. Precipitation sampling is carried out for two purposes, firstly to measure the quantity falling and secondly to assess its composition. Quantitative measurement is usually undertaken to assess either the adequacy of rainfall for public supply, or agricultural and horticultural purposes, or the likelihood of flooding due to excess run-off. For most purposes, the measurement required is the amount falling, but for some purposes a knowledge of the amount of solid water (snow, frost and hail) remaining on the ground at the thaw may be useful, in which case evaporation and drifting complicate the measurements. Compositional sampling is usually undertaken to determine the extent of pollution by specific materials of interest, and possibly the source of pollution.

The sampling techniques used are dependent both on the form in which the precipitation occurs and on the nature of the determinands. Sample container material and sample preservation for compositional analysis are the same as those for other types of sample—see Chapter 5 for details.

10.2 Measuring the amount of precipitation

10.2.1 General

The total amount of precipitation which reaches the ground in a stated period at any given place is expressed as the depth to which water would cover the earth's surface at the place, assuming no run-off. Snow, hail, ice and other solid forms are measured as the depth of fresh material covering this same surface.

The aim of any measurement of precipitation is to obtain a sample representative of the area concerned, so that the choice of the site for the measurement, the type of gauge and the number of gauges in the network are important considerations, as well as such factors as observer practice. These points apply equally to measurements of quantity and quality.

10.2.2 Gauge location

The choice of gauge site is critical to the measurement of precipitation. The perfect site would provide an ideal representation of the precipitation falling on the area. In practice, sites are not perfect, largely because of the effects of wind, which acts both on the gauge and on the site around the gauge.

The effect of wind is generally to reduce the amount of catch that would have reached the ground in the absence of the gauge. The gauge itself, in standing above the ground surface at a height between 30 cm and 2 m, depending on type, creates an obstacle in the air stream. Acceleration takes place in the space above the gauge and this alters the trajectory of the falling drops or particles, the smaller ones being carried over the gauge. The higher the windspeed, the greater the loss of catch; a loss which will be greater for taller gauges and for smaller drops and lighter particles.

10.2.2.1 Gauge design

Designs of gauge have been developed which attempt to reduce the effect of wind. The aim of shields placed around the gauge is to induce uniform flow of air over it and thus to avoid local acceleration. Surrounding the gauge by a turf wall about 3 m in diameter and the same height as the gauge reduces the effect of wind, and a satisfactory arrangement is the ground level or pit gauge. This consists of a shallow pit in the centre of which stands a gauge, the top of which stands level with the ground. A grid is placed around the gauge in the intervening space in the pit to stop eddies. Gauges of this type generally catch 4% to 25% more rain on an annual basis, than do nearby elevated gauges, depending on location. They are not suitable for solid precipitation, however, and have no equivalent for snowfall measurement.

</td></tr>
</table>

10.2.2.2   Effect of site

A gauge site should be on level ground, and surrounding objects such as trees, fences and buildings should be more than four times their height away from the gauge. The site should be sheltered from the full force of the wind, but the shelter should not induce larger disturbances in the wind field than the effects which are being avoided. Sites on sloping ground should be avoided, especially if the slope is into the prevailing wind. The best sites are often in clearings in trees, or where surrounding bushes form a wind break. Sites where eddies might be induced by buildings or the topography should be avoided.

10.2.2.3   Systematic error of measurement

The effect of wind on the normally exposed gauge causes a loss of catch which may be exacerbated by the site of the gauge. This systematic error in measurement, affects both quantity and quality alike and is much worse for snow than for rain.

10.2.3   Types of gauge

Gauges can be divided into recording and non-recording types. The former may record rainfall or they may transmit data to a distant base. All types of gauge have several elements in common, in particular the collector (see Figure 42). However, they may differ in how the collected rain or snow is measured.

10.2.3.1   The collector

The collector varies in the area presented to the falling rain, usually between 200 and 1000 cm^2 depending on the type of gauge. The interior of the collector is designed to stop water splashing out, while the height of its rim and external shape are aimed at preventing splash in, or the blowing of material into the gauge.

10.2.3.2   The receiver and recording

In observer-read gauges, the collected rainwater falls from the funnel of the collector into a bottle. The bottle may be emptied into a measuring cylinder or a dip rod may be used to measure the depth of water.

Three types of recording gauges have been in general use, the weighing type, the float type and the tipping bucket type. Only the weighing type can measure all forms of precipitation. In all three cases, the increase in weight, the rise of the float or the tipping of the buckets is recorded mechanically or electrically. Each method has advantages and disadvantages and is subject to errors.

10.2.4   Errors of measurement

Apart from systematic error, the various types of gauge are subject to a range of errors. Evaporation can take place from the collector and from the bottle in which the rainwater is collected. Splashing out and splashing in can occur and the sample can be contaminated by material blown in, or dropped in. Snow can be blown in and out of gauges. Observers can introduce a range of errors depending on the practice adopted and on how well the gauge is maintained. Recording gauges suffer from mechanical problems; freezing in cold weather, clock failure and other problems. Snow causes bridging of gauges. Generally, errors increase as the time between visits to a site increases.

10.2.5   Measurement networks

The design of precipitation networks requires considerable research and there are a number of basic questions which need to be addressed when establishing new networks or evaluating the performance of existing networks. These include:

i.   the number of sites to be instrumented;

ii.   the location of sites; and

iii.   maintenance.

For an area where no measurements have been made there are no immediate answers to these questions. Indeed for virgin territory, it is invariably necessary to install a pilot network of a few instruments to provide some information as a basis for the design of a permanent network.

In the case of existing networks there are methods of investigating the mean, in relation to the number of gauges, to establish what is the error of the estimate of the mean. Increasing the number of gauges in the network reduces the error and there is usually a point where there is a balance between the value of the information from the network and the cost of obtaining it. Alternatively, correlograms can be constructed relating the measurements from pairs of gauges to their distance apart. This correlation/distance relationship calculated for different time periods can indicate the optimum spacing for a network.

10.2.6   Other forms of precipitation

Most of the previous remarks have been concerned with rain but problems are invariably larger for other forms of precipitation, particularly snow. Snow is best measured by clearing an area of ground between snowfalls and measuring the depth after each fall. However, accurate measurements are difficult to make due to the effect of drifting.

10.2.7   Other techniques

Other forms of measurement are becoming more useful, for example ground-based weather radar and satellite-based remote sensing imagery. However, these methods require calibration against the normal type of instrument located on the ground. Thus, 'measurements' made with them frequently compound the existing errors.

For additional information on gauges, refer to the Meteorological Observers Handbook (242).

10.3   Sampling to determine the composition of precipitation

10.3.1   General sampling of rainfall

This section considers the collection of precipitation when the composition is to be determined. As always, the aim is to obtain a representative sample of the precipitation. Differences between the compositions of precipitation and collected water can arise because of:

i.   different collection efficiencies of rain collectors for different sizes of rain drops;

ii.   evaporation of water from the receiver;

iii.   changes in the composition of collected water caused by chemical or biological activity;

iv.   reactions between the rainwater and the materials of the collector;

v.   contamination of the collector by soil or other particles or biological material; and/ or

vi.   dry deposition of gases or aerosols on to the collector surfaces.

All of these processes, with the exception of some types of biological contamination can lead to systematic rather than random errors, resulting in differences between the measure composition and its true value.

Although they may not always be eliminated, a number of steps can be taken to minimise these potential errors. To minimise contamination of the precipitation sample by wind-blown soil particles or other debris, collectors used in composition studies are usually located at a height of 1–2 m. As a result, they receive less rain than those at ground level, the under-catch being influenced both by the height and aerodynamics of the collector as discussed in the preceding section (see also 243). For example, certain bulk collectors can typically collect 90% of the rainfall collected by others, although values may be as low as 65% at exposed high-altitude sites (244). Many collectors do not catch snow efficiently (245); hence large anomalies can occur at northern sites during winter months. There is the additional problem of bias against smaller drops which may have higher solute concentrations (246, 247), but this is only likely to have a major effect with very short sampling periods.

In order to minimise the contribution of dry deposition, wet-only collectors which open only during periods of precipitation are available (248–251). These collectors are designed to avoid splash and are capable of recording the time and duration of precipitation events and other relevant environmental data, for example wind speed and direction. In addition, they may be refrigerated to maximise sample stability between collection and analysis. Automation enables a number of daily samples to be collected without the constraint of daily visits to the site which may otherwise result in compromises regarding siting. Sequential sampling can also permit the investigation of changes in composition within an individual event.

While wet-only collectors provide very useful data it should be noted that reliability problems can result in decreased data capture. Furthermore, problems can occur in detecting the onset of light rain.

In the case of bulk collectors, or those which are open all the time, the collected rainwater should be protected from light and direct solar radiation to minimise evaporative losses, chemical degradation and also biological action. One way in which this may be done is to locate the collecting bottle in a close-fitting canister surrounded by a polished concentric sleeve (252).

Contamination of the sample by birds can be discouraged by incorporating some form of bird guard, usually an arrangement of inert line adjacent to but not crossing over the funnel, or a circle of spikes surrounding it (252, 253).

10.3.1.1   Materials of construction

The collecting funnel and bottle should be inert to the species of interest. When sampling for major ions, high-density polyethylene, polypropylene and PTFE (usually as a coating) have been found to be satisfactory. Stainless steel may be used for sampling for pesticides and trace organics. See Chapter 5 for more details of compatibility of materials and determinands.

10.3.1.2   Sampler siting criteria and network design

The design of any monitoring network is dictated by the aims of the exercise. Whatever these aims, each collector should be located so as to collect as representative a sample of precipitation as possible. A number of comprehensive guides to network design have been published (254) and the subject is not considered in detail here. A useful technique for assessing site density relates measurements in pairs of collectors. The method provides an estimate of the interpolation error between collectors, and hence the site density necessary to achieve a particular variance can be calculated.

10.3.1.3   Sample preservation, storage and transport

The general principles given in earlier sections of this book apply to the sampling of precipitation. However, the following references may be consulted for additional details on sampling for measurement of radioactivity (157), pesticides and other trace organic substances (255, 256), and acidity and related ions (257, 258).

10.4   Information on sampling problems still under investigation

10.4.1   Sampling snow

Over large areas of the United Kingdom a significant part of the winter precipitation occurs as snow. Snowflakes and rain drops differ somewhat in their removal of pollutants from the atmosphere and snowfall may have a different chemical composition from rainfall under otherwise similar environmental conditions. Hence the relative contributions of snow and rain may influence the acidic input over any one year. Snowfall introduces another dimension to acidic deposition. The character of the 'acidic flush' which occurs on a snowbelt depends, in part, on pollutant distribution in the snowpack, as well as on snow depth, and the earlier evolution of the snowpack.

The accurate measurement of snowfall in other than calm conditions is much more difficult than that of rainfall and remains an intractable problem (259). The major difficulties are listed below.

i. When brisk winds blow across loose surfaces 'snow drifting', occurs (260). The process is called 'saltation,' and the snow grains proceed by a series of jumps of limited height, frequently of a few centimetres and rarely more than 1 metre. The minimum wind-speed for this process depends on conditions, but can be as low as 3 ms^{-1}.

    In very strong winds, snowflakes are suspended in the air by turbulent eddies. Deposition will then occur by turbulent transfer or inertial impaction, very much in the manner in which cloud droplets are deposited in occult deposition.

ii. Aerodynamic disturbance by the collector causes the displacement and acceleration of the airflow over the collector opening. As a result, collection efficiency is reduced by an increasing amount with increasing wind speed. Deficiencies for snowfall are much greater than for rainfall due to the smaller inertia and lower settling velocities of snowflakes compared to raindrops.

iii. A further aerodynamic problem, 'blow out', may arise because strong circulating flows are induced inside many collectors which may blow out snow that has settled.

iv. The very low density of snow means that it rapidly fills most collectors, especially those not designed for snow and unless attended to promptly, undercatching will result.

In forested areas it is possible to avoid most of the aerodynamic difficulties by installing the collectors, with suitable precautions, in clearings (261). This procedure is clearly not possible everywhere and many empirical attempts have been made to improve snow collection (259, 261–263). Most have been based on aerodynamic shielding of the collector. Additional wind sheltering by snow fences (or dual snow fences) is sometimes employed.

A new approach based on the principles of aerofoil and wing design has been tried. The collector, suitably curved shaped, reduces the streamline displacement over the opening, which in turn reduces the disturbance to the trajectories of the snow flakes which diminishes the catch (245).

10.4.2   Sampling mist and cloud etc

Measurements made from both aircraft and at hilltop sites have shown that cloud and fog water contain significantly larger ionic concentrations than rain (258). Instruments to collect cloud water are still at a development stage and many designs are under consideration, but one approach is to allow the droplets to impact on polyethylene or polypropylene strings arranged in a cylindrical or conical configuration. The droplets failing to follow the streamline of airflow round the strings are interrupted, coalesce and drain down through a polyethylene funnel into a sample bottle. The collection efficiency of such a collector is both wind speed and droplet size dependent. The performance of the collector may be modelled, using data on the capture of moving droplets and cloud droplet size spectra, to determine the expected sample flow (264). On site calibration is essential if deposition is to be estimated.

10.5   Sampling of airborne dust deposition

This is a complex problem, and for advice see appropriate BSI and ISO standards in the reference section (265–271).

11 Sampling potable water, including piped water supplies and water in bottles, cans, containers, siphons and vending machines

11.1 General information

Public supplies of drinking water are usually distributed by pipework systems, but drinking water may also be supplied in bottles or other containers, and may occasionally be obtained from wells, springs, surface waters or even water butts. Storage tanks may also be used to contain drinking water in ships, aircraft, trains, etc. The following sections give advice on sampling water from such sources, but reference should also be made to Chapter 9 for wells and springs, and Chapters 7 and 8 for surface waters. Sampling of water butts can be carried out using the procedure for tanks, etc given in this chapter.

Samples are taken for four basic purposes, which in some cases may be combined. These are: for verification of whether the water meets legal or other requirements; investigation of complaints; assessing the consequences of changes in treatment or of untoward events; and to assist with process control. The ways in which these samples are taken are similar, but are dependent on the location being sampled.

11.2 Piped water supplies—sampling frequency and sites

For UK regulatory sampling requirements, see the appropriate Statutory Instruments in force. See also the publication "Guidance on Safeguarding the Quality of Public Water Supplies" (272).

There are many ways of making a random selection of properties whose supply is to be sampled and the actual location of the sample points needs to take into account the flow, mixing of waters and general layout of the distribution system, and the roads and access to these points. When planning samplers' routes, care needs to be taken that the progress of water along a main is not followed unwittingly. It is also essential to remember that, even in one street, there may be several supply mains and connections may be in an irregular order (12).

It is important when sampling routinely, to ensure that the samples from a locality are not always taken at the same time on the same week day, in case there is a time-related cause of contamination which may go unnoticed. Where the sources used to supply an area are changed periodically, there must be liaison between samplers and operators to ensure that over a period of time, water from all sources is sampled. If problems are suspected, samples should be taken when each source is in use, or over any period of possible variation.

Sampling for the investigation of complaints, for studying the consequence of changes in supply, treatment or distribution, or for monitoring operational requirements needs to be planned with the purpose of the investigation in mind.

If investigating a problem which may have a cause within a consumer's property, ensure that sufficient samples are taken to locate the source of the problem. It may be necessary to sample the supply before it reaches the property, as well as to take samples close to and on either side of any storage tank or suspect fitting, all in one trip. Likewise it is recommended that a sufficient volume of sample is taken to allow checking of the analysis if problems occur.

When looking for a source of contamination, note that whilst most leaks are outwards, high flow rates, and fluctuating pressure (especially water hammer) can cause suction into a main, despite an apparently positive pressure within.

A knowledge of approximate flow rates is required when planning studies on distribution systems carrying waters from different sources.

When samples are taken to ascertain whether the cause of an earlier contamination has been rectified, ensure that the water sampled has been water produced after the changes and does not contain contaminated water produced before those changes. Ensure that all spur connections and dead ends, and other unused pipes which might contribute to the sample, have been adequately flushed with considerably more than their own volume of water. The only purpose served by sampling before such a thorough flushing has been completed would be to ascertain the extent of the contamination, or whether all contaminated water has been removed from the system.

In distribution systems where several sources are used alternately, when checking a positive analytical result ensure that a re-sample is included from the same source as that which gave the positive result, and under the same conditions.

For the sampling of animalcules (macroinvertebrates) see ref. 273.

11.3 Sampling from taps

First consider whether the tap chosen is appropriate to the reason for sampling. Secondly, consider whether a flushed or first draw sample is required.

When sampling to ascertain the quality of the water originally supplied, note that water can be contaminated by faulty storage tanks, pick ups or other reaction with pipes, and by dirt in or on the tap outlet washer or gland. The degree and method of cleansing is dependent on the parameters to be examined and the material of construction of the taps.

Detailed advice on microbiological sampling methods is given in ref 67.

For chemical analysis, after any requisite initial wiping clean, it usually suffices to flush the tap thoroughly. The problem is to know when the tap has been thoroughly flushed without unduly wasting water. The most common method is to flush until the temperature of the water no longer varies. An alternative method is to estimate the volume in the pipes between the sample tap and the main, and flush at least double the estimated volume prior to taking the sample. If in doubt, take a second sample from the same point after a delay of several minutes additional flushing.

First-draw samples are used when checking whether water is being contaminated or changed by the local pipe work, or by tap or local tank contamination. Tap cleaning should be omitted, or if necessary kept to a minimum, with only sufficient flushing to rinse out cleaning material. For checking for microbiological contamination of the tap spout, consider swabbing techniques.

It is possible, by rapid flushing and sudden closing of valves, to disturb pipe scale and corrosion products which would not normally be found in the water. Water hammer can have a similar effect. Avoid creating such conditions unless their effect is being investigated.

Sometimes it is necessary to sample from a tap with a leaking gland without contamination from the leak. First clean the tap outlet. Then, using suitable tubing, make a swan-neck extension to the tap so that the leak drips off the first bend, well clear of the exit. After first flushing out the apparatus, sample in the usual way taking the sample at the end of the swan-neck as shown in Figure 43 (40).

11.4 Sampling from hydrants

If this is necessary, first ensure there is no water in the sump below the valve. If there is, it should be removed. Ensure that the connections and connecting pipe work are clean.

Assemble and flush thoroughly, being careful to keep water out of the valve box, to avoid risk of entrainment. If sampling for microbiological determinands, follow the detailed procedure given in ref 67. Care should be taken so as to avoid contaminating the sample.

11.5 Sampling from tanks, towers, wells and butts

If sampling taps, cocks, or sample lines are provided, ensure that these are so sited as to give representative samples. If necessary, sample from several cocks etc, with multiple or composite samples being analysed. Note that in addition to contamination leaching into the water, the material from which sample fittings are made can kill micro-organisms, or adsorb determinands. Check construction materials prior to use. Adequate flushing is essential and a drain to receive the flushings should be provided.

If dip samples have to be taken ensure that the outside of the vessel used for dipping is as clean as the inside and that it will not change the composition of the sample. Dip samples are usually taken using a 1-litre (or other appropriate size) stainless steel can attached to the appropriate length of stainless steel chain. The whole is pre-cleaned and heat sterilised if necessary, sealed into a sterile bag for transport to the site, and only opened when required. A fresh can is used for each sample. Cans may be re-used after cleaning or sterilising as appropriate. If sampling for metals present in stainless steel, use metal-free plastic equipment. This needs to be clean but not necessarily sterile (see Chapter 5).

The sample, once taken, is immediately poured into a sample bottle previously cleaned and sterilised as for tap samples. Bottles are then stoppered, labelled and handled in the usual way. Avoid contaminating the water being sampled by knocking debris or dust into it while opening the tank or well etc., when taking the sample, or when resealing the tank. Visual inspection is usefully carried out at the same time. Foreign matter and scale can cause contamination, but may be missed from the sample.

11.6   Sampling from drinking fountains and vending machines

These are rarely sampled for the quality of the water used, but mainly to check for contamination in the appliance. The supply is sampled in the same way as an ordinary tap by shutting off the supply, disconnecting the fountain or machine and then treating the supply side of the disconnection as the end of a tap. The machine is subsequently reconnected. Avoid contamination in so doing. If the fountain or machine is itself being sampled, operate the device in the normal way and collect the water in an appropriate pre-cleaned metal, glass or plastic container (dependent on the determinand sought). Cool if necessary and then transfer carefully to a suitable clean stoppered bottle. Treat as a normal tap sample.

11.7   Sampling of water in sealed bottles, containers, and siphons

11.7.1   Sampling of water from containers

Bottles etc should be selected at approximately equal intervals through a production run or stock in store, the total number selected having regard to the volume of the container and the total volume of water to be sampled.

Except when sampling for free carbon dioxide and pressurising gases, bottles or containers should be well mixed by turning end over end for up to 15 minutes prior to analysis. Bottles for free carbon dioxide and gas analysis should not be shaken.

For any analysis except for free carbon dioxide and other gases, pressured containers may have their pressure released slowly. However, for siphons it may be more convenient to use the siphon pressure to expel the requisite sample volume into a clean glass or plastic bottle or flask (depending on determinand) and stopper this container after gas evolution has ceased. Bottles after release of any pressure, should be treated as sample bottles for ordinary tap water analysis, samples being taken carefully to avoid any contamination and bottles re-closed immediately. Do not reuse crown corks. Use a new clean well fitting stopper.

Where a determinand requires a larger volume of sample than can be contained by a single bottle or container, either make special arrangements to sample at the bottling plant, or alternatively take a sufficient number of bottles or containers from the same batch to provide an adequate sample.

11.7.2   Sampling for determination of free carbon dioxide and inert pressurising gases

In addition to carbon dioxide, samples usually contain natural or added carbonate salts. For a complete analysis, at least three measurements are necessary requiring at least two separate samples. The measurements are:

i.   total gas pressure (see method E of ref. 274);

ii.   total carbon dioxide plus carbonates; and

iii.   combined carbonates.

The following sections are each subdivided accordingly. Measurements (i) and (iii) can often be made on the same sample. Determination (ii) requires a separate sample but this should be taken from a bottle or container as closely as possible in production order to the bottle used for the other determinations.

The sampling procedures for these three determinations vary with bottle or container type. There are three variants:

i.   bottles and cans with thin metal, cork or plastic closures penetrable by a hypodermic needle;

ii.   bottles and siphons etc. under pressure and fitted with valves; and

iii.   containers sealed with glass, hard plastic or porcelain balls or stoppers.

11.7.2.1   Containers penetrable by a hypodermic needle

i.   *For gas pressure*

Fix or clamp a rubber pad over the cap or top and insert a small volume stiff metal capillary tube with a point at one end, fitted with a pressure measuring device at the other. There must be no gas leakage until the measurement is completed. After measurement of total gas pressure, provided no contamination has occurred this sample may be vented to remove dissolved gases and used for other tests except total carbon dioxide. Because of the risk of contamination, this sample is not valid for bacteriological examinations.

ii.   *For total carbon dioxide and carbonate*

With a fresh bottle or container, fit a rubber pad as in (i), then using a similar stiff metal capillary tube and a syringe or piston pipette inject a known volume of accurately known strength sodium hydroxide solution into the sample, sufficient to convert all free carbon dioxide to bicarbonate. Set aside a similar portion of the same sodium hydroxide solution in a stoppered container for use as a reagent blank.

Rinse out the syringe or pipette by sucking the sample into it and re-injecting several times. The syringe or pipette must have been thoroughly pre-cleaned before use.

As the volume that can be injected may be very small, the hydroxide solution may need to be concentrated. Having spare space in the syringe or pipette, withdrawing a small portion of sample and premixing this with the sodium hydroxide may facilitate the subsequent injection if the container is very full.

Allow the sample and excess sodium hydroxide to mix thoroughly, then vent the can or bottle and proceed as for tap water samples. (Note: absence of excess pressure after sodium hydroxide addition indicates absence of inert pressurising gas). Prior to analysis, measure the volume of the sample plus alkali and thus obtain the sample volume.

iii.   *For combined carbonates*

Vent the sample and proceed as for water samples in Section 11.7.1.

11.7.2.2   Bottles and siphons etc under pressure and fitted with valves

i.   *For gas pressure*

Fix the pressure measuring device to the valve outlet by as short a length of suitable pressure tubing as possible. Slowly open the valve. Re-close the valve at the end of the test.

ii.   *For total carbon dioxide and carbonate*

Using a fresh bottle, fix the valve outlet with a delivery tube dipping to the bottom of a tall jar, cylinder, or a beaker containing an excess known volume of pre-analysed sodium hydroxide solution. The container should be large enough to hold the whole contents of the sample. Very slowly, controlling by the valve, transfer the whole contents of the sample to the vessel containing the sodium hydroxide, ensuring that all free carbon dioxide reacts. Rinse off the dip tube with a known amount of water. Prior to analysis, measure the volume of the sample plus alkali and rinse water and thus obtain the sample volume. Mix well and store the sample in a clean stoppered glass bottle until required.

iii. *For combined carbonate*

As in Section 11.7.1 above.

11.7.2.3 Containers sealed with glass, hard plastic or porcelain balls or stoppers

i. *For gas pressure*

Measurements are not readily made with these types of containers, but collection of gas samples is possible (see Section 11.7.3), free carbon dioxide being determined by difference between (ii) and (iii) below.

ii. *For total carbon dioxide and carbonate*

Thoroughly clean the bottle and its cap, without loosening the cap. Clean a pair of tongs. Take a clean beaker large enough to contain at least twice the contents of the container to be sampled. To this beaker add a known volume of known strength sodium hydroxide solution and, if necessary, a sufficient known volume of water to ensure that when inverted in the beaker the top of the bottle to be sampled is several centimetres below the liquid surface. Invert the bottle and immerse the neck in the liquid in the beaker. Then by means of the tongs loosen the bottle cap or stopper and slowly let sample and gas flow into the beaker. Mix thoroughly, remove the bottle, stopper and tongs, allowing them to drain thoroughly into the beaker. Measure the sample volume and store the sample in a clean stoppered bottle until required.

iii. *For combined carbonate*

Transfer the contents of the bottle to a clean stoppered bottle. Allow gases to vent before stoppering tightly.

11.7.3 Collection of gases for analysis

Take a glass sampling cylinder fitted with a single tap vent at one end and two tap vents at the other. This should be of sufficient volume to hold all the gas expected to be evolved from the sample. Fill the whole cylinder including vent nipples with water, close all three taps, and suspend over a tank of water (large enough to hold the container to be sampled), with the double valve end dipping under the water. Care should be taken so as not to get air into the nipples. Immerse a funnel in the water in the tank, and connect one of the two adjacent cylinder vents to the funnel. Place the container to be sampled into the water under the funnel, and open both adjacent vents (which should still be below the water surface). Slowly open the container, allowing gas to escape into the funnel. The gas will then rise into the sampling cylinder, displacing water downwards through the vent not connected to the funnel. When no more gas is given off, close the two taps and assemble the cylinder into a gas dispensing device or gas analyser using one tap at each end. For more accurate results, measure the volume of the water used in the procedure and determine any gas that may have dissolved in it during collection.

12 Sampling effluents

12.1 Reasons for sampling effluents

Effluents are sampled for several, related reasons. These are:

i.   as part of a quality control programme to minimise the risk of accidental discharge of a harmful waste or the loss of valuable process materials (this usually consists of regular monitoring of effluent quality plus additional checks when there is reason to suspect that the process producing the effluent is not running correctly or efficiently);

ii. to investigate whether the effluent has altered due to changes in the process or because of operational problems;

iii. an unknown effluent might be investigated in order to discover where it originates or what it contains; and

iv. to provide or refute evidence of pollution, in which case great care has to be taken to ensure that the sample is representative of the effluent when analysed.

110

12.2 Sample site

To avoid dilution, thereby making analysis easier, and to minimise the risk of contamination with other materials complicating the interpretation of the analysis and possibly interfering with the analysis itself, it is advisable to sample as close to the effluent discharge point and even at a convenient place prior to discharge.

If the discharge is to a river, lake or similar open water, biological monitoring techniques have frequently proved useful in locating the source of the discharge. Transport and industrial accidents, fires, the unwitting release of long forgotten waste or effluent, and also fly dumping and overuse of harmful chemicals can cause effluent plumes which can only be sampled well after release. Occasionally, effects on wall and bottom slime, or on the sewer lining may provide similar indication of the source of the effluent. In these cases, sampling must be as opportunity permits.

Finally, effluents may be sampled either at the intake to a sewage treatment works for record or control purposes or during treatment. Treatment works effluents are usually sampled as above.

12.3 Hazards

Almost all effluents are hazardous and no risks should be taken. Forethought and careful preparation can often enable an emergency sampling of an unexpected hazardous effluent to be carried out safely. Protective clothing and remotely operated sampling gear should be available and properly maintained. Hazards fall into two broad categories both of which can be subdivided. These are (i) hazards due to the sample site environment, and (ii) hazards due to the material being sampled. The former hazards only relate to the actual sampling operation; the latter hazards may sometimes even increase after the sample has been brought into the laboratory.

Hazards due to sample site environment include:

slipping and falling;
being struck by falling or overhanging objects;
drowning, and being overwhelmed by an increased flow;
a poisonous, irrespirable, flammable or explosive atmosphere;
harmful flora and fauna; and
negligence.

The effluent being sampled is part of the site environment too, but will be considered separately below.

For sites sampled regularly, properly-maintained walkways, ladders and guard rails complying with Health and Safety Regulations should be provided. Appropriate footwear should be worn and where advisable, protective clothing, hard hat, goggles or face shield, safety harness and lines should be used. Adequate permanent lighting should be provided, or portable lamps carried. If flammable gases and vapours are possible, lamps must be flameproof.

The air in all confined spaces and pits should be checked and declared safe, otherwise proper breathing apparatus should be used. If there is risk of skin absorption of chemicals or parasites, adequate protective clothing is essential. Be alert and avoid hazardous plants and mammals. The sampler should be familiar with the appearance of such biota beforehand and also of any useful first aid treatment.

If there is a possibility of a sudden discharge, or of closure or blocking of any exit, ensure that others, especially works operators, know when and where work is in progress. Issue of a clearance certificate or tally system is advocated to ensure that all workers are safe. Prior risk assessment is essential.

First aid and rescue equipment should be available and properly stored near the site. Rescuers must always inform headquarters and don appropriate protective gear, respirators, safety harness, etc before attempting a rescue, lest they too require to be rescued. If in any doubt the worst should be assumed and prepared for accordingly.

Installation of sampling lines or robot samplers may be a solution for difficult or hazardous sites. If sampling lines are used, it may be necessary to purge or flush the line to remove any material in it from previous sampling before taking the sample. Equipment must not contaminate or cause loss of material from the sample. If possible, such lines should be capable of being drained after use.

As mentioned above, the material sampled may itself be hazardous or become hazardous on storage. If possible, knowledge of the nature of the sample should be obtained in advance.

Samples may be hazardous due to toxicity by inhalation, ingestion, or skin or eye contact. They may be corrosive to protective clothing, the sample bottle and sampling gear as well as the sampler.

Samples may be directly or indirectly explosive or flammable. The risk of this can vary with temperature, exposure to air, or even contact with fittings.

Samples can be supersaturated at ambient conditions and de-gas, crystallise or precipitate on being taken. Such samples may need to be diluted as they are taken, for example with the sample delivery immersed in a known amount of water, especially if supersaturated with a gas. If there is risk of bursting the sample bottle, consider using a sampling bomb with leakproof cocks, purged with inert gas or evacuated if the sample requires this.

The material sampled may be infectious. If so, consider the risks from skin contact, inhalation, splashes in the eyes and ingestion and take appropriate precautions. Note that aerosols are easily made accidentally and can travel far. All actual sample handling equipment should be sterile before use. Contaminated equipment and clothing should be disinfected, cleaned and either sterilised before re-use or safely destroyed. For further details see "The Microbiological Examination of Waters, Prevention of Laboratory Acquired Infection", PHLS Safety Handbook.

If organisms are present which may start fermentation and evolve gas, keep samples cool during transport to the laboratory (but do not freeze), and analyse as quickly as possible. When handling subsequently, wear protective gloves, clothing and face shield in case the bottle bursts. Use of metal or wicker outer containers is suggested.

All spillage must be thoroughly cleaned up and decontaminated and/or disinfected. Do not handle broken glass. Use dustpans, brushes and tongs.

12.4 Sampling techniques

The technique used is highly dependent on the material sampled, the nature of the sample location and the circumstances. For information on types of bottle, stabilisers and storage conditions see by determinand in Table 1, Chapter 5.

For transport to the laboratory, use of plastic or metal carrying boxes with internal racks is suggested. Coolant containers or ice should, if used, be stored in leakproof containers in each box. In the event of leakage such boxes should be easy to clean, decontaminate and sterilise.

Samples from taps and small pipes can be taken directly into the sample bottle. Samples from large bore pipes can be taken into clean buckets and poured into bottles using a clean funnel or ladle. Care should be taken to note whether the sample is multiphase with separate surface or bottom layers or with suspended solids. In the event of a segregatable sample being taken in a bucket, all the sample taken should be sent to the laboratory with an explanatory note, where it can be separated into components. The amount of each phase can be measured and analysed separately, or if required, the sample can be homogenised. Samples from larger conduits, sewers, tanks, rivers, etc should be taken with due regard to depth and width using sample bottles, ladles, buckets, pumps, etc.

Thick or viscous effluents may need to be sampled in a similar manner, but using scoops, a pressure egging device, or gear or cam pumps designed for slurries. It is advisable to check, by using methods or tests which involve additions to the sample, that segregation and preferential sampling are not occurring.

Inhomogeneous bulk effluents may vary in composition with time, so that even two samples taken in immediate succession may differ. If approximately representative samples are required, it is best to sample repeatedly at intervals. These can either be analysed separately, giving an indication of the variability and (if the time interval is sufficient) of trends, or the samples can be used to prepare a composite sample.

Deep flowing effluents with discrete surface, middle and bottom layers usually need to be treated as three separate samples, with an estimate made of the flow of each. Flow rates can vary between layers and an attempt may need to be made to estimate these rates. See the second part of this booklet. The cross-section of each layer also needs to be estimated. This is usually done by a dip stick coated with suitable absorbents. It may be necessary to provide the dip stick with an easily removable protective sheath so that absorption of upper layers does not mask the mark made by lower layers.

Effluents discharged into a greater flow usually form widening plumes before complete mixing takes place. It usually suffices to sample from the centre of the plume as close to the source as possible, though for some purposes a multi-sample profile with width and depth may be necessary (see Chapter 7).

It is sometimes necessary to take an effluent sample of an illegal discharge. Occasionally, by skilful observation of macrophytes, macroinvertebrates and vertebrates and a knowledge of their variations with season, it may be possible to estimate when a surreptitious discharge is being made and take samples in the normal manner. Remotely controlled sampling devices are usually preferred for taking extra samples. Such samplers can also be actuated by a continuously monitoring sensor. Typical sensors are electrodes sensitive to pH, conductivity, reduction-oxidation potential, dissolved oxygen, ammonia, specific ions or temperature. Colorimeters and turbidimeters can also be used. If the output from the electrode or meter moves outside a predetermined range, the sampling device is actuated. The sampler itself can consist of an evacuated bottle fitted with a magnetic valve or pinch cock, a sampling pump connected to a sample bottle, two interconnected bottles, one full, one empty, such that emptying one fills the other and sets up a measured amount of the sample to be supplied directly to an automated analyser.

Continuous sampling for parameters such as pH, etc can be carried on by electrodes fitted to recorders, by land lines or other devices. Care should be taken to ensure that neither the instrument nor the sample line feeding it becomes fouled or blocked by algae or sediment.

Semi-continuous sampling can be carried out by having time-actuated remote sampling devices feeding automatic analysers, situated nearby. Though possible, these latter devices can prove expensive to install and maintain in reliable working order. More usually, a series of samples are taken which are returned to a central laboratory for analysis.

13 Biological sampling

13.1 Introduction

Sampling of biota in rivers, streams, estuaries, coastal waters and associated banks, beds and sediments is usually carried out for either of two purposes: (i) the assessment of the presence, or the virtual absence of certain species, or (ii) a general assessment of the quality of the system.

As the measurements made involve living organisms which can multiply, often migrate and which may have other constraints other than water quality on their occurrences, the results obtained need careful interpretation even though they may often be as useful as chemical analyses, or even more so. Thus, while no viable counts of organisms indicative of the presence of harmful substances may be obtainable, this does not absolutely guarantee that such organisms are completely absent from the body of water sampled, but with sufficient properly taken samples it can be shown that the probability of finding such organisms is so exceedingly small that for practical purposes they are virtually absent. On the other hand, the inability to find a certain water quality indicator species in a stretch of water does not necessarily mean that the water quality would be detrimental to such a species if it were present. Conversely, while the presence of a species in relatively large numbers does mean that the water can accommodate them, the presence of only one or two specimens of a readily-migrating indicator organism may, if unsupported by other evidence, only represent migrants from a healthy population elsewhere, which are now present in a water not sufficiently harmful to cause instant death.

Lethal effects associated with pollution include toxic substances, lack of sufficient oxygen and water temperatures either too high or too low. However, these effects can also be caused naturally. Other reasons for the absence of species are predation, the inability to migrate into that area due to natural barriers, storm or flood damage, water depth and current.

For convenience, this chapter has been divided into two parts—freshwater and marine biota.

13.2   Sampling freshwater biota

13.2.1   Methods

As biota vary in size, form and habitat, a range of sampling methods is needed which must be suited to the organisms and habitats concerned. This series therefore includes a variety of booklets on the sampling of macro invertebrates, macrophytes and micro-organisms in a variety of habitats, using sample bottles, swabs, nets, grabs skimmers, hand sampling, artificial substrates and direct observation. Most of these methods are intended primarily for use in rivers and streams, but the others listed are readily capable of adaptation to rivers (48, 67, 119, 189–193, 275). Similarly many can be used, possibly with modification, for the sampling of lakes, reservoirs, estuaries and coastal waters. Similar methods of sampling have been recommended in North America (78) and New Zealand (276). Other useful books are listed in refs 196 and 277–283.

13.2.2   Optimum season for sampling

The best season for sampling varies widely with the organism sought and the purpose of sampling. Thus, sampling for pathogenic organisms, in water for human or animal consumption or other sensitive use, should be as frequent as possible, taking into account the ability to take effective remedial or protective action in time, the hazard from the organism and the risk that the supply may be contaminated. On the other hand, unless there is reason to suspect an anomalous occurrence, there is little point in looking for a species of an organism at a period in the year when its life cycle indicates that it will be absent from that habitat or present in another form. Environmental monitoring must therefore take the form of a general survey of the species present, or at least be a survey for the presence of indicator species typical of certain water qualities, and, except when all that is required is knowledge of whether a given species is present, environmental assessments must use a range of indicator species suited to the particular habitat being examined, There are several reasons other than water quality which can cause absence of a species; for example, due to natural barriers its range has not yet reached that stretch of water, or the species was completely destroyed or considerably reduced by some previous natural disaster and due to natural or other barriers has not been able to re-establish itself. Other reasons include the presence or absence of some physical constraint such as suitable areas for breeding, light, water flow conditions and nutritional requirements. Introduction of a competitive species can also upset the distribution pattern of a particular species.

Finally, it must be remembered that if species are removed, damaged or frightened during a sampling period or assessment, the original balance may be disturbed and may take time to re-establish. Thus, the removal of plants or flowers can result in a depleted zone extending some way downstream in the following season due to the consequent lack of seed. Allowance for this effect should be made when planning a continuing surveillance lasting several years. Either the methods used should not themselves substantially affect the ecosystem, a series of virtually identical but different sampling areas must be compared, or a standard renewable habitat should be used.

The months mentioned in the subsections which follow, vary slightly with yearly climatic variations and also from south to north. Note that some pollutant discharges can also be seasonal.

13.2.2.1 Macroinvertebrates

Gammarus and *Asellus* may be looked for at any time of the year, but the nymphs of stoneflies and mayflies are most easily identified in March/April (for winter developing species) and late July early August (summer nymphs). The nymphs of some species may be quite small at the beginning of these periods but if sampling is left too late many or most adults will have emerged. Cladocera, in particular the acid sensitive *Daphnia* species are best looked for during the summer months, but may be collected from May to October—later in some cases.

13.2.2.2 Fish

Since fish are more active in warm water, sampling is best done in summer, (June to September) but qualitative work with nets (in lochs) or by electro-fishing (in streams) may be done in mild weather at most times of the year. To determine whether there has been a successful hatching of salmonids, sampling should be done in streams from June onwards, or August onwards if there is a need to distinguish between trout and salmon fry. Since the species of coarse fish spawn at different times during spring and early summer (March to June) the fry also appear at different times. It is usually possible to collect fry of most species from late July onwards.

13.2.2.3 Plants (Macrophytes)

Apart from emergent species which colonise the littoral zone and are usually identifiable throughout the greater part of the year, many macrophytes begin growing in April or May (depending on temperature) and may not be easy to sample until June or later. The various species mature at different times during the summer so that if flower heads or seeds are required for identification (for example some of the sedges) it will be necessary to check on the time of maturation for the given area.

13.2.2.4 Algae

As with macrophytes different species are more easily sampled at different times of the year. Spring diatom "blooms" may be followed by blooms of species of green algae in summer and blue-green algae (cyanobacteria) in later summer and autumn. In many lakes and lochs this would be an oversimplified picture since the increase in any one species depends on local chemical and physical characteristics. Regular sampling from spring to autumn may be necessary unless it is known when a specific indicator alga is likely to appear.

Filamentous algae in streams, including acidophilic species such as *Mougeotia* may be sampled from May until late summer, but again the times depend on temperature and other physical characteristics of the stream.

13.2.2.5 Diatoms

Some of the organisms can be collected throughout the year but other species have a distinct seasonality. Consequently, the particular time of year for the specific indicator species should be known.

13.2.3 Sampling location

In addition to the above mentioned requirement that for several but not all methods of examination entailing the removal of species, reliable results will not be obtained if a single location is re-sampled too frequently. Firstly, it should be accessible and safe, but secure from unwanted disturbance. Secondly, the habitat must be correct for the species sought. A variety of factors contribute to the habitat of a species, some of which are interdependent (48, 277) such as:

> water speed;
> water depth;
> water turbulence;
> water surface area;
> suspended solids content;

temperature pattern over the year;
wind;
light and shade;
bottom form, penetrability and geochemical nature;
presence of adequate nutrients (both macro- and micro-);
oxygen content;
water hardness; and
acidity or alkalinity.

It should be noted that while plants can metabolise dissolved carbon dioxide and take other nutrients from the bed, paradoxically some of the most pollution-sensitive animals will not survive in the purest waters, and that while some species may be highly sensitive to a certain substance, others may tolerate it, and a few may actually need it. Calcium, oxygen, nitrogen, phosphorus and silicon are well known examples of essential elements which can be harmful to certain species; but species are known with nutritional requirements for elements such as boron, fluoride, molybdenum, selenium, copper, nickel and zinc. It is also known that certain plants have special soil and climate requirements. The same is also true for the nutritional and climatic requirements of animals and micro-organisms.

Sometimes even the form in which these elements occur may be important. Examples are known of deficiency diseases due not to the absence of an element, but rather the absence of it in an available form.

13.3 Sampling of marine biota

As the source material is not so readily available, and as sampling methods may vary widely depending on the organisms of interest, this section is arranged as a bibliography.

13.3.1 Introduction

There is an enormous diversity of sampling methods for marine organisms, reflecting the variety of target groups and their supporting habitats and the objectives for study, ranging from the identification of micro-organisms to commercial fish stock assessment. The bibliography reflects this variety and, for convenience references have been classified under the following broad headings: microbes, larger benthos, plankton and fish (inevitably, there is some degree of overlap between these groups).

Historically, the global nature of the interests in fisheries resources and closely linked with this, the determination of primary and secondary production in the water column, accounted for an early concentration of effort on the development of methods in these subject areas.

As a general rule, monitoring programmes have placed the emphasis on internal rather than "global" consistency with respect to sampling methods. With only a relatively limited number of options to choose from, however, this has not necessarily precluded wider comparisons.

With a recent upsurge in interest in the biological condition of whole sea areas, for example the North Sea, in relation to anthropogenic inputs, the concern with method standardisation across all biological groups is receiving greater attention than hitherto in international meetings. Higher priority is also now being given to standard methods for nationally co-ordinated programmes, for example for the monitoring of sites used for marine disposal from ships. Various initiatives have undoubtedly led to some duplication of effort, but at present this can be viewed as a desirable trait, as it is probably the best means by which an eventual consensus on a standard suite of methods can be achieved.

The present bibliography—which is wide-ranging in scope—is intended as a precursor to one or more SCA manuals specifying protocols for marine sampling in order to meet a range of biological monitoring requirements.

13.3.2 Microbes

In view of the extensive activity elsewhere within the SCA on microbiological sampling and analytical methods (67), most of which is connected with public health issues, it is not the intention here to provide a detailed bibliography. However, by way of introduction to this subject area, the following two references are recommended for their coverage of methods and as sources of further information.

1. Austin B (ed.), *Methods in Aquatic Bacteriology*. J Wiley and Sons, Chichester, 1988, 425pp.

2. Austin B and Austin DA (Eds), *Methods for the Microbiological Examination of Fish and Shellfish*. Ellis Horwood, Chichester, 1989, 317pp.

13.3.3 Benthos

This term describes the biota within or closely associated with the sea bed. For the purposes of scientific study, the benthos are usually subdivided by size class (see Table 8).

To the above groups may be added the "hyperbenthos", ie free-swimming species (especially crustaceans) which tend to be associated with the water column immediately above the sea bed, and are sampled using specially designed sledges.

The following list gives publications dealing with estuary and marine benthic sampling methods relevant to UK studies.

1. Anon., *Procedures for the Monitoring of Benthic* Communities around Point-Source Discharges. In *Report of the ICES Advisory Committee on Marine Pollution*. ICES Co-operative Research Report No 160, 1988, 28–45.

2. Anon., *Examples of the Application of ICES Guidelines for the Monitoring of Benthic* Communities around Point-Source Discharges. In *Report of the ICES Advisory Committee on Marine Pollution*. ICES Co-operative Research Report No 167, 1989, 150–164.

3. Anon., *Procedures for the Monitoring of Marine Benthic Communities at UK Sewage Sludge Disposal Sites*. (Prepared by the Biology Task Team for the MPMMG Co-ordinating Group on the Monitoring of Sewage Sludge Disposal Grounds). DAFS Technical Report Series.

4. Association of Directors and River Inspectors of Scotland, *Standardisation of Freshwater and Marine Biological Methods used by the Scottish River Purification Boards. II. Marine and Estuarine Methods*.

5. Baker JM and Wolff WJ (eds), *Biological Surveys of Estuaries and Coasts*. Cambridge University Press, Cambridge, 1987, 449pp.

6. Crapp GB, The distribution and abundance of animals on the rocky shore of Bantry Bay. *Irish Fish. Invest. (B),* 1973, **9**, 1–3.

7. Elliott JM and Tullett PA, *A Supplement to a Bibliography of Samplers for Benthic Invertebrates*. Freshwater Biological Association, Occasional Publication No 20, 1983, 26pp. See also Occasional Publication No 30, 1993.

8. Forth River Purification Board, *Marine Biological and Sedimentological Methods*. Report TW2/88, 1988, 39pp.

9. George JD, Lythgoe GI and Lythgoe JN (eds), *Underwater Photography and Television for Scientists*. Clarendon Press, Oxford, 1985, 184pp.

10. Hartley JP, Methods for sampling offshore macro-benthos. *Mar. Poll. Bull.,* 1982, **13**, 150–154.

11. Higgins RP and Theil H (eds), *Introduction to the Study of Meiofauna*. Smithsonian Institution Press, Washington and London, 1988.

12. Hiscock K (ed.), *Rocky Shore Survey and monitoring Workshop, 1–4 May 1984*. BP International, London, 1985.

13. Holme NA and McIntyre AD (eds), *Methods for the Study of Marine Benthos*. IBP Handbook No 16, 2nd Edition. Blackwell Scientific Publications, Oxford, 1984, 387pp.

14. Holme NA and Nichols D, *Habitat Survey Cards for the Shores of the British Isles*. Field Studies Council, London, 1980.

15.   McIntyre AD, The benthos of the western North Sea. *Reun. Cons. Int. Explor. Mer,* 1978, **172**, 405–417.

16.   Morris AW (ed.), *Practical Procedures for Estuarine Studies.* National Environmental Research Council, 1983, 262pp.

17.   MPMMG, *First Report of the Marine Pollution Monitoring Management Group's Co-ordinating Group on Monitoring of Sewage Sludge Disposal Sites,* (compiled Portmann JE). Aquat. Envir, Monit. Report No 20. MAFF Directorate of Fisheries Research, Lowestoft, 1989, 64pp.

18.   Nichols D (ed.), *Monitoring the Marine Environment.* Proceedings of a Symposium of the Institute of Biology No 24. The Institute, London, 1979.

19.   Price JH, Irvine DEG and Farnham WF (eds), *The Shore Environment, Volumes 1 and 2.* Academic Press, London and New York, 1980.

20.   Rumohr H (ed.), *Collection and Treatment of Soft Bottom Macrofauna Samples.* ICES Techniques in Environmental Science.

13.3.4   Attached flora

In contrast to many other groups, there has been relatively little published on the sampling of attached macro and microflora. Workers in this field have often developed their own methods or have followed protocols evolved from techniques used in the terrestrial environment.

1.   Baker and Wolff, see 13.3.3 ref 1.

2.   Chapman ARO, *Demography,* in *Handbook of Phycological Methods. Ecological Field Methods: Macroalgae,* (Eds Littler MM and Littler DS). Cambridge University Press, Cambridge, 1985, pp 251–256.

3.   Hartnoll RG and Hawkins SJ, Monitoring rocky shore communities: a critical look at spatial and temporal variation. *Helgol. Meeresunters.,* 1980, **33**, 484–495.

4.   Hawkins SJ and Hartnoll RG, Changes in a rocky shore community: an evaluation of monitoring. *Mar. Environ. Res.,* 1983, **9**, 131–181.

5.   Jones WE, Fletcher A, Bennett SJ, McConnell BJ and Mack-Smith J, *Changes in Littoral Populations as Recorded by Long Term Shore Surveillance. I. Selected Examples of Cyclic Changes,* in *Cyclic Phenomena in Marine Plants and Animals,* (eds Naylor E and Hartnoll RG). Pergamon Press, Oxford, 1979, 93–100.

6.   Jones WE, Fletcher A, Bennett SJ, McConnell BJ, Richard AVL and Mack-Smith J, *Intertidal Surveillance,* in *Monitoring the Marine Environment,* (ed. Nicholls D). Proceedings of a Symposium of the Institute of Biology No 24. The Institute, London, 1979.

7.   Littler MM and Littler DS, *Non-destructive Sampling,* in *Handbook of Phycological Methods. Ecological Field Methods: Macroalgae,* (Eds Littler MM and Littler DS). Cambridge University Press, Cambridge, 1985, pp 161–176.

8.   Russell G, Phytosociological studies on a two-zone shore. I Basic pattern. *J. Ecology,* 1972, **62**, 539–545.

9.   Wilkinson M, *Estuarine Benthic Algae and their Environment: A Review,* in *The Shore Environment, Volumes 1 and 2,* (eds Price JH, Irvine DEG and Farnham WF). Academic Press, London and New York, 1980.

13.3.5   Plankton and fish

The diversity of sampling methods reflects the enormous size range of organisms in these two large groups. They can be classified as described in Table 9.

The literature is both extensive and firmly international in flavour. Several of the references cited below are to manuals dealing with standard methods for use by scientists in Europe and North America, ie in the Northern Atlantic and Pacific Oceans, and are therefore applicable to the seas around the British Isles.

Where thought to be relevant, references to the original manuals or books are included along with updates or new editions.

13.3.6 Phytoplankton and zooplankton

This list includes some references to oceanographic and chemical methods which link with plankton sampling. Also, most surveys of phytoplankton made before 1979 overlooked the presence of algal picoplankton (<2 μm in largest dimension). This should be borne in mind when using the older literature. References concerning the latter are listed under a separate subheading.

1. Anon., *Determination of Photosynthetic Pigments in Seawater.* UNESCO Monograph on Oceanographic Methodology No 1, 1966.

2. Anon., *A Guide to Measurement of Marine Primary Productivity under some Special Conditions.* UNESCO Monograph on Oceanographic Methodology No 3, 1973.

3. Edmondson WT and Winberg GG (eds), *A Manual of Methods for Measuring Secondary Productivity in Fresh Waters.* IBP Handbook No 17. Blackwell Scientific Publications, Oxford, 1971.

4. Hyatt E, *Keyguide to Information Sources in Remote Sensing.* Mansell Publishing Ltd., London and New York, 1988.

5. Jerlov NG, *Optical Oceanography,* Elsevier Oceanography Series, 1968.

6. Kentish MJ, *Practical Handbook of Marine Science.* CRC Press, 1989.

7. Parsons TR, Maita Y and Lalli CM, *A Manual of Chemical and Biological Methods for Sea Water Analysis.* Pergamon Press, Oxford, 1984.

8. Platt T, Mann KH and Vlanowicz RE, *Mathematical Models in Biological Oceanography.* UNESCO Monograph on Oceanographic Methodology No 7, 1981.

9. Shearer JA, DeBruyn ER, Deleclercq DR, Schlinder DW and Fee EJ (eds), *Manual of Phytoplankton Primary Production Methodology.* Can. Tech. Rep. Fish. Aquat. Sci. No 1341, 1985.

10. Smith PE and Richardson SL, *Standard Techniques for Pelagic Fish Egg* and Larva Surveys. FAO Fisheries Technical Paper FIR/T175, 1977.

11. Sournia A (ed.), *Phytoplankton Manual.* UNESCO Monograph on Oceanographic Methodology No 6, 1978.

12. Steedman HF, *Zooplankton Fixation and Preservation.* UNESCO Monograph on Oceanographic Methodology No 4, 1976.

13. Strickland JDH, Solar radiation penetrating the ocean. A review of requirements, data and methods of measurement with particular reference to photosynthetic productivity. *J. Fish. Res. Bd Can.,* 1958, **15**, 453–493.

14. Strickland JDH, Measuring the Productivity of Marine Phytoplankton. *Bull. Fish. Res. Bd Can.,* 1960, **122**, 172pp.

15. Strickland JDH and Parsons TR, *A Practical Handbook of Seawater Analysis.* Bull. Fish. Res. Bd Can., 1968, **167**, 311pp.

16. Tett PB, *Plankton*, in *Biological Surveys of Estuaries and Coasts*, (eds Baker JM and Wolff WJ). Cambridge University Press, Cambridge, 1987, 280–341.

17. Tranter DJ (ed.), *Zooplankton Sampling Manual.* UNESCO Monograph on Oceanographic Methodology No 2, 1968.

18. Tyler JF and Smith RC, *Measurements of Spectral Irradiance Underwater.* Gardner and Breach, London, 1970.

19. Vollenweider RA, *A Manual on Methods for Measuring Primary Production in Aquatic Environments.* IBP Handbook No 12 (2nd Edition). Blackwell Scientific Publications, Oxford, 1974, 225pp.

13.3.7 Algal picoplankton

The following research papers and reviews include information relevant to sampling

1.   Craig SR, Picoplankton size distributions an marine and freshwaters: problems with filter fractionation studies. *FEMS Microbiology Ecology,* 1986, **38**, 171–177.

2.   El Hag AGD and Fogg GE, The distribution of coccoid blue-green algae (cyanobacteria) in the Menai Straits and the Irish Sea. *Br. Phycol. J.,* 1986, **21**, 45–54.

3.   Glover HE, Phinney DA and Yentsch CS, Photosynthetic characteristics of picoplankton compared with those of larger phytoplankton populations in various water masses in the Gulf of Maine. *Biological Oceanography,* 1985, **3**, 223–247.

4.   Kuosa H, Occurrence of autotrophic picoplankton along an open sea-inner archipelago gradient in the Gulf of Finland, Baltic Sea. *Ophelia,* 1988, **28**, 85–93.

5.   Stockner JG and Antia NJ, Algal Picoplankton from marine and freshwater ecosystems: a multidisciplinary perspective. *Can. J. Fish. Aquat. Sci.,* 1986, **43**, 2472–2503.

6.   Takahashi M, Kikuchi K and Hara Y, Importance of picocyanobacteria biomass (unicellular blue-green algae) in the phytoplankton population of the coastal waters off Japan. *Marine Biology,* 1985, **89**, 63–69.

7.   Waterbury JB, Watson SW, Valois FW and Flants DG, *Biological and Ecological Characterisation of the Marine Unicellular Cyanobacterium* Synechococcus, in *Photosynthetic Picoplankton*, (eds Platt T and Li WKW). *Can. Bull. Fish. Aquat. Sci.,* 1986, **214**, 71–120.

13.3.8 Fish and fisheries

1.   Anderson KP, *Manual of Sampling and Statistical Methods for Fishery Biology.* FAO Fisheries Technical Paper FIb/T26, Suppl. 1, 1965.

2.   Brander K, *Guidelines for Collection and Compilation of Fishery Statistics.* FAO Fisheries Technical Paper FIRS/T148, 1975.

3.   Burezynski J, *Introduction to the Use of Sonar Systems for Estimating Fish Biomass.* FAO Fisheries Technical Paper FIRM/T191, 1979.

4.   Butler MJA, Leblanc C, Belbin JA and MacNeill JL, *Marine Resource Mapping: An Introductory Manual.* FAO Fisheries Technical Paper No 274, 1986.

5.   Butler MJA, Mouchot MC, Barale V and Leblanc C, *The Application of Remote Sensing to Marine Fisheries: An Introductory Manual.* FAO Fisheries Technical Paper No 295, 1988.

6.   Caddy JF and Bazigos GP, *Guidelines for Statistical Monitoring.* FAO Fisheries Technical Paper FIRM/FIDI/T257, 1985.

7.   Everhart WH, Eipper AW and Youngs WD, *Principles of Fisheries Science.* Cornell University Press, 1975.

8.   Forbes ST and Naaken O, *Manual of Methods for Fish Resource Survey and Appraisal. Part 2. The Use of Acoustic Instruments for Fish Detection and Abundance Estimation.* FAO Fisheries Technical Paper FIR, 1972.

9.   Gulland JA, *Manual of Methods of Fish Stock Assessment. Part 1. Fish population Analysis.* FAO Fisheries Technical Paper FIb/40 (Rev 1), 1965.

10.   Gulland JA, *FAO Manual of Sampling and Statistical Methods for Fisheries Biology. Part 1. Sampling Methods.* FAO Fisheries Technical Paper FRs/M3, 1966.

11.   Gulland JA, *Manual of Methods for Fisheries Resource Survey and Appraisal. Part 5. Objectives and Basic Methods.* FAO Fisheries Technical Paper FIRS/T145, 1978.

12.   Hall WB, *Manual of Sampling and Statistical Methods. Chapter 66. Continuous Distributions.* FAO Fisheries Technical Paper FRS/T26 (Suppl. 2), 1968.

13.   Holden MJ and Raitt DFS, *Manual of Fisheries Science. Part 2. Methods of Resource Investigation and their Application.* FAO Fisheries Technical Paper FIRS/T115.

14. Johannessen KA and Mitson RB, *Fisheries Acoustics. A Practical Manual for Aquatic Biomass Estimates.* FAO Fisheries Technical Paper FIRM/T240, 1983.

15. Jones R, *Manual of Methods of Fish Stock Assessment. Part 4. Marking.* FAO Fisheries Technical Paper FRs/T51, 1966.

16. Kesteven GL, *FAO Manual of Field Methods in Fisheries Biology No 1*, 1960.

17. Kesteven GL, *Manual of Fisheries Science. Part 1. An Introduction to Fisheries Science.* FAO Fisheries Technical Paper FIRM/T118, 1973.

18. Laevastu T, *Manual of Methods in Fisheries Biology*, FAO Fisheries Technical Paper FIb/M1, 1965.

19. Mackett DJ, *Manual of Methods for Fisheries Resource Survey and Appraisal. Part 3.* Standard Methods and Techniques for Demersal Fisheries Resource Survey. FAO Fisheries Technical Paper FIRD/T124, 1973.

20. Nedelec C, *Definitions and Classification of Fishing Gear.* FAO Fisheries Technical Paper FIDI/T222, 1982.

21. Nielsen LA and Johnson DL (eds), *Fisheries Techniques.* American Fisheries Society Publications, 1983.

22. Pope JA, Akyuz EF, Margretts AR and Hamley JM, *Manual of Methods of Fish Stock Assessment. Part 3. Selectivity of Fishing Gear.* FAO Fisheries Technical Paper FIRS/T41 (Rev. 1), 1975.

23. Potts GW and Reay PJ, *Fish,* in *Biological Surveys of Estuaries and Coasts,* (eds Baker JM and Wolff WJ). Cambridge University Press, Cambridge, 1987, pp342–373.

24. Ricker WE, *Methods for Assessment of Fish Production in Freshwaters.* IBP Handbook No 3. Blackwell Scientific Publications, Oxford, 1971.

25. Saville A, *Survey Methods of Appraising Fisheries Resources.* FAO Fisheries Technical Paper FIRS/T171.

13.4 Summary

For a survey to be meaningful, it must be made at the right time, in the right place with the right equipment, and take into account the effects of sampling and the consequent disturbance of the ecosystem entailed.

Table 8   A scheme for classifying benthos by size

Category	Size	Biological features	Sampling techniques	Taxonomic position
Microbenthos	Pass finest sieves	High rates of respiration and reproduction.	Plating and culturing. Cores of <2 cm diameter.	Bacteria, viruses, yeasts, fungi, actinomycetes, cyanobacteria, most protozoa, some eukaryotic algae.
Meiobenthos	Pass 0.5–1 mm sieves	Medium respiration rates. Two or more generations per year.	Cores of 2–10 cm diameter.	Large protozoa, small metazoa.
Macrobenthos	Retained on 0.5–1 mm sieves	Low respiration rates. Two or less generations per year. Mostly infauna.	Grab sampling at least 0.1 m².	Medium-sized metazoa.
Megabenthos	Hand picked from samples	As above. Mostly epifauna.	Towed gear, trawls, dredge.	Large metazoa.

Table 9   A classification of size of plankton and fish

Category	Size	Type of organism	Collecting method
Plankton:			
Ultra-nanoplankton (picoplankton)	<2 μm	Bacteria, algae, etc.	Sterile water samplers.
Nanoplankton	2–20 μm	Micro-flagellates.	Water samplers.
Microplankton	20–200 μm	Diatoms, nauplii, veligers.	Fine mesh (200 mesh per inch) tow nets, water samplers.
Macroplankton (Mesoplankton)	200–2000 μm	Fish larvae, copepods, mysids, etc.	Coarse mesh (40–60 mesh per inch) tow nets.
Megaplankton	2000 μm	Colonial forms of zooplankton, eg medusae, euphasids.	Small mesh (5–20 mm) pelagic trawls.
Fish and aquatic animals:			
Pelagic fish	5 cm–<8 m	Sprat, herring, tuna, basking sharks.	Pelagic trawls, long-lines, purse-seines
Demersal fish	5 cm–<3 m	Codfishes, flatfishes, sharks, skates.	Demersal trawls, long-lines, seines, traps.
Pelagic and semi-pelagic	1 m–<25 m	Seals, whales, porpoises.	Harpoons, narcotising agents.

Figure 1

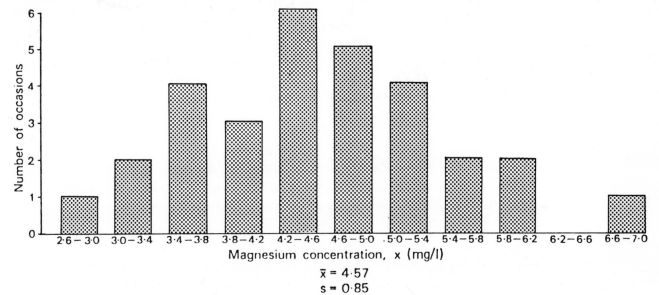

$\bar{x} = 4.57$
$s = 0.85$

Results of magnesium determinations, mg/l:

3·98	4·38	4·55	4·95	3·62	5·03
5·23	3·79	4·57	3·30	4·50	4·72
3·78	4·65	5·12	5·84	6·62	4·91
3·61	4·34	5·62	2·91	3·02	5·44
4·12	4·87	5·22	5·90	4·42	4·15

Figure 2

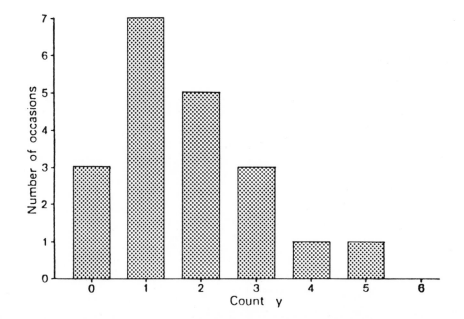

Counts observed in 10 ml portions

2	1	2	1
2	2	1	0
3	0	3	4
1	1	1	5
2	3	0	1

Figure 3

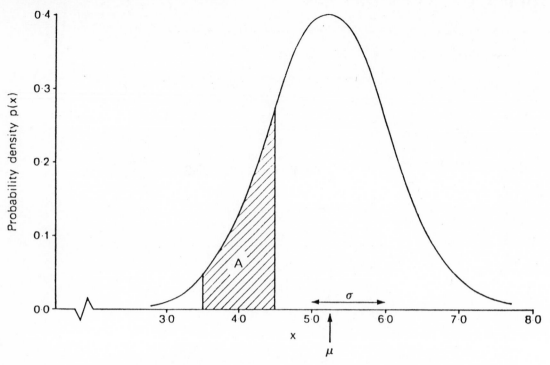

Area A gives probability of observing x between 3·5 and 4·5

Figure 4

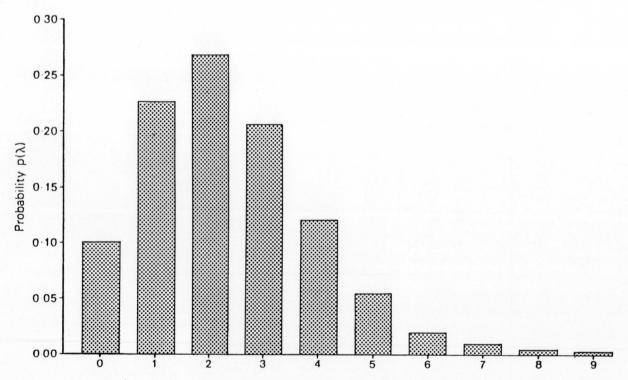

Figure 5   Sequential consideration of factors involved in the design of sampling programmes

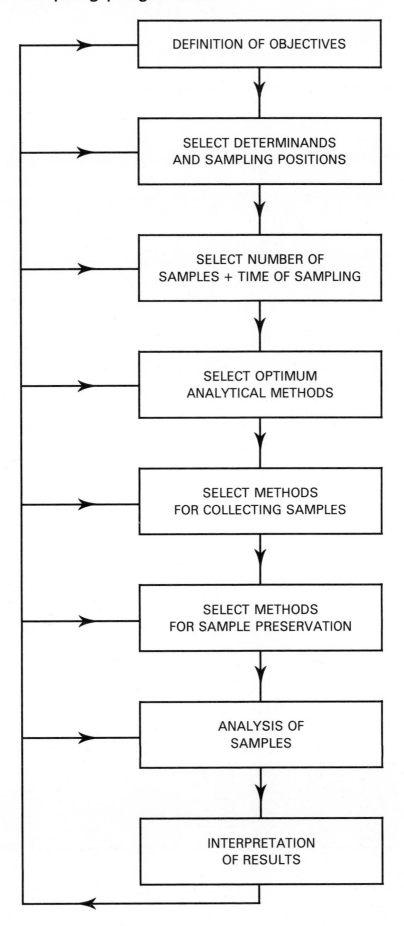

Figure 6 Selection of sampling location and position

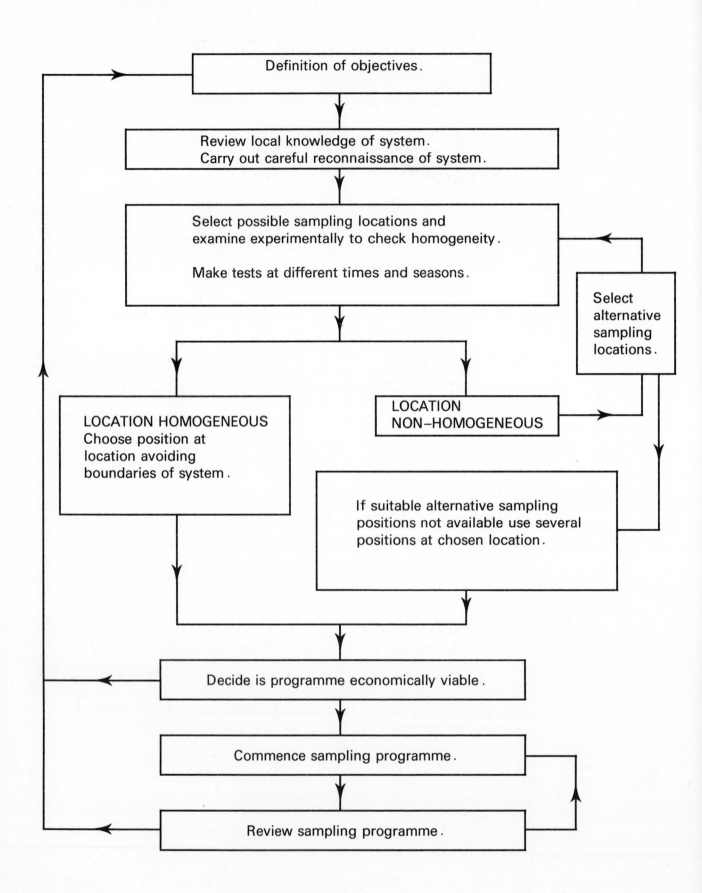

Figure 7   Schematic representation of mixing of an effluent with a river

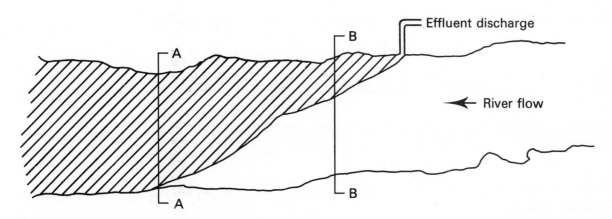

Sampling location should be downstream
of A − A

(a) Lateral dispersion of effluent

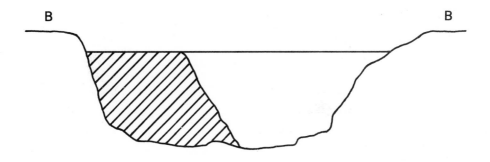

(b) Vertical and lateral dispersion of effluent

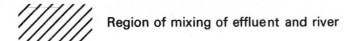   Region of mixing of effluent and river

Figure 8   Choice of sampling frequency and time of sampling

1.   Quality — Characterisation

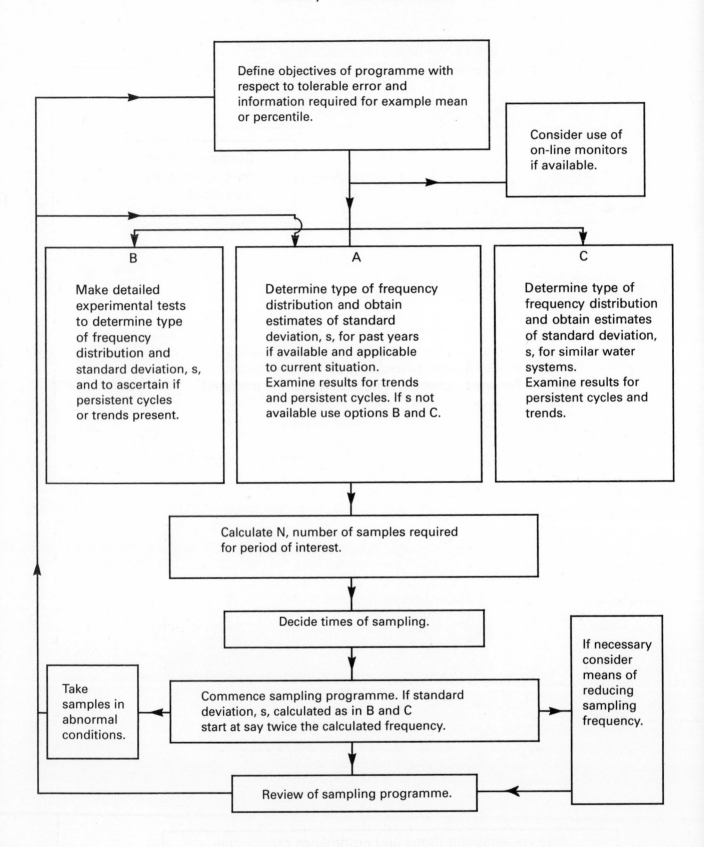

Figure 9   Choice of sampling frequency and time of sampling

2.   Quality — Control Programmes

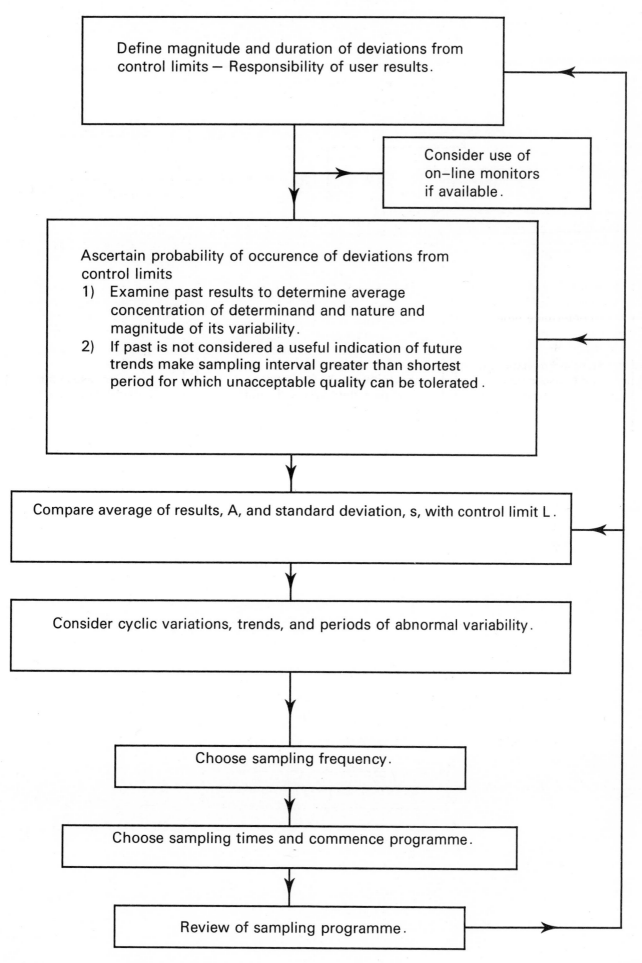

Figure 10   Effect of variability of quality on the accuracy of estimating

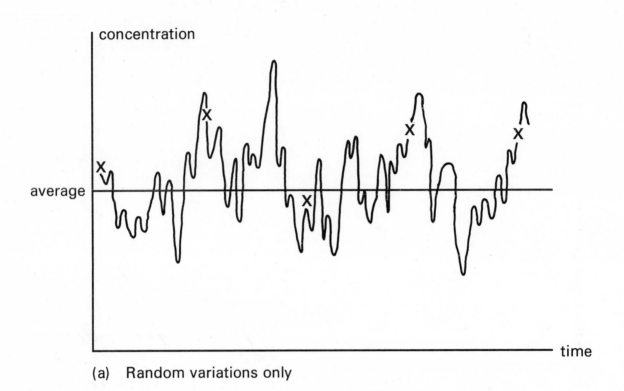

(a)   Random variations only

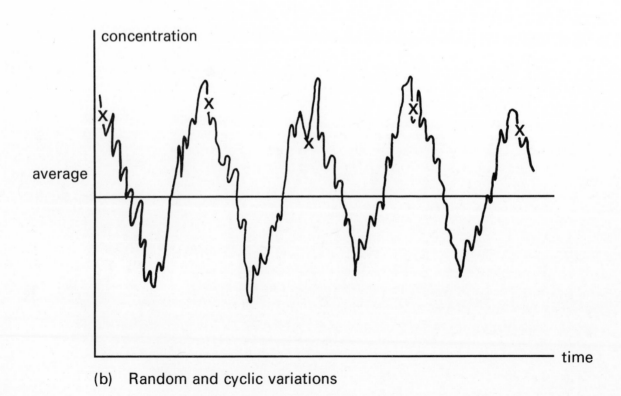

(b)   Random and cyclic variations

X   Analytical results

Figure 11   Approximate number of samples required in estimating a mean concentration

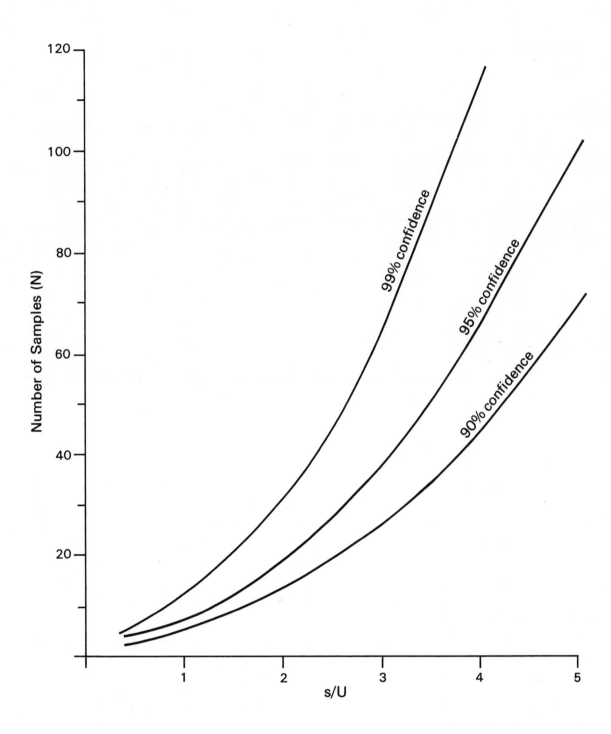

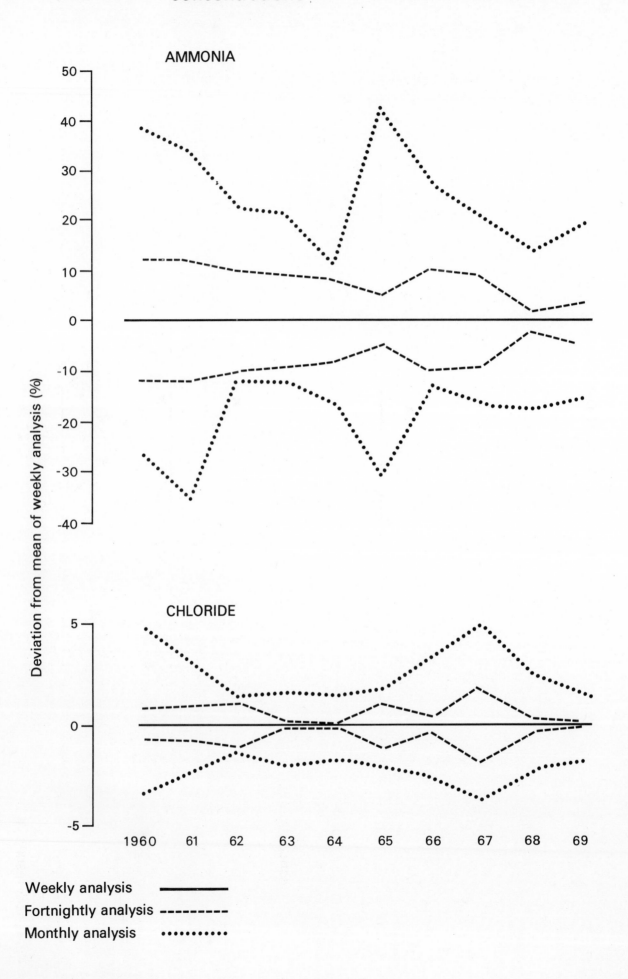

Figure 12   Effect of sampling frequency on annual mean concentrations

Figure 13   Examples of different quality control situations

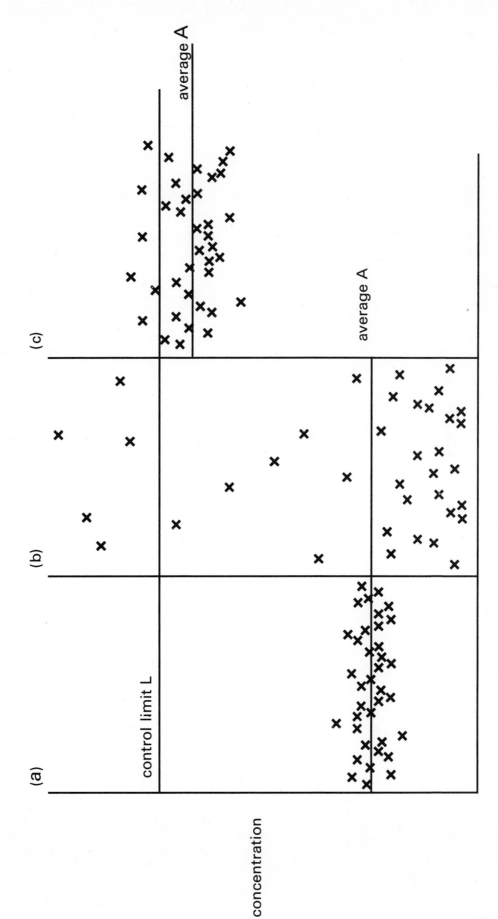

Analytical results ✕

Figure 14   Estuarine circulation patterns

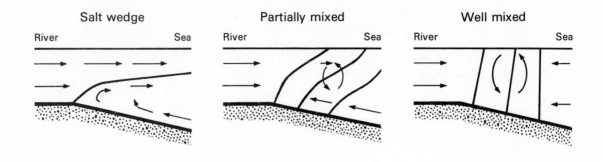

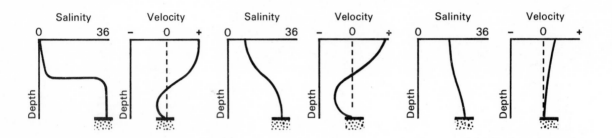

After Morris (159)

Figure 15   Immersion samplers for waters

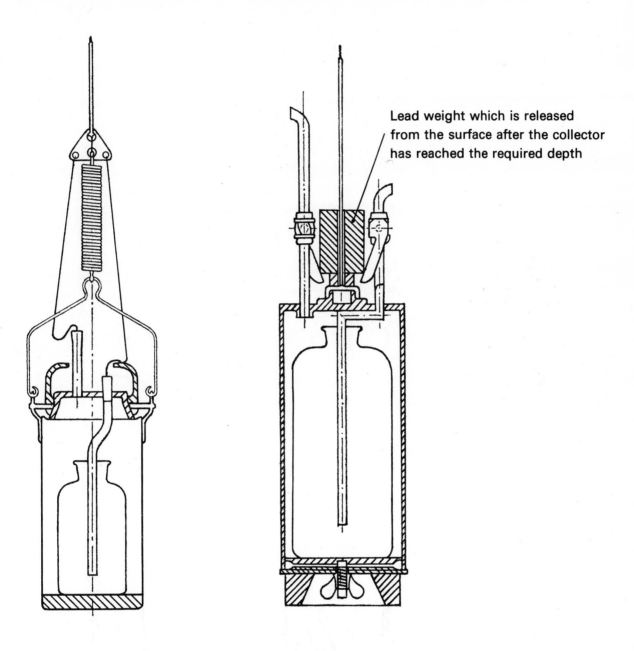

Lead weight which is released from the surface after the collector has reached the required depth

Note: the sample bottle and outer container should be filled with an inert gas

Figure 16   Double-bottle sampling systems

(For simplicity, weighting system omitted)

(from Reference 285)

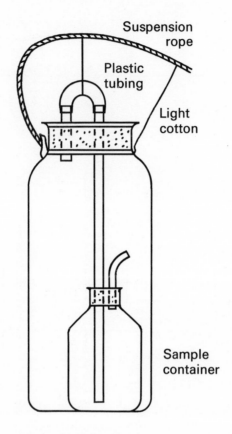

Figure 17 Double-bottle sampling systems

(For simplicity, weighting system omitted)

(from Reference 285)

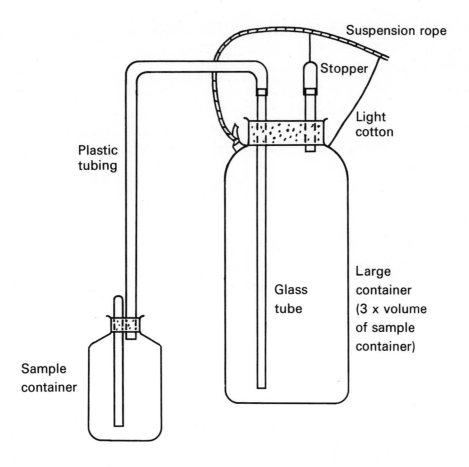

Figure 18   The Dussart sampler

(from Reference 285)

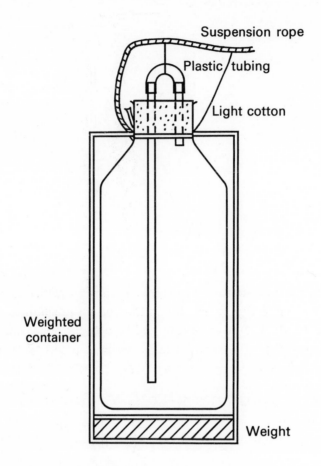

Suspension rope

Plastic tubing

Light cotton

Weighted container

Weight

Figure 19   The rat-trap bottle

(from Reference 286)

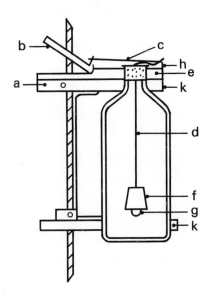

a, Rat–trap; b, trigger platform; c, trigger arm; d, cord attached to upper greased bung e, and then to lower greased bung f, which has a glass weight g, to ensure that it remains in the correct position to close the neck of the bottle. h, Anti–pressure pad to prevent bung e, being forced into the bottle. The whole apparatus is attached to the table with clamps, k.

Figure 20   Longitudinal section of Ruttner's water-bottle

(from Reference 76)

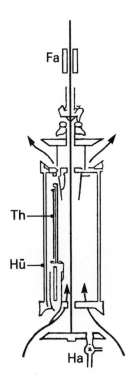

Fa, the drop–weight (messenger); Hū, the protective cover for the thermometer, Th; Ha, the drainage cock (see text).

Figure 21

(from Reference 78)

Kemner Sampler

Figure 22   Van Dorn water sampler in operation

(from Reference 285)

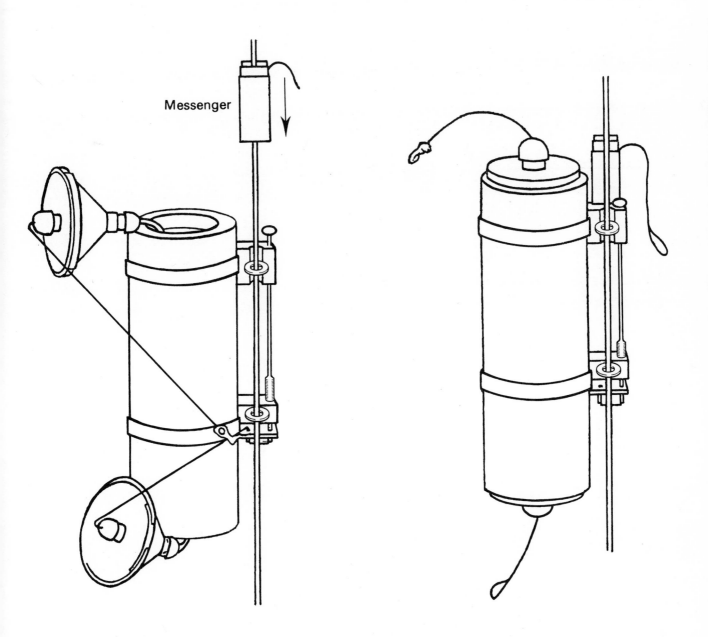

Messenger

Figure 23   Freidinger "open cylinder" sampler

(from Reference 287)

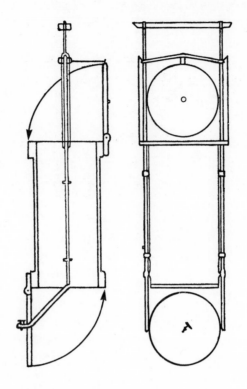

Figure 24   Shallow water sampler

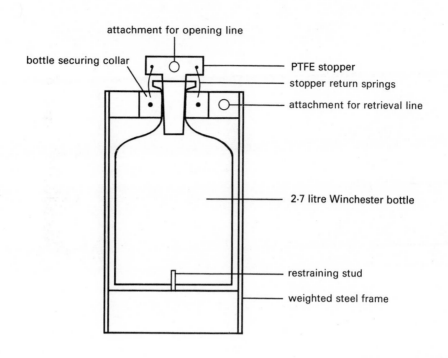

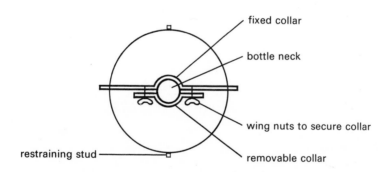

The sampling depth is set by a buoy fixed to the retrieval line

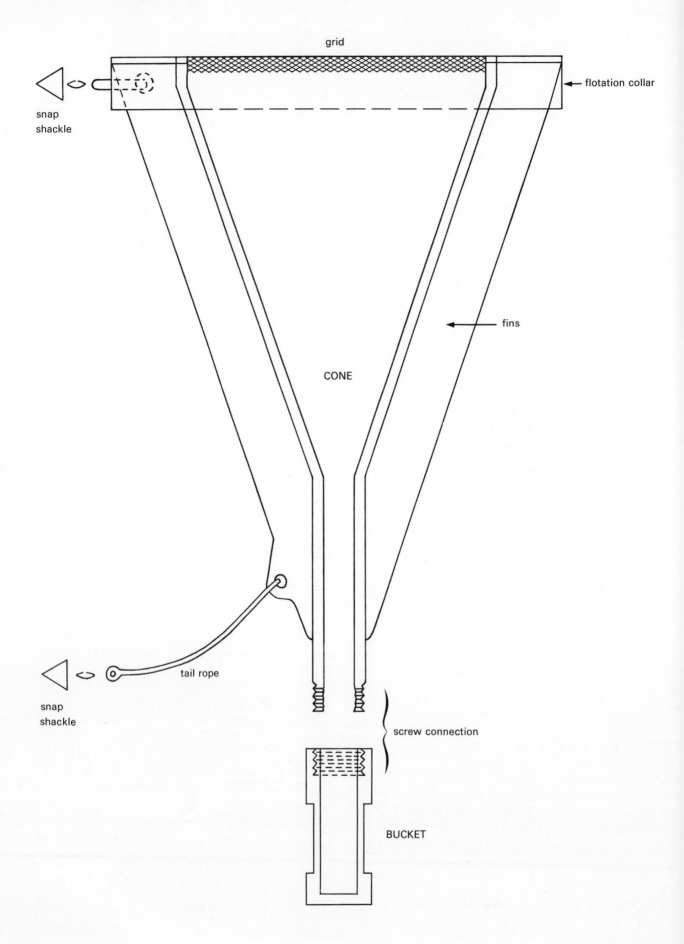

Figure 25   The Aberdeen sedimentation trap

Figure 26   The sedimentation rig

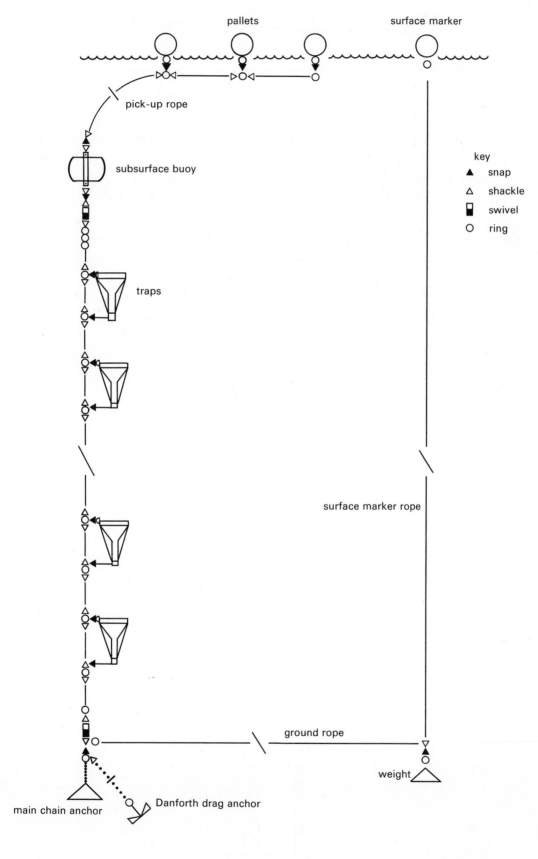

(Reproduced by kind permission of Department of Agriculture and Fisheries Scotland DAFS)

Figure 27   Schematic diagram of dependence of variations in
              quality on the distance downstream from a cyclically-
              varying waste discharge

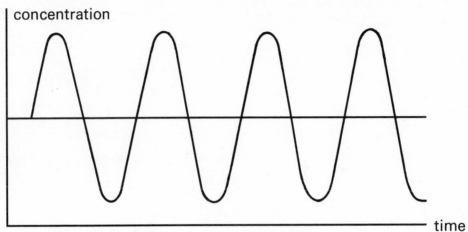
(a)   Sampling location close to discharge

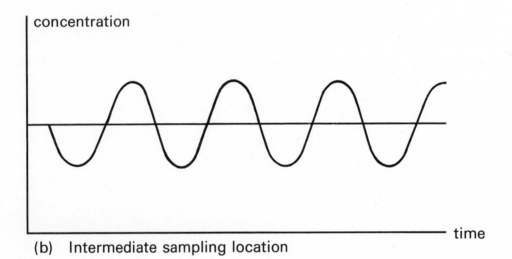
(b)   Intermediate sampling location

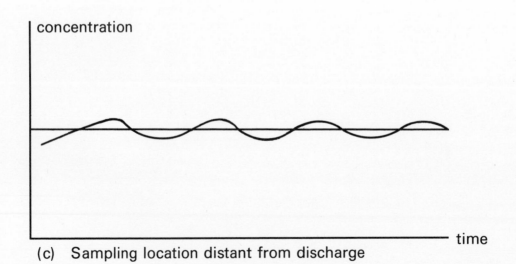
(c)   Sampling location distant from discharge

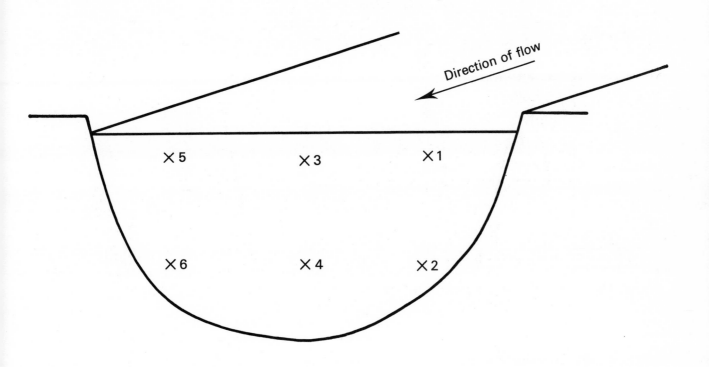

Figure 28   Checking spatial distribution of determinands

Figure 29

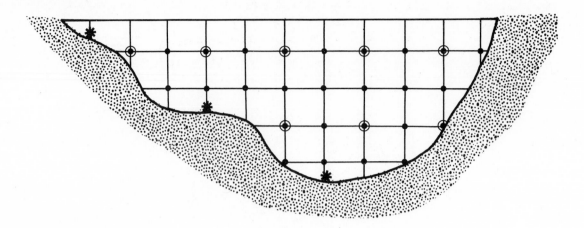

(a) Typical cross sectional (depth), sampling grid. Use all points or only those ringed depending on variation in quality and dimensions. Additional useful sites are shown by asterisks. The surface may also need to be sampled.

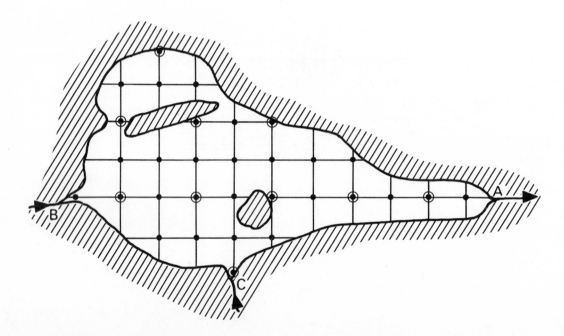

(b) A typical grid plan of sampling stations, points and rings as in (a). A indicates the outlet sample point. B and C indicate inlet sample points, alternatively the two lake points close to them can be used.

Figure 30

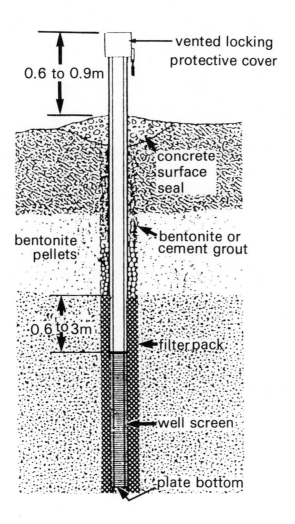

vented locking protective cover

0.6 to 0.9m

concrete surface seal

bentonite pellets

bentonite or cement grout

0.6 to 3m

filter pack

well screen

plate bottom

Figure 31

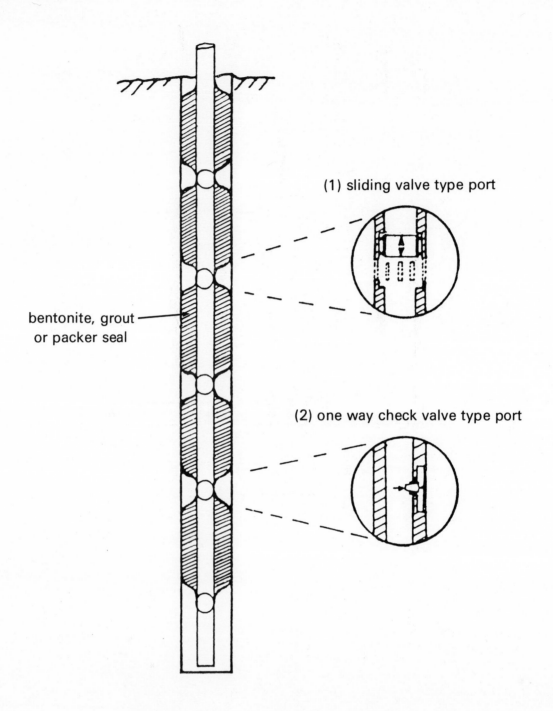

bentonite, grout
or packer seal

(1) sliding valve type port

(2) one way check valve type port

Figure 32

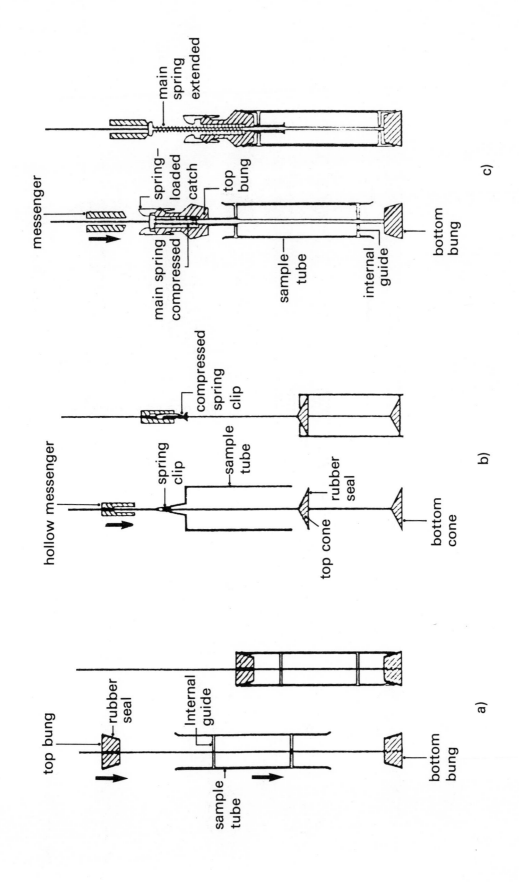

Figure 33

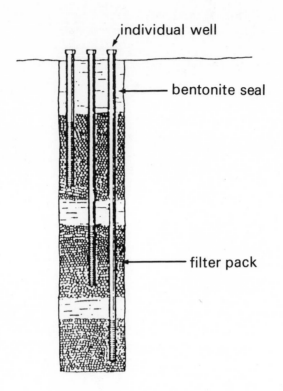

individual well

bentonite seal

filter pack

Figure 34

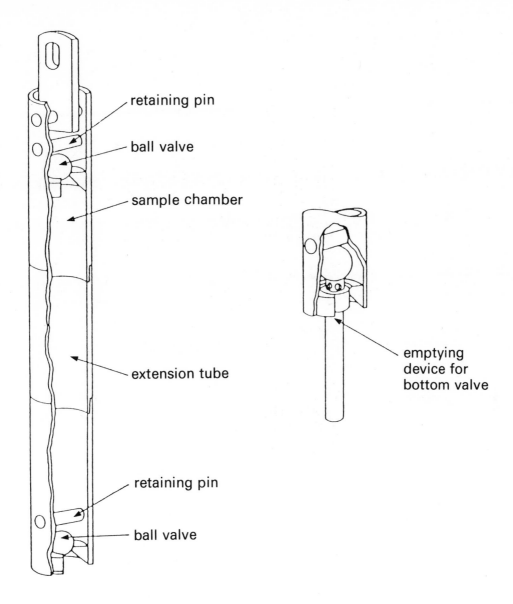

retaining pin

ball valve

sample chamber

extension tube

retaining pin

ball valve

emptying
device for
bottom valve

Figure 35

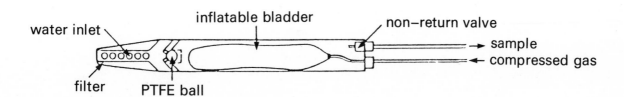

water inlet

inflatable bladder

non–return valve

→ sample

← compressed gas

filter

PTFE ball

Figure 36

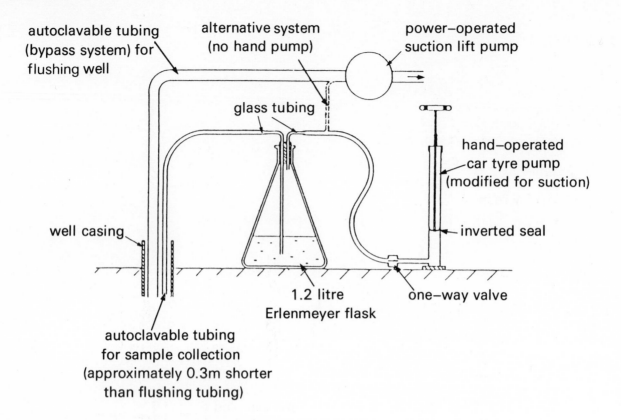

autoclavable tubing (bypass system) for flushing well

alternative system (no hand pump)

power-operated suction lift pump

glass tubing

hand-operated car tyre pump (modified for suction)

inverted seal

well casing

one-way valve

1.2 litre Erlenmeyer flask

autoclavable tubing for sample collection (approximately 0.3m shorter than flushing tubing)

Figure 37

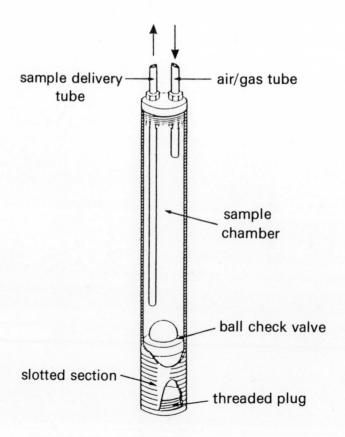

sample delivery tube

air/gas tube

sample chamber

ball check valve

slotted section

threaded plug

Figure 38

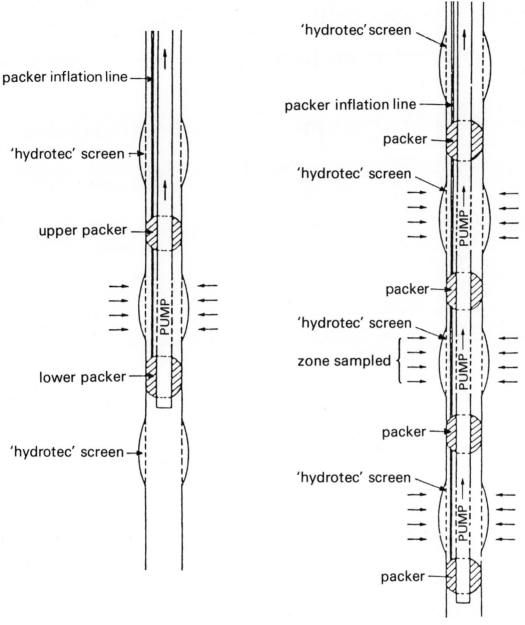

a) Isolation of one zone for sampling within a borehole

(b) 4–Packer system for sampling central zone of three

Figure 39

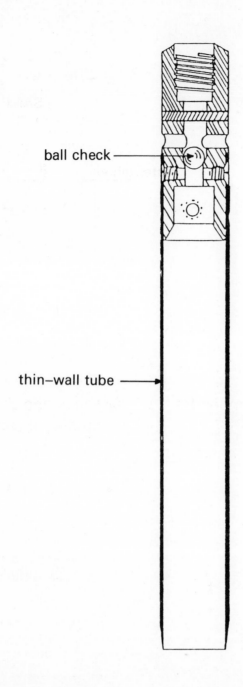

ball check

thin-wall tube

Figure 40

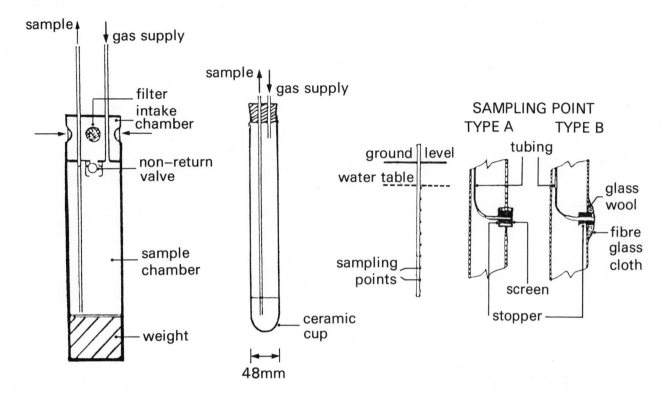

a) WRc in situ sampler

b) soil moisture sampler

c) schematic diagram of the multilevel sampling device

Figure 41

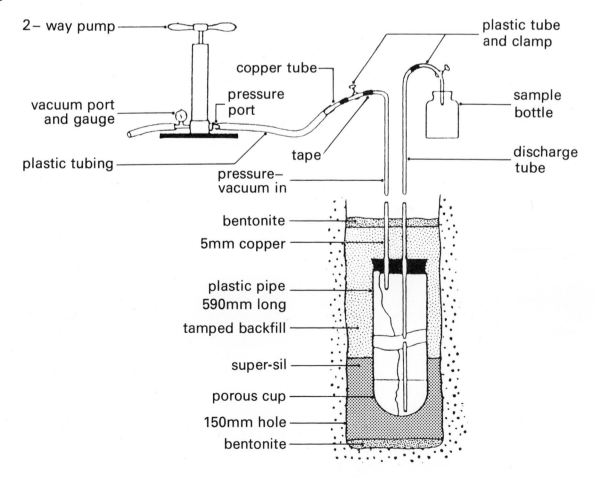

Figure 42

Typical rain gauges

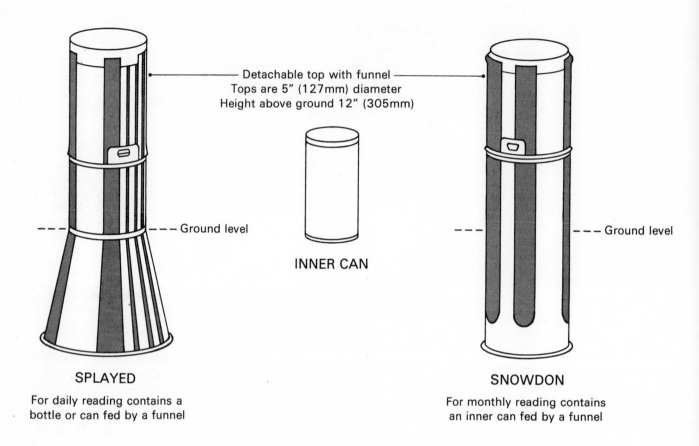

Detachable top with funnel
Tops are 5″ (127mm) diameter
Height above ground 12″ (305mm)

Ground level

INNER CAN

Ground level

SPLAYED

For daily reading contains a
bottle or can fed by a funnel

SNOWDON

For monthly reading contains
an inner can fed by a funnel

Figure 43

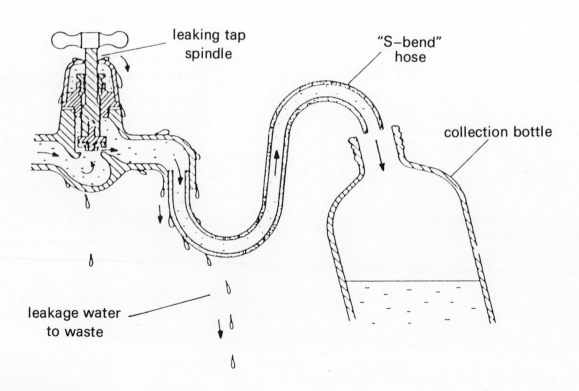

leaking tap
spindle

"S−bend"
hose

collection bottle

leakage water
to waste

14 References

1. Davies OL and Goldsmith PL (eds), *Statistical Methods in Research and Production, 4th Edition.* Oliver and Boyd, Edinburgh, 1972.

2. Massart DL, Dijkstra A and Kaufman L, *Evaluation and Optimization of Laboratory Methods and Analytical Procedures.* Elsevier Scientific Publishing Co., 1978.

3. *Protocol for Analytical Quality Assurance in Public Analyst Laboratories.*

4. Wilson AL and Hunt DTE, *The Chemical Analysis of Water,* 2nd Edn. The Royal Society of Chemistry, London, 1986.

5. Cheeseman RV and Wilson AL, *A Manual of Analytical Quality Control for the Water Industry,* (revised Gardner MJ). Water Research Centre Report NS30. Medmenham, 1989.

6. Moroney MJ, *Facts from Figures, 4th Edition.* Penguin, London, 1969.

7. Cormack, RM, *The Statistical Argument.* Oliver and Boyd, Edinburgh, 1971.

8. Miller JC and Miller JN, *Statistics for Analytical Chemists.* Ellis Horwood (Wiley) 1974.

9. Campbell RC, *Statistics for Biologists, 2nd Edition.* Cambridge University Press, Cambridge, 1974.

10. Cox DR, *Planning of Experiments.* Wiley, New York, 1958.

11. Skoog DA, West DM and Holler FJ, *Fundamentals of Analytical Chemistry, 5th Edition.* Saunders College Publishing, 1988.

12. Ellis JF, *Handbook of Design and Interpretation of Monitoring Programmes.* Water Research Centre Report NS29, Medmenham, 1989.

13. Pomeroy RD and Orlob GT, *Problems of Setting Standards and of Surveillance for Water Quality Control.* California State Water Quality Control Board, Sacramento, 1967.

14. Kittrel FW, *A Practical Guide to Water Quality Studies of Streams.* United States Government Printing Office, Washington, 1969.

15. Federal Water Quality Administration, *Design of Water Quality Surveillance Systems.* United States Government Office, Washington, 1980.

16. Hem JD, *Study and Interpretation of the Chemical Characteristics of Natural Water, 2nd Edition.* United States Government Printing Office, Washington, 1970.

17. Beckers CV, Chamberlain SG and Grimsrud GP, *Quantitative Methods for Preliminary design of Water Quality Surveillance Systems.* United States Government Printing Office, Washington, 1972.

18. Montgomery HAC and Hart IC, *Water Pollution Control* (London), 1974, **73,** 3–27.

19. Weber CI (Ed.), *Biological Field and Laboratory Methods.* United States Natural Environmental Research Centre, Cincinatti, 1973.

20. Wilson AL, in *Manual of Analysis for Water Pollution Control.* World Health Organisation, 1981.

21. Kerrigan JE (ed), Proc. *National Symposium on Data and Instrumentation for Water Quality Management.* University of Wisconsin, Madison, 1970.

22. Deininger RA (ed), Proc. *Seminar on Design of Environmental Information Systems.* Ann Arbor Science Publishers, Ann Arbor, 1974.

23. Rainwater FH and Thatcher LL, *Methods for Collection and Analysis of Water Samples.* United States Government Printing Office, Washington, 1960.

24. Holden WS (ed), *Water Treatment and Examination.* Churchill, London, 1970.

25. United States Environmental Protection Agency, *Handbook for Monitoring Industrial Wastewaters.* United States Government Printing Office, Washington, 1973.

26. Institution of Civil Engineers, *Safety in Sewers and at Sewage Works, 2nd edition.* The Institution, London, 1972.

27. Link LE and Shindala, A, *Water Resources Bull.,* 1973, **9**, 901–907.

28. Ball MD, in *Reference 22*, pp 283–292.

29. Palmer MD and Izatt JB, *Water Res.,* 1970, **4**, 773–786.

30. Palmer MD and Izatt JB, in *Reference 22*, pp 406–418.

31. Wilson JF, in *United States Geol. Surv.Water Supply Paper 1892.* United States Government Printing Office, Washington, 1968, pp 5–8.

32. Dunn B, in *Reference 31*, pp 9–14.

33. Cobb ED, in *Reference 31,* pp 15–22.

34. Collings MR, in *Reference 31*, pp 23–29.

35. Stoner JD, in *Reference 31*, pp 30–33.

36. Buchanan TJ, in *Reference 31,* pp 43–36.

37. Wilson JF, in *Reference 31*, pp 37–43.

38. Chase EB and Payne FN (compilers), *Selected* Techniques in Water Resources Investigations, 1966–67. United States Government Printing Office, Washington, 1968.

39. Feder GL, *Ann. New York Acad. Sci.,* 1972 **199**, 118–123.

40. Sinton LW, *A Guide to Ground Water Sampling Techniques. Water and Soil Miscellaneous Publication No 99.* National Water and Soil Conservation Authority, Wellington, New Zealand, 1986.

41. Palmer MD, *Required Density of Water Quality Sampling Stations at Nanticoke, Lake Erie.* Ontario Water Resources Commission, Toronto, 1968.

42. Pakalnins A and Pollock DC, *Water Pollution Control (Ontario)*, 1971,**109**, 32–33, 35.

43. Wastler TA and Walter CA, *Proc. Am. Soc. Civ.Engrs. J. Sanit. Eng. Div.,*1968, **94** (SA6), 1175–1194.

44. Hilder DW and Wilson AL, *Water Research Association Technical Memorandum TM 72.* The Association, Medmenham, 1972.

45. Wilson AL, *Water Research Association Technical Memorandum TM 71.* The Association, Medmenham, 1972.

46. Anon., *Trib. CEBEDEAU,* 1963, **16**, 184–189.

47. Masch FD and Wilson JR, in *Advances in Water Quality Improvement* (eds Gloyna EF and Eckenfelder WW). University of Texas Press, London, 1968, pp 103–110.

48. *Methods for the Use of Aquatic Macrophytes for Assessing Water Quality in Rivers and Lakes,* 1985–6. HMSO in this series.

49. Gunnerson CG, *Proc. Am. Soc. Civ.Engrs, J. Sanit. Eng. Div.,* 1966, **92** (SA2), 103–125.

50. Meynell GG and Meynell E, *Theory and Practice in Experimental Biology.* Cambridge University Press, Cambridge, 1965.

51. Moody DW, in *Reference 22*, pp 325–335.

52. Allen HE and Mancy KH, in *Water and Water Pollution Handbook, Vol. 3* (ed. Ciacciio LL). Dekker, London, 1972.

53. Rainwater FH and Avrett JR, *J. Am. Water Wks Ass.,* 1962, **54**, 757–768.

54. Wilson AL, in *Reference 22*, pp 199–227.

55. Steele TD, in *Reference 22*, pp 346–363.

56. Thomann RV, *Proc. Am. Soc. Civ.Engrs, J. Sanit. Eng. Div.,* 1967, **93** (SA1), 1–23.

57. Demayo A, *Technical Bulletin No 16.* Department of Energy, Mines and resources, Ottawa, 1969.

58. Kothandaraman V, *Proc. Am. Soc.* Civ.Engrs, J. Sanit. Eng. Div., 1971, **97** (SA1), 19–31.

59. Fuller FC and Tsolos CP, *Biometrics,* 1971, **27**, 1017–1034.

60. Shastry JS, Fan LT and Erikson LE, *Water, Air and Soil Pollution,* 1972, **1**, 233–256.

61. Edwards AMC and Thornes JB, *Water Resources Res.,* 1973, **9**, 1286–1295.

62. Thomann RV, *Proc. Am.* Soc. Civ.Engrs, J. Sanit. Eng. Div., 1970, **96**, 819–837.

63. World Health Organisation, *International Standards for Drinking Water, 3rd edition.* The Organisation, Geneva, 1971.

64. World Health Organisation, *European Standards for Drinking Water, 2nd edition.* The Organisation, Geneva, 1970.

65. United States Public Health Service, *Drinking Water Standards.* United States Government Printing Office, Washington, 1962.

66. Department of National Health and Welfare, *Canadian Drinking Water Standards and Objectives.* Queen's Printer for Canada, Ottawa, 1969.

67. *The Microbiology of Water 1994—Part 1—Drinking Water.* Report on Public Health and Medical Subjects No 71. HMSO, London, in this series.

68. Deininger RA, in *Instrumental Analysis for Water Pollution Control* (ed. Mancy KH). Ann Arbor Science Publishers, Ann Arbor, 1972, pp 299–319.

69. Itskovitch BL, *Automation and Remote Control,* 1961, **22**, 186–192.

70. Thomann RV, in *Reference 22*, pp 76–86.

71. Ward RC and Vanderholm DH, *Water Resources Res.,* 1973, **9**, 536–545.

72. Little AH, *Water Pollution Control,* 1973, **72**, 606–617.

73. *The Sampling and Initial Preparation of Sewage and Waterworks Sludges, Soils, Sediments, Plants and Contaminated Wildlife, 2nd Edition,* 1986. HMSO in this series.

74. *The Sampling of Oils, Fats, Waxes and Tars in Aqueous and Solid Systems,* 1983. HMSO in this series.

75. Hutchinson GE, *A Treatise on Limnology, Vol. 1.* Wiley, London, 1957.

76. Ruttner F, *Fundamentals of Limnology.* University of Toronto Press, Toronto, 1953.

77. American Society for Testing and Materials, *1969 Book of ASTM Standards: Part 23, Atmospheric Analysis.* The Society, Philadelphia, 1969.

78. American Public Health Association *et al., Standard Methods for the Examination of Water and Wastewater, 16th and subsequent editions.* The Association, New York, 1982.

79. Department of the Environment, *Analysis of Raw, Potable and Waste Waters.* HMSO, London, 1972.

80. Golterman HL (ed.), *Methods for Chemical Analysis of Fresh Waters.* Blackwell, Oxford, 1969.

81. Riley JP, in *Chemical Oceanography, Vol. 3, 2nd edition* (eds Riley JP and Skirrow G). Academic Press, London, 1975, pp 193–477.

82. Collins VG, Jones JG, Hendrie MS, Shewan JM, Wynn-Williams DD and Rhodes ME, in *Sampling—Microbiological Monitoring of Environments* (eds Board RG and Lovelock DW). Academic press, London, 1973, pp 77–110.

83. *Dissolved Oxygen in Natural and Waste Water,* 1979. HMSO in this series.

84. British Standards Institution, *British Standard BS1328*. The Institution, London, 1969.

85. Mancy KH and Weber WJ, in *Treatise on Analytical Chemistry, Part III, Vol. 2* (eds Kolthoff IM, Elving PJ and Stross FH). Wiley-Interscience, London, 1971, pp 413–562.

86. Anderson PW, Murphy JJ and Faust SD, in *Reference 22*, pp 261–281.

87. Wilson AL, *Chem. Ind.,* 1969, 1253–1260.

88. Wood LB and Stanbridge HH, *Water Pollution Control,* 1968, **67**, 495–520.

89. Bouveng HO, *Pure Appl. Chem.,* 1969, **19**, 267–290.

90. Tarazi DF, Hiser LL, Childers RE and Boldt CA, *J. Water Pollution Control Fed.,* 1970, **42**, 708–732.

91. Cottrell DR, Kitchen D and Whitby FJ, *Imperial Chemical Industries, Brixham Laboratory Report No BL/A/1582*. Imperial Chemical Industries, Brixham, 1974.

92. Schwoerbel J, *Methods of Hydrobiology*. Pergamon Press, London, 1970.

93. Holme NA and McIntyre AD, *Methods for the Study of Marine Benthos*. Blackwell, Oxford, 1971.

94. *Biological Methods for Water Quality Surveys. Water and Soil Miscellaneous Publication No 54*. Ministry of Works and Developments, Wellington, New Zealand.

95. Beak TW, Griffing TC and Appleby AG, in *American Society for Testing and Materials Special Technical Publication 528* (eds Cairns J and Dickson KL). Philadelphia, 1973, pp 227–241.

96. *NAMAS Document M10*. National Measurement Accreditation Service, London.

97. *NAMAS Document M17*. National Measurement Accreditation Service, London.

98. Everitt GE, Potter EC and Thompson RG, *J. Appl. Chem.,* 1965, **15**, 389–402.

99. Spencer DW and Brewer PG, *Crit. Revs. Solid State Sci.,* 1970, **1**, 409–478.

100. Hamilton EI and Minski MJ, *Environm. Lett.,* 1972, **3**, 53–71.

101. BS 6068 Part 6 (and ISO 5667, various parts).
     Section 6.1, 1981, *Guidance on the Design of Sampling Programmes.*
     Section 6.2, 1986, *Guidance on Sampling Techniques.*
     Section 6.3, 1986, *Guidance on the Preservation and Handling of Samples.*
     Section 6.4 onwards, *Guidance on Sampling from Various Special Types of Water.*

102. Ryden JC, Syers JK and Harries RF, *Analyst,* 1972, **97**, 903–908.

103. Skougstad MW and Scarbro GF, *Environm. Sci. Technol.,* 1968, **2**, 298–301.

104. Robertson DE, *Analytica Chim. Acta,* 1968, **42**, 533–536.

105. Bowen VT, Strohal P, Saiki M, Ancellin J, Merten D and Ganguly AK, in *Reference Methods for Marine Radioactivity Studies*. International Atomic Energy Agency, Vienna, 1970, pp 7–40.

106. Bowditch DC, Edmond CR, Dunstand PJ and McGlynn JA, *Australian Water Resources Council Technical Paper No 16*. Australian Government Publishing Services, Canberra, 1976.

107. *US Federal Register, Vol 52*. 171. 33550 V.

108. Shannon JE and Lee GF, *Air, Water Pollut.,* 1966, **10**, 735–756.

109. Burton JD, Leatherland TM and Liss PS, *Limnol. Oceanogr.,* 1970, **15**, 473–476.

110. Heron J, *Limnol. Oceanogr.,* 1962, **7**, 316–321.

111. *Mercury in Waters, Effluents, Soils and Sediments etc. Additional methods* 1985. HMSO in this series.

112. Feldman C, *Anal. Chem.,* 1974, **46**, 99–103.

113. Christman DR and Ingle JD, *Anal. Chim. Acta.,* 1976, **86**, 53–62.

114. Carr RA and Wilkniss PE, *Envir. Sci.Technol.*, 1973, **7** 62–63.

115. Rosain RM and Wai CM, *Anal. Chim. Acta,* 1973, **65**, 297–284.

116. Harper DJ, Fileman CF, May PV and Portmann JE, *Methods of Analysis for Trace Metals in Marine and Other Samples*, MAFF Aquatic Environment Analytical Methods, 1991.

117. *Silver in Waters, Sewages and Effluents by AAS* 1982. HMSO in this series.

118. Waldock MJ, Miller D, Waite ME, Smith DJ and Portmann JE, *Methods of Analysis for Total ands Organotin Compounds in Environmental Samples.* MAFF Aquatic Environmental Analytical Methods, 1991.

119. *Handnet Sampling of Aquatic Benthic Macroinvertebrates* 1978. HMSO in this series.

120. Strickland JDH and Parsons TR, *A Practical Handbook of Seawater Analysis.* Fisheries Research Board of Canada, Ottawa, 1968.

121. Coyne RV, Campbell JM and Robles EG, *Report No AD-75237.* United States National Technical Information Service, Springfield, 1972.

122. Kobayashi J, reported in *Methods of Seawater Analysis, 2nd Edition*, eds Grasshoff K, Eberhardt M and Kremling K. Verlag Chemie, Weinheim, 1983.

123. Fitzgerald GP and Faust SL, *Limnol. Oceanogr.,* 1967, **12**, 332–334.

124. Hager SW, Atlas EL, Gordon LI, Mantyla AW and Park PK, *Limnol. Oceanogr.,* 1972, **17**, 931–937.

125. Nelson DW and Romkens MJM, *J. Environ. Qual.,* 1972, **1**, 323–324.

126. Morgan PE and Clarke EF, *Public Wks.,* 1964, **95**, 73–75.

127. Agardy FJ and Kidds ML, *Proc. 21st Indiana Waste Conference 1966.* Purdue University, Lafayette, undated, pp 226–233.

128. Institut für Wasserwirtschaft, *Ausgewahlte Methoden der Wasseruntersuchunger, Band 1.* Gustav Fischer Verlag, Jena, 1971.

129. United States Environmental Protection Agency, *Methods for Chemical Analysis of Water and Wastes, 1974.* United States Government Printing Office, Washington.

130. Marvin KT, Proctor RR and Neal RA, *Limnol. Oceanogr.,* 1970, **15**, 320–325.

131. Cheeseman RV and Wilson AL, *Water Research Association Technical Memorandum TM78.* The Association, Medmenham, 1978.

132. Traversy WJ, *Methods of Chemical Analysis of Waters and Wastewaters*, Department of Fisheries and Forestry, Ottawa, 1971.

133. Chao TT, Jenne EA and Heppting LN, in *United States Geological Survey Professional Paper 600-D.* United States Government Printing Office, Washington, 1968.

134. Hegi HR and Fischer E, *Schweitz. Z. Hydrol.,* 1969, **31**, 162–174/

135. Thayer GW, *Chesapeake Sci.,* 1970, **11**, 155–158.

136. Brezonik PJ and Lee GF, *Air Water Pollut.,* 1966, **10**, 549–553.

137. Jenkins D, in *Trace Organics in Water,* (ed. Gould RF). American Chemical Society, Washington, 1968, pp 265–280.

138. Howe LH and Holley CW, *Environ. Sci.Technol.,* 1969, **3**, 478–481.

139. Henriksen A, *Vatten,* 1969, **25**, 247–254.

140. Charpiot R, *Can., Oceanogr.,* 1969, **21**, 773–793.

141. Henriksen A, *Vatten,* 1971, **27**, 44–50.

142. Grunnet TK, *Vatten,* 1971, **27**, 220–233.

143. Benedek A and Jajak A, *Water and Pollution Control,* 1975 (September), 20–24, 31.

144. Riley JP, in *Analytical Chemistry of Sea Water, Volume 3, 2nd Edition,* (eds Riley JP and Skirrow G). Academic Press, London, 1975, pp 211–218.

145. Grasshof K, *Methods of Sea Water Analysis.* Verlag Chemie, New York, 1976, pp 21–24.

146. Wang W and Schnepper DH, *Water Sewage Wks.,* 1971, **117** 257–259.

147. Sheldon RW, *Limnol. Oceanogr.,* 1972, **12**, 494–498.

148. Brewers JM, *Marine Pollution Bulletin,* 1985, **16**, 277–281.

149. Campbell JA, Gardner MJ and Gunn AM, *Anal. Chim. Acta,* 1985, **176**, 193–200.

150. Gardner MJ, *Water Research Centre Technical Report TR 172.* The Centre, Medmenham, 1978.

151. Mizuno K, *Bunseki Kagaku,* 1971, **20**, 1235–1240.

152. Zirino A and Healey ML, *Limnol. Oceanogr.,* 1971, **16**, 773–778.

153. Van Steenderen RA, *Water SA,* 1976, **2**, 156–159.

154. Malcolm RL and Leenheer JA, *Inst. Environ. Sci.Tech. Meet. Proc.,* 1973, **19**, 336–340.

155. Schmitz W and Bauer L, *Haus Tech., Essen, Vortragsveröff.,* 1970, No 231, 12–28.

156. *Phosphorus in Water, Effluents and Sewage,* 1980. HMSO in this series.

157. *Determination of Radioactivity in Water by Multinuclide Gamma Ray Spectrometry,* 1989. HMSO in this series.

158. Morris AW, in *Practical Estuarine Chemistry,* (ed. Head PC). Cambridge University Press, Cambridge, 1985, pp 1–60.

159. Morris AW, in *Practical Procedures for Estuarine Chemistry,* (ed. Morris AW). NERC, 1983, pp 1–17.

160. Gunnerson CG, *Proc. Am. Soc. Civ.Engrs,* 1966, **92 (SA2)**, 103–125.

161. Wastler TA and Walter CM, *J. Sanit. Engng Div.Am. Soc. Civ.Engrs,* 1968, **SA6**, 1175–1194.

162. Ibanez F, *Limnol. Oceanogr.,* 1981, **26**, 336–349.

163. Head PC, in *Practical Estuarine Chemistry,* (ed. Head PC). Cambridge University Press, Cambridge, 1985, pp 278–330.

164. Hooper DJ, in *Estuarine Hydrography and Sedimentation,* (ed. Dyer KR). Cambridge University Press, Cambridge, 1979, pp 41–56.

165. Lion LW and Leckie JO, *Limnol. Oceanogr.,* 1982, **27**, 111–125.

166. Platford RF, Carey JH and Hale EJ, *Environmental Pollution Series B,* 1982, **3**, 125–128.

167. Hamilton CI and Clifton RJ, *Limnol. Oceanogr.,* 1979, **24**, 188–193.

168. David PM, *J, Mar. Biol. Assoc.,* 1965, **45**, 313–320.

169. Wellman AD and Wellman WJA, *Lab. Practice,* 1975, 31–33.

170. Hatcher RF and Parker BC, *Limnol. Oceanogr.,* 1974, **19**, 162–165.

171. Ritall WF, *Proceedings of Seminar on Methodology for Monitoring the Marine Environment, Seattle, October 1973.* United States Environmental Protection Agency, Washington, 1974, pp 55–71.

172. Liss PS, in *Chemical Oceanography, 2nd Edition, Vol. 2,* (eds Riley JP and Skirrow G). Academic Press, London, 1975, pp 193–244.

173. Smith KL, *Limnol. Oceanogr.,* 1971, **16**, 675–677.

174. Joyce JR, *J, Mar Biol. Assoc. UK,* 1973, **53**, 741–744.

175. Petty RL, *Marine Chemistry,* 1981, **10**, 409–416.

176. Law RJ, Fileman TW and Portmann JE, *The Analysis of Hydrocarbons in Marine and other Samples.* MAFF Aquatic Environment Analytical Methods, 1991.

177. Harper DJ, *Mar. Chem.,* 1987, **21**, 183–188.

178. Mart L, *Fresenius Z. Anal. Chem.,* 1979, **299**, 97–102.

179. Bewers JM and Windom HL, *Mar. Chem.,* 1982, **11**, 71–86.

180. Eagle RA, Norton MG, Nunny RS and Rolfe MS, *The Field Assessment of Effects of Dumping Wastes at Sea. 2. Methods.* MAFF Fisheries Research Technical Report No 47. MAFF, Lowestoft, 1987.

181. Holme NA and McIntyre AD, *Methods for the Study of Marine Benthos.* Blackwell Scientific, London, 1984.

182. Reineck HE, *Senckenbergi.Analyt.,* 1958, **39**, 42–48, 54–56.

183. Reineck HE, *Nat. und Mus.,* 1963, **93**, 102–108.

184. Craib JS, *J Cons. Perm. Int. Explor. Mer.,* 1965, **30**, 34–39.

185. Bouma AH, *Methods for the Study of Sedimentary Structures.* Wiley Interscience, New York, 1969.

186. Bricker OP, *Biogeochemistry of Estuarine Sediments. Proceedings of the 1976 UNESCO/SCOR Workshop.* UNESCO, Paris, 1978, pp 75–79.

187. Kriukov PA and Manheim FT (eds), *Dynamic Environment of the Ocean Floor.* Lexington Books, Lexington MA, 1982, pp 3–26.

188. *MPMMG Report, 1988.*

189. *Quantitative Sampling for Benthic Macroinvertebrates in Shallow Waters* 1980. HMSO in this series.

190. *Sampling Methods for Non-Planktonic Algae (Benthic Algae and Periphyton)* 1982. HMSO in this series.

191. *Sampling of Benthic Macroinvertebrates in Deep Rivers* 1983. HMSO in this series.

192. *A Colonization Sampler for Collecting Macroinvertebrate Indicators of Water Quality in Lowland Rivers* 1983. HMSO in this series.

193. *Methods of Sampling Fish Populations in Shallow Rivers and Streams* 1983. HMSO in this series.

194. *The Direct Determination of the Biomass of Aquatic Macrophytes and Measurement of Underwater Light,* 1985. HMSO in this series.

195. *The Enumeration of Algae. Estimation of Cell Volume and use in Bioassays,* 1990. HMSO in this series.

196. *A Review and Methods for the Use of Epilithic Diatoms for Detecting and Monitoring Changes in River Water Quality* 1993. HMSO in this series.

197. *Estimation of Flow and Load.* See second part of this booklet.

198. Miles DL and Cook JM, in *Quality of Groundwater. Proceedings of an International Symposium, Noordwijkerhout, The Netherlands.* Studies in Environmental Science, **17**. Elsevier, 1981, pp 725–731.

199. Wilkinson WB and Edworthy KJ, in *Quality of Groundwater. Proceedings of an International Symposium, Noordwijkerhout, The Netherlands.* Studies in Environmental Science, **17**. Elsevier, 1981, pp 629–642.

200. Foster SSD and Gomes DC, *Groundwater Quality Monitoring: An Appraisal of Practices and Costs.* Pan American Health Organisation, Lima, 1989.

201. Van Ec JJ and McMillion LG, in *Groundwater Contamination: Field Methods,* (eds Collins AG and Johnson AI). ASTM STP 963. American Society for Testing and Materials, Philadelphia, 1988.

202. Brassington FC and Walthall S, *Quarterly Journal of Engineering Geology,* 1985, **18**, 181–194.

203. Ward RC, *J. Wat. Poll. Con. Fed.,* 1979, **51**, 2292–2300.

204. Bachmat Y and Ben-Zvi M, in *Quality of Groundwater. Proceedings of an International Symposium, Noordwijkerhout, The Netherlands.* Studies in Environmental Science, **17**. Elsevier, 1981, pp 605–615.

205. *The Nitrogen Cycle of the United Kingdom. A Study Group Report.* The Royal Society, London, 1983.

206. Foster SSD, Bridge LR, Geake AK, Lawrence AR and Parker JM, *British Geological Survey Hydrogeology Report No 86/2.* NERC, 1986.

207. Freeze RA and Cherry JA, *Groundwater,* Prentice-Hall Inc., 1979.

208. *Safety in Wells and Boreholes,* Institution of Civil Engineers, London, 1972.

209. Edmunds WM, Miles DL and Cook JM, in *Hydrochemical Balances of Freshwater Systems.* IASH Publication No 150, 1984, 55–70.

210. Valeton I and Klint W, *Geol. Runsch.,* 1962, **52**, 475–492.

211. Valeton I, *Proc. Int. Clay Conf. Stockholm,* 1963, **2**, 241–247.

212. Valeton I, *Beitr. Mineral Petrog.,* 1965, **11**, 217–246.

213. Valeton I, *Bull. Soc. Geol. Fr.,* 1966, **7 (VIII)**, 685–701.

214. Pittwell LR, *Chem. Geol.,* 1973, **12**, 39–49.

215. Wilson LC and Rouse JV, *Ground Water Monitoring Review,* 1983, **3**, 103–109.

216. Clark L and Baxter KM, *Quarterly Journal of Engineering Geology,* 1989, **22**, 159–168.

217. Parker JM, Perkins MA and Foster SSD, in *Proceedings of the Symposium Methods and Instrumentation for the Investigation of Groundwater Systems, Noordwijkerhout, The Netherlands.* May 1983, pp 43–54.

218. Marsh JM and Lloyd JW, *Ground Water,* 1980, **18**, 366–373.

219. Parker CV, Hewitt AD and Jennings TF, *Groundwater Monitoring Review,* 1990, 146–156.

220. Keeley JF and Boating K, *Ground Water,* 1987, **25**, 300–313.

221. Walker SE, in *Proceedings of the Third National Symposium on Aquifer Restoration and Ground-water Monitoring.* (Watlington DH: NWWA), 1983.

222. Driscoll FG, *Groundwater and Wells, 2nd Edition.* Johnson Division, Minnesota, 1986.

223. Barcelona MJ, Gibb JP, Helfrich JA and Gaske EE, *Illinois State Water Survey Contract Report No 374,* 1985.

224. Pohlmann KF and Hess JW, *Ground Water Monitoring Review,* 1988, **8 (4)**, 82–84.

225. Neilsen DM and Yeates GL, *Ground Water Monitoring Review,* 1985, **5**, 83–99.

226. Gillham RW, *Ground Water Monitoring Review,* 1982, 36–39.

227. Pankow JF, Isabelle LM, Hewetson JP and Cherry JA, *Ground Water,* 1984, **22**, 330–339.

228. Emenhiser TC and Singh UP, *Ground Water Monitoring Review,* Fall 1984, 35–37.

229. Edge RW and Cordry K, *Ground Water Monitoring Review,* 1989, 177–183.

230. Rannie EH and Nadon RL, *Ground Water Monitoring* Review, 1988, **8 (4)**, 100–107.

231. Patton FD, *Proceedings of the First International Mine Drainage Symposium,* Denver, Colorado, 1979.

232. Kinniburgh DG and Miles DL, *Environmental Science and Technology,* 1983, **17**, 362–368.

233. Entwhistle DC and Reeder S, *Geological Soc. Newsletter,* 1990, **19 (4)**, 32.

234. Norman WR, *Ground Water Monitoring Review,* Spring 1986, 56–60.

235. Bishop P, Burston MW, Chen T and Lerner DN, *Quarterly Journal of Engineering Geology,* 1991, **24**, 311–322.

236. Gillham RW, *Ground Water Monitoring Review,* Spring 1982, 36–39.

237. Harrar JE and Rober E, *Ground Water,* 1982, **20**, 479–481.

238. Wilson LC, *Ground Water Monitoring Review,* Winter 1983, **3**, 156–166.

239. Wagner GH, *Soil Science,* 1962, **94**, 379–386.

240. Hansen EA and Harris AR, *Proc. Soil Science Soc. of America,* 1975, **39**, 528–536.

241. Parizek RR, *J. Hydrol.,* 1970, **11**, 1–21.

242. *Meteorological Observer's Handbook.* HMSO, London.

243. Sevruk B, Hertig JA and Spiess R, *Atmos. Environ.,* 1991.

244. Stone BH, *A Preliminary Assessment of United Kingdom Precipitation Collectors.* Warren Spring Laboratory, Stevenage, 1990.

245. Hall DJ, Cottrill SM, Goldsmith AL, Upton SL, Waters RA and Wright P, *The Development and Field Use of a Snow Collector for Acid Precipitation Studies.* Report No LR 585 (PA), Warren Spring Laboratory, Stevenage, 1987.

246. Georgii HW and Wötzel D, *Geophys. Res.,* 1970, **75**, 1727–1731.

247. Adams SJ, Bradley SG, Stow CD and de Mora SJ, *Nature,* 1986, **321**, 842–844.

248. Asman WAH, *Water, Air and Soil Pollut.,* 1980, **13**, 235–245.

249. Coscio MR, Pratt CG and Krupa SV, *Atmos. Environ.,* 1982, **16**, 1939–1944.

250. Galloway JN and Likens GE, *Water, Air and Soil Pollut.,* 1976, **6**, 241–258.

251. Slanina J, Mols JJ, Board JH, von der Sloot HA, von Raaphorst JG and Asmon W, *Intern. J. Environ. Anal. Chem.,* 1979, **7**, 161–176.

252. Hall DJ, *The Precipitation Collector for use in the Secondary National Acid Deposition Network.* Report No LR 561 (AP), Warren Spring Laboratory, Stevenage, 1986.

253. Asman WAH, Riddler TB, Rejnders HF and Slanina J, *Water, Air and Soil Pollut.,* 1982, **17**, 415–420.

254. Zolitz, *Optimization of the Background Monitoring Net for Air Pollutants in the Federal Republic of Germany, by Aid of Geostatistics.* 1988.

255. Wu TL, *Water, Air and Soil Pollut.,* 1981, **15**, 173–184.

256. Richards RP, Kramer JW, Baker DB and Kriegar KA, *Nature,* 1987, **327**, 129–131.

257. *United Kingdom Review Group on Acid Rain, Future Acid Deposition Monitoring in the United Kingdom.* Warren Spring Laboratory, Stevenage, 1986.

258. United Kingdom Review Group on Acid Rain, *Acid Deposition in the United Kingdom, 1981–1985.* Warren Spring Laboratory, Stevenage, 1987.

259. Kurtyka JC, *Precipitation Measurements Study.* Report of Investigation No 20, State Water Survey Division, Urbana Ill., USA, 1953.

260. Kind RJ, in *Handbook of Snow, Principles, Processes, Management and Use* (eds Gray DM and Male DH). Pergamon Press, Toronto, 1981, pp 338–359.

261. Granat L, in *Proc. Symp. Monitoring and Assessment of Airborne Pollutants with Special Emphasis on Long-Range Transport and Deposition of Acidic Materials* (eds Pierce RC, Whelpdale DM and Sheffer MG). Environmental Secretariat, National Research Council of Canada, Ottawa, 1982, pp 281–314.

262. Goodison BE, *J. Applied Met.,* 1978, **17**, 1542–1548.

263. Goodison BE, Ferguson HL and McKay GA, in *Handbook of Snow, Principles, Processes, Management and Use* (eds Gray DM and Male DH). Pergamon Press, Toronto, 1981, pp 191–274.

264. Gervat GP, Clark PA and Kallend AS, *A Ground Based Cloudwater Collector; Design, Estimated Performance and Preliminary Samples from the North Downs.* Note No TPRD/L/2701/N84, CERL, Leatherhead, 1984.

265. BS 1747. *Method for Measurement of Air Pollution.*

266. BS 1747/1. *Deposit Gauges 1969.*

267. BS 1747/2. *Determination of Concentration of Suspended Matter 1969.*

268. BS 1747/5. *Directional Dust Gauges 1972.*

269. ISO 4222. *Ambient Air—Measurement of Particle Fallout.*

270. ISO 5667/8. *Guidance on Sampling of Wet Deposition.*

271. ISO 9835. *Ambient Air—Determination of Black Smoke.*

272. *Guidance on Safeguarding the Quality of Public Water Supplies.* Department of the Environment and Welsh Office. HMSO, London, 1989.

273. *Methods of Biological Sampling, Sampling of Macroinvertebrates in Water Supply Systems* 1983. HMSO, London in this series.

274. *The Determination of Carbon Dioxide in Natural, Treated and Beverage Waters, with a Supplement on Sampling Boiled and Canned Waters* 1986. HMSO in this series.

275. *Methods for the Isolation and Identification of Salmonellae from Water and Associated Materials* 1982. HMSO in this series.

276. Biggs DJ, Gifford JS and Smith DG, *Biological Methods of Water Quality Survey.* Water and Soil Miscellaneous Publication No 54, Nature, Water and Soil Conservation Organisation, Wellington, New Zealand, 1983.

277. Pittwell LR, *Biological Monitoring of Rivers in the Community*, in *The Principals and Methods for Determining Ecological Criteria Hydrobiocenoses* (eds Amavis R and Smeets J). CEC/Pergamon Press, Oxford, 1976, pp 225–262.

278. Hellawell JM, *Biological Monitoring and Surveillance of Rivers.* Water Research Centre, Notes on Water Research No 3, 1976.

279. Elliot JM, *A Statistical Analysis of Samples of Benthic Invertebrates.* Freshwater Biological Association, Ambleside, 1977.

280. Haslam SM, *River Plants of Western Europe.* Cambridge University Press.

281. Haslam SM and Walseley PA, *River Vegetation.* Cambridge University Press.

282. Haslam SM, *River Pollution. Some Methods for the Ecological Perspective.* Belhaven, London, 1990.

283. Elliot JM, Tullett PA and Elliot JA, *A New Bibliography of Samplers for Freshwater Benthic Invertebrates.* Freshwater Biological Association, Ambleside, 1993.

284. Edmunds AW, Bath AH, 1976. *Centrifuge extraction and chemical analysis of interstitial waters.* Environmental Science and Technology, Vol 10, 467–472.

285. Kingsford M, *Sampling of surface waters.* Technical Publication No 2. Water and Soil Division, Ministry of Works and Development, Wellington, New Zealand, 1977.

286. Ormerod K, Bonde GJ and Kirstensen KK, *Bacteriological Examination of Water for Pollution Control.* Ed M J Suess. Vol 3, pp273–461. Pergamon Press for World Health Organisation, 1982.

287. Golterman HL, Clymo RS and Ohnsted MAM, *Methods for Physical and Chemical Analysis of Fresh Waters.* International Biological Programme, Handbook No 8, Second Edition. Blackwall Scientific Publications, Oxford, 1979.

Estimation of Flow and Load 1996

Methods for the Examination of Waters and Associated Materials

CONTENTS

While many analyses are carried out to measure the concentration of determinands in water or solids, for many purposes the ultimate requirement is not the concentration itself but the load of the determinand being transported in a given time. Basically, load is the product of concentration and flow rate:

mass per unit volume × volume per unit time = mass per unit time

$$gl^{-1} \times lhr^{-1} = ghr^{-1}$$

This booklet is concerned with the estimation of flow and other variables which complicate this simple relationship. The total load is the integrated product of flow and concentration, integrated both over the total cross-section of the system and over the time interval under study. In practice, load can be very difficult to estimate. For example, there is the problem of load determination at very high flow rates when the determinand concentration is below the limit of detection. If the concentration is only just below the limit of detection, the amount transported could in reality be significant. The load might equally be close to zero. The converse case of a significant concentration moving at an extremely slow rate may also be a problem. In both the above instances no single load figure should be given, but an explanation of the facts should be reported, mentioning the range within which the true value might lie.

Concentrations in rivers usually vary with time. Variations depend on the system, but daily, yearly and irregular fluctuations are all common. Sufficient data have already been accumulated to show that correlations between determinand concentration and water flow can differ widely.

For certain rivers, the peak concentration levels are at times of low flow, either because there is less water to dilute an effluent stream or because the water draining into the river has been longer in contact with the ground and therefore has had more opportunity to leach out solutes. In the former instance, loads may remain constant, while in the second, the seasonal variation may differ between determinands. In some rivers, especially for sediment loads, determinand concentration and flow may vary together so that as much as 80% of the total annual load may be concentrated into only 3% of the time.

For some very soluble determinands, the peak concentrations may occur as sharp peaks during the initial increase in flow, falling again before peak flow. In the case of biological nutrients such as nitrate, even more complex variations occur dependent on climate, plant growing cycles and farming practices.

Changes in chemical form can be important, especially when distinction is made between soluble, insoluble and total determinand. As is mentioned below, weather effects can also affect results in several ways by mixing and by aeration.

Adsorption, desorption and leaching by soil or rock also play a part in changing the composition of waters.

Mixing of chemically different waters can lead to precipitation as sediment below a confluence, or where a river joins a lake or the sea. Velocity changes can cause deposits or scouring.

The overall layout and shape of the system can likewise cause concentration patterns to vary, especially if there are several inputs or sources which differ in quality, several outlets or abstractions and intermediary loops, networks, islands or braided channels. Only rarely is the time taken for water to flow round an island identical in both channels and the mixing of dissimilar streams can take many kilometres to complete.

Channelling is a common phenomenon, especially if there are density or other differences. The rafting of one water over a more dense one is very common, especially when due to temperature or dissolved solids content. The existence of layers arranged across a water course is well known, especially where tidal or current effects occur, and extreme examples such as a right bank tributary water channelling across to the left bank are not unknown. On the other hand, several examples are known of complete mixing of large rivers within a few hundred metres, as when they pour over a waterfall. Eddies and back (or upstream) flow can further complicate the load profile, as when one or more tributaries are in sudden spate and others are not.

Flood relief channels interconnecting different river systems also occur naturally as well as artificially, with very intermittent but large flows in them. Mixing is highly dependent on the shape of the rivers at, and downstream from, the confluence and on the amount of turbulence. Turbulence is dependent not only on flow rate but also on obstructions to flow and on air (or wind) speed above the surface.

The nature of the permeability of the strata of banks and the level of the groundwater table can also be important. Studies have revealed quite large exchanges taking place between the river and the groundwater when the banks and beds are relatively porous.

Intermittently moving sediment load can present a problem when a measurement of long term total load is required, as the rate of transport is very variable and dependent on stream velocities being high enough to suspend or slide the deposits. At very high flow rates sediment burdens approaching mud flows can be attained (when the suspended solids content exceeds the water content). Rapid transport of boulders has been recorded and the shifting of hill stream cobbles and the reworking of mud banks are well known.

Flow in closed pipes can be complicated by sediments, wall friction, water hammer and variable flows (especially in grids and networks, due to variation in demand) but is easy to measure. For groundwaters, flow can be a very difficult parameter to measure and sometimes relies on the use of and detection of markers.

If load estimates need to be accurate, flow and concentration data must be typical. The reason for which the measurements are being taken determines the degree of thoroughness (and the cost) of the investigation. It is also important to ascertain the required accuracy of any estimate and to ensure that the effort and expenditure on obtaining flow and concentration data are in proportion (23). Samples and flow measurements must be representative.

Additional information can be found in references 1, 2 and 3.

When assessing load the total load of an element may not be the same as the available load. This is dependent on the purpose the water is subsequently put to. For instance, if water is subsequently to be heated, it is pertinent whether calcium is present as bicarbonate, sulphate or phosphate.

2.1 Introduction

Flow is a general term referring to movement of a liquid. The volumetric flow rate, or discharge, of a liquid expresses the flow past a given cross-section, for example in cubic metres per second, or litres per second. Estimates of flow may achieve an accuracy of about ± 2 % (23).

Load is a general term which refers to the average rate at which some substance is transported by a liquid, normally water, past a given point. Load is intimately related to flow.

The substance constituting the load can be dissolved in solution, when it is referred to as solute load, or can be insoluble, forming a sediment load. Sediment loads may be:

i.   bed material load, moving along the bed of the channel and within the bottom of the water column;

ii.   suspended bed material load which is dispersed through the water column; or

iii. wash load which is maintained in suspension at all times that flow is taking place.

Estimates of solute load are generally more accurate than those of sediment load. Suspended sediment and washload estimates are more accurate than those for bed material load, but both are dependent on flow and turbulence. All load measurements are dependent on the representativeness of the sample and the accuracy of the analysis. The former is dependent on knowledge of the river and its variations, the latter on the analytical laboratory.

Load can be measured directly only under very specialised conditions, normally involving pipe flow. Usually, load is estimated indirectly using separate measurements of discharge and concentration. This approach, involving two sources of experimental error, combines with the extreme variability of solute and sediment loads, to produce estimates of load which may contain appreciable errors.

The accuracy and precision of estimates of load can be increased by the correct choice of:

i.   sampling sites;

ii.   sampling programmes (in time);

iii. sampling patterns (in space, at a sampling site);

iv.   sampling and sample handling procedures; and

v.   data analyses.

2.2 Computation of mass flow, load and yield

2.2.1 Definitions and introduction

This chapter describes the main methods of estimating load. Sampling patterns, their advantages and disadvantages and the relevant computations are discussed in detail.

The basic data required to compute loads are the volumetric flow rate of water (ie the discharge) (see Table 1), and the concentration of the solute or sediment of interest. Different ways of measuring discharge and concentration produce three basically different ways of expressing load (see Table 1).

Estimates of mass flow and load are usually based on simultaneous measurements of discharge and concentration at the same site. The two parameters can be measured at different, but closely spaced, sites if the discharge is adjusted to allow for the difference in areas draining to the two sites.

The measurements of suspended sediment and wash load concentration and bed material concentration, usually require different techniques. Total sediment concentration can occasionally be measured in highly turbulent flow when all the sediment is thrown into a uniform suspension. These conditions may exist in flumes during moderate and high discharges.

Estimates of mass flow, load and yield can be computed using:

(a) Mass flow/load

i. simultaneous measurements of discharge and concentration;

ii. direct measurement of bed material load;

iii. indirect estimates based on rating curves of concentration versus discharge;

iv. indirect estimates based on theoretical relationships; and

v. direct measurement of mass flow in pipes.

(b) Yield

i. indirect estimates using correlations between yield and catchment characteristics;

ii. direct estimates using lake or reservoir sedimentation;

iii. direct estimates using bed material traps.

2.2.2 Computation of mass flow

The relationship between discharge, concentration and mass flow given in Section 2.2.1 forms the basis of all computations of mass flow. The methods used to measure discharge and concentration vary with the conditions at the sampling site and alter the form of the computation and the accuracy of the estimate.

When the concentration in a channel or pipe is uniform throughout the cross-section, the basic relationship can be used unaltered with a single sample taken to establish the concentration and the discharge measured in any suitable manner.

If the discharge measurements are based on measurements of velocity on several verticals then the increments of discharge in each segment of cross-section can be used to estimate the areal variation of, and total, mass flow (Figure 1).

$$\text{mass flow through each segment} = q \cdot C$$
$$\text{total mass flow} = q_1 C + q_2 C + q_3 C + q_4 C$$
$$= C(q_1 + q_2 + q_3 + q_4)$$
$$= C \cdot Q$$

The mass flows within each segment are determined by the variations in velocity, and discharge, within the cross-section. This variation in mass flow can be important if part of the flow in the channel is diverted *en masse* for use.

If there are sufficient velocity measurements to plot isovels (ie contours of equal velocity) then a more detailed analysis of mass flow variation within the cross-section can be undertaken (Figure 2). Increments of mass flow between adjacent isovels are computed,

$$\text{mass flow between adjacent isovels} = \frac{(V_n + V_{n-1})}{2} \cdot A_{n-1} \cdot C$$

$$\text{total mass flow} = \frac{(V_m + V_1)}{2} \cdot A_{10} \cdot C + \frac{(V_1 + V_2)}{2} \cdot A_{12} \cdot C +$$
$$\frac{(V_2 + V_3)}{2} \cdot A_{23} \cdot C + \ldots + \frac{(V_5 + V_6)}{2} \cdot A_{56} \cdot C + \frac{V_6}{2} \cdot A_6 \cdot C$$

Where V_n, V_{n-1} are adjacent isovels, V_m = maximum velocity (estimated) A_{12}, A_{23}, etc are areas of cross-section between isovels for velocities V_1 and V_2, V_2 and V_3, etc.

$$\text{total mass flow} = q_{m1} \cdot C + q_{12} \cdot C + q_{23} \cdot C + \ldots + q_{56} \cdot C + q_6 \cdot C$$

$$\text{as} \quad \frac{(V_1 + V_2)}{2} \cdot A_{12} = q_{12}$$

$$\text{so that total mass flow} = C \cdot Q$$

177

The practical result for a situation with uniform concentration is the same as before, but this approach indicates the dependence of mass flow variations in a channel or pipe on velocity variations when concentration is uniform.

If concentration and velocity vary within the cross-section, the procedure adopted depends on the amount of information available on velocity and concentration variations.

If contours of velocity and concentration can be drawn, then the cross-section is subdivided into a set of cells defined by adjacent pairs of contours (Figure 3). The mass flow through each cell is computed as

$$\text{cell mass flow} = \frac{(V_n + V_{n-1})}{2} \cdot \frac{(C_n + C_{n-1})}{2} \cdot A$$

Where V_n and V_{n-1} are adjacent isovels, C_n and C_{n-1} are adjacent concentration contours, A is the area defined by the bounding contours, and total mass flow $= \sigma(\bar{v}.\bar{c}.A)$

The estimate of mass flow in each cell can be used as the basis for contours indicating variations in mass flow within the cross-section.

A simpler approach results if a grid is drawn across the pattern of velocity and concentration contours (Figure 4). Weighted mean values of velocity and concentration are estimated for each cell of the grid and used to compute mass flow through each cell. Total mass flow is then obtained by summing contributions from individual cells. If detailed information on mass flow variations within a cross-section is required on a regular basis, this approach has the advantage over that in the previous paragraph in that it provides a consistent framework for data analysis.

When current velocity and concentration are measured at the same points along several verticals in the cross-section, the same rectangular grid approach can be adopted. Cell limits are defined by vertical lines midway between the verticals along which velocity and concentration are measured and horizontal lines midway between sampling points (Figure 5).

$$\text{total mass flow} = \Sigma(V_n \cdot A_n \cdot C_n)$$
$$\Sigma(q_n \cdot C_n)$$

Where q_n is the increment of discharge through each cell.

If current velocity and concentration are measured at different points in the same verticals, then the mean concentration in each segment can be used to compute mass flow through the segment (Figure 6).

$$\text{segment mass flow} = q \cdot C$$

$$\text{total mass flow} = q_1.C_1 + q_2.C_2 + ... + q_n.C_n$$

$$= \Sigma(q_n.C_n)$$

Where C is the mean concentration in the segment.

The mean concentration may be an arithmetic mean of the measured concentrations or, preferably, a mean based on a plot of concentration against depth. If concentrations are measured in samples taken with an integrating sampler then the preferred mean value is obtained directly.

If the boundaries between segments of cross-section are chosen to give a set of equal fractions of the discharge and mean concentrations are found along verticals passing through the centroids of segments then

$$\text{total mass flow} = q \cdot C_1 + q \cdot C_2 + \ldots + q \cdot C_n$$
$$= q(C_1 + C_2 + \ldots + C_n)$$
$$= \frac{Q(C_1 + C_2 + \ldots + C_n)}{n}$$

as $q \cdot n = Q$

This approach provides a convenient basis for routine determinations of mass flow, if the limits of segments conveying equal fractions of discharge can be defined and do not vary with changing discharge.

If only one sample can be taken to measure concentration in a stream where concentration is not uniform, then the approaches discussed in previous paragraphs (ie Figures 3–6) must be modified. Instead, either:

i.   the sample must be taken from a point, chosen to give a consistent relationship between sample concentration and mean concentration, in the cross-section; or

ii.   the sampling point is determined by practical considerations (accessibility etc) and the relationship between the concentration in samples taken at that point and the mean concentration in the cross-section is determined. This is the basis for many routine sampling sites, particularly with large rivers and rivers in flood.

Both these approaches require detailed investigations of concentration variations within the cross-section at different discharges. The relationships between selected point samples and mean concentration can then be investigated.

The aim is to establish a relationship of the form:

$$\overline{C} = f \cdot C_s$$

Where C_s = concentration determined in point sample, $\overline{C}$ = mean concentration in cross-section, f = correction factor.

Ideally, the correction factor value should be independent of discharge.

The problem of validating a single sampling point in a cross-section is analogous to the problem of determining a single point for velocity measurement in a cross-section or on a vertical (see Chapter 3).

Ideally, if the sampling site has been selected correctly then solute and wash load concentrations should vary little over the cross-section. Detailed investigations can then be restricted to sites at which suspended sediment concentration is required.

If detailed field data are not available, an initial relationship between point and cross-section concentrations may be obtainable from published information. This initial relationship must be checked.

2.2.3   Computation of solute and suspended sediment load

Solute and suspended sediment load computations are based on detailed records of discharge and concentration, or mass flow, over the period of interest. This period may be of any duration depending on the intention of the study.

These records may range in detail and accuracy from continuous discharge and concentration records, providing a continuous record of mass flow, through records based on the conversion of a discharge record using a rating curve, to records based on a few estimates of mass flow. The accuracy of the estimated load will depend on the quality of this basic information.

In all cases, the basic computation is the same:

$$L = \frac{1}{T} \int_0^T M \cdot dt = \frac{\sum (M \cdot t)}{T} = \frac{\sum (C \cdot Q \cdot t)}{T}$$

Where T is the time interval over which load is to be estimated.

The computational procedure chosen depends on:-

i.   the variability of the discharge and concentration (mass flow);

ii.   the sampling frequency; and

iii.   the volumes of samples taken.

When both discharge and concentration have been virtually constant over the period of interest, the load is given by

$$L = C \cdot Q$$

When discharge is constant and the concentration varies in time, the most accurate estimate of concentration will be obtained from a continuous record of concentration, or from a curve of concentration versus time, interpolated between discrete samples.

$$L = \frac{1}{T}\int_0^T Q \cdot C \cdot dt = \frac{Q}{T}\int_0^T C \cdot dt = Q \cdot \overline{C}$$

The integral or mean value of concentration can be evaluated by measuring the area under the concentration/time graph.

If discharge is constant, but the frequency of sampling is insufficient to justify the construction of a continuous curve joining individual points, then a bar graph should be used (Figure 7). Each sample is represented by a bar extending on either side of the sample time to points midway between it and neighbouring samples. The equation given in the previous paragraph can be applied. In this case, the integral or mean value of concentration can be evaluated by simple geometry using concentration values and sampling times.

$$L = \frac{Q}{T}\left[C_1\left(t_1 + \left(\frac{t_2 - t_1}{2}\right) - t_0\right) + C_2\frac{(t_3 - t_2)}{2} + C_n\left((t_0 + T) - \frac{(t_n - t_{n-1})}{2}\right) \right]$$

Where t_0 is the beginning of the period of interest and t_1, t_2, etc are sampling times and T is total time duration (Figure 7).

If earlier data are available for a sample time $t_{(-1)}$, and $t_0 < (t_1 - t_{(-1)})$, the first term is replaced by

$$C_{(-1)}\frac{(t_1 - t_{(-1)})}{2} - t_0 + C_1\frac{(t_2 - t_{(-1)})}{2}$$

If data are also available after the finishing time T, and

$$(t_0 + T) > \frac{(t_2 - t_{(n+1)})}{2}$$

the final term is replaced by

$$C_n\left(\frac{(t_{n+1} - t_{n-1})}{2}\right) + C_{n+1}\left((t_0 + T) - \frac{(t_{n+1} + t_n)}{2}\right)$$

This form of the computation can be used if samples were taken irregularly. If samples were taken at regular intervals, this becomes:-

$$L = \frac{Q}{T}(C_1 \cdot t + C_2 \cdot t + \ldots + C_n \cdot t)$$

$$= \frac{Qt}{T}(C_1 + C_2 + \ldots + C_n)$$

$$= Q\left(\frac{C_1 + C_2 + \ldots + C_n}{n}\right)$$

$$= Q \cdot C$$

as $t = T/n$, and n = number of samples

If both discharge and concentration vary in time, then estimates of load must be based on records of mass flow. It must be stressed that

$$\overline{C} \cdot \overline{Q} \cdot t = M$$

so that

$$\overline{C} \cdot \overline{Q} = L$$

If a continuous record of mass flow is available then

$$L = \frac{1}{T}\int_0^T M \cdot dt$$

If only a bar-graph presentation of mass flow variations is possible, the equations can be as those given for Figure 7, except that concentration C is replaced by mass M.

All the sampling and computation techniques for estimating load, described in preceding paragraphs, depend on individual samples and the concentration in each sample. An alternative approach is to take flow proportional samples.

In proportional sampling, samples are taken at regular intervals and combined to give a single bulk sample representing the period during which load is to be estimated and the concentration of the bulk sample determined. The load is then given by the relation:-

$$C_B \cdot \overline{Q} = \overline{M} = L$$

where C_B = concentration in bulked sample, and $\overline{Q}$ = mean discharge during sampling period.

Sample volumes are related to discharge magnitude using previously known or assumed relationships between mass flow and discharge. The volume of each sample is chosen so that the mass of solute or sediment in each sample is proportional to the mass flow at the sampling time.

Table 1 Summary of definitions

Term (and synonyms)	Symbol	Definition	SI units	Other units	Notes
Discharge	Q	The volumetric flow rate of water *or* the volume of water passing a given point in unit time	m^3s^{-1}	ft^3s^{-1} Mld^{-1}	
Concentration	C	The mass of solute or sediment per unit volume of water (instantaneous or average value)	kgm^{-3}	mgl^{-1} parts per million (ppm)	
Mass flow (instantaneous flux, solute/sediment discharge)	M	The rate of transport of solute or sediment	kgs^{-1}	kgd^{-1}	$C \cdot Q = M$
Load	L	The average mass flow during a given time interval	kgs^{-1}	kgd^{-1} $kgyr^{-1}$	$\dfrac{1}{T}\displaystyle\int_0^T C \cdot Q \cdot dt$ *or* $\dfrac{1}{T}\displaystyle\int_0^T M \cdot dt = L$
Yield	Y	The accumulated mass flow over a relatively long time period (usually a year)	kg (state time period)		$\displaystyle\int_0^T C \cdot Q \cdot dt$ or $\displaystyle\int_0^T M \cdot dt = Y$
Unit yield	U	The yield per unit area of catchment (A)	$kgkm^{-2}$ (state time period)		$U = Y/A$

3 Measurement of flow or discharge in open channels

3.1 Introduction

The general objective for the collection of stream-flow data is to provide information on flow characteristics at any point on any channel. Purposes for which stream-flow data are used include the design and operation of water supply systems, control of pollution, design of highway bridges and culverts, management of flood plains, development of recreation facilities, forecast and management of floods, production of energy, design and maintenance of navigation facilities and allocation of water for irrigation and industry.

This chapter describes the establishment and operation of gauging stations on lakes, rivers or open channels for the measurement of water level (stage) or discharge, or both.

3.2 Summary of methods

The methods of measurement of discharge in open channels is summarised below.

3.2.1 Velocity area method

The discharge is derived from the sum of the products of stream velocity, depth and distance between observation points, the stream velocity being normally obtained by current meter. For a continuous record of discharge in a stable prismatic open channel with no variable backwater effects, a unique relation is established between water level (stage) and discharge. Once established, this stage-discharge relation is used to derive discharge values from recordings of stage.

3.2.2 Weirs and flumes

The relation between stage (or head) and discharge over a weir or through a flume is established from laboratory or field calibration. The discharge is subsequently derived from this rating formula.

3.2.3 Moving boat method

A current meter is suspended from a boat which traverses the channel normal to the stream flow. The component of the velocity in the direction of the stream is computed from the resultant velocity and the angle of this resultant. The discharge is the sum of the products of the stream velocity, depth and distance between observation points. The moving boat method is therefore in effect a velocity-area method.

3.2.4 Ultrasonic method

The velocity of flow is measured by transmitting an ultrasonic pulse diagonally across the channel in both directions simultaneously. The difference in time transits is a measure of the velocity which requires to be multiplied by the cross-section area to derive discharge. The ultrasonic method therefore also follows the principles of velocity-area measurement.

3.2.5 Electromagnetic method

The discharge is found by measuring the electromotive force, emf, produced by a moving conductor (the flowing water) through a magnetic field produced by a coil placed below or above the open channel.

3.2.6 Slope-area method

The discharge is derived from measurements of the slope of the water surface and the cross-section over a fairly straight reach of channel assuming a roughness coefficient for the channel boundaries.

3.2.7 Fall-discharge method

In a stable open channel affected by backwater, a relation is established between fall (slope) and discharge.

3.2.8 Dilution method

A tracer liquid is injected into the channel and the water is sampled at a point further downstream where turbulence has mixed the tracer uniformly throughout the cross-section. The change in concentration between the solution injected and the water at the sampling station is a measure of the discharge.

3.2.9 Floats

The velocity is measured by recording the time taken for a float to travel a known distance along the channel. Observations are made using floats at different positions across the channel and discharge is derived from the sum of the products of velocity, width and depth.

Generally, this method is used only when the flow is too fast or too slow to use a current meter.

3.2.10 Measurement of water level (stage)

All of the methods used to measure discharge in open channels depend on the measurement of stage. In fact, stage is one of the most important single measurements in hydrometry. Certainly this is the case in measurement by weirs and in stage-discharge measurements where a small relative uncertainty in stage may produce a significant relative uncertainty in discharge.

In the United Kingdom hydrometric network, the objective is to measure stage to ± 3 mm and in most cases this can generally be achieved by the use of digital float operated recorders installed in stilling wells. To calibrate such instruments it is normal to use some more accurate means to read outside river levels, such as a portable vernier on the staff gauge or a separate device such as a datum plate and point or tape gauge.

Where the bank is sloping, inclined gauges are to be preferred to vertical staff gauges: they are best installed so as to closely follow the contour of the river bank. Usually it is necessary to construct the gauge in several sections, each with a different slope.

The types of recording gauges most common for the continuous measurement of stage in open channels are:

i.   digital punched tape or solid state float recorders;

ii.   autographic chart (float) recorder; and

iii.   servo-manometer and servo-beam balance.

A comprehensive illustrated description of instruments for the measurement of stage is given by Smoot (4). See also ISO 4373 (5) and ISO 3454 (6).

3.2.11 Single or continual measurements

The continuity of use of a discharge measuring station falls into two headings:

i.   Individual measurements (Section 3.4). These include methods suitable for a single measurement of discharge or a limited number of measurements often used to calibrate a station.

ii.   Continual or regular measurements (Section 3.5). These include continuous recordings and methods suitable for continual frequent measurements often made over many years.

Before dealing with flow measurement, the establishment and operation of water level gauging stations on lakes, rivers or open channels will be considered. Such measurements are readily adapted to continuous recording.

3.3 Measurement of water level (stage)

3.3.1 Principle

The stage of a stream or lake is the height of the water surface above an established datum plane. Water levels of rivers, lakes and reservoirs are used directly in hydrological forecasting, in delineating flood hazard areas and in the design of structures in, or near, water bodies. When correlated with discharge of streams, or with the volume of storage in reservoirs and lakes, water levels are used as the basis for computation of records of discharge, or changes in storage. Records of water level are obtained by systematic observations on a reference gauge, or from a water level recorder.

3.3.2 Preliminary survey

A preliminary survey is made of the physical and hydraulic features of the proposed site to ensure that it conforms to the requirements necessary for the measurement of water level (5).

3.3.3 Selection of site

The site selected for observation of stage is governed by the purpose for which the records are collected, the accessibility of the site and the availability of an observer if the gauge is non-recording. Gauges on lakes and reservoirs are normally located near the outlet, but upstream from the zone where an increase in velocity causes a draw down in water level. Gauges on large bodies of water are located so as to reduce the fetch of strong currents which may cause damage or misleading data. Hydraulic conditions are an important factor in site selection on channels, particularly where water levels are used to compute discharge records.

A water level gauging station depends on:

i.   a direct visual measurement of water level, or

ii.   an indirect measurement, for example via a pressure transducer.

A continuous record of stage may not always be required. Commonly, a very accurate visual reference gauge, for example needle gauge or graduated staff gauge can be used to calibrate and check the recording device.

3.3.4 Vertical 'staff' gauges and inclined 'ramp' gauges

Such gauges comprise a graduated scale marked on or attached to a suitable surface. The scale is immersed in the flowing water channel or in an embayment or stilling well. It should be:

i.   accurate and clearly marked;

ii.   durable and easy to maintain; and

iii.   simple to install and use.

The reading where the water level intersects the graduations can be made by eye, possibly assisted by binoculars.

3.3.4.1 Graduation

i.   The scale graduations of a vertical gauge should be clearly and permanently marked directly on a smooth surface or on a gauge board. The numerals should be distinct and placed so that the lower edge of the numeral is close to the graduation to which it refers. The smallest graduation depends on the accuracy required, but is normally 10 mm.

ii.   The graduations of an inclined gauge may be directly marked as described in (i) or may be on manufactured gauge plates designed to be set for particular slopes. Except in the latter case, an inclined gauge should be calibrated *in-situ* by precise levelling from the station bench mark.

iii. Gauge plates are generally manufactured in suitable lengths with, for example, the face of the scale not less than 50 mm in width and the markings on the gauge are in multiples of millimetres.

iv. The markings of the subdivisions should be accurate to ± 0.5 mm, and the cumulative error in length should not exceed 0.1% or 0.5 mm, whichever is greater.

3.3.4.2 Installation and use

Preferably a staff or ramp gauge is placed near the bank so that a direct reading of water level may be made. If this is impracticable, the measurement can be made in a suitable permanent stilling bay or stilling well in which the wave actions are damped and the level of the water surface closely follows the fluctuations of the water level in the channel. To ensure this, intakes to stilling wells should be properly designed and located.

The gauge is located as closely as possible to the measuring section without affecting the flow conditions at this point. It should not be placed where the water is disturbed by turbulence, or there is danger of damage by drift. Bridge abutments or piers are generally unsuitable locations. Wherever the gauge is situated, it should be readily and conveniently accessible so that the observer may take readings as nearly as possible at eye level. Where necessary, the construction of a flight of steps to give convenient access is useful. The gauge board or plate should be securely fixed to the backing, but provision should be made for maintenance or adjustment. The edges of the gauge board should be protected.

The material of which a gauge is constructed should be durable, particularly for alternating wet and dry conditions and also in respect to the resistance to wear or fading of the markings. The material should have a low coefficient of expansion with respect to temperature or wetting effects.

A suitable backing for a vertical (staff) gauge is provided by the surface of a wall having a vertical or nearly vertical face, parallel to the direction of flow. The gauge board or backing plate is attached to the surface so as to present a truly vertical face to receive the graduations. The gauge board and backing plate are securely fastened to the wall. Gauges may be fixed to piles, either driven firmly into the bed or banks, or set in concrete so as to be free from sinking, tilting, or being washed away. In either case, the anchorage is extended below the ground surface to a level free of disturbance by frost. In order to avoid velocity effects which may hinder accurate reading, a pile may be shaped to present streamlined cut waters upstream and downstream, or the gauge may be situated in a bay where it will not be exposed to the force of the current. Where the range of water levels exceeds the capacity of a single vertical gauge, additional sections may be installed on the line of the cross section normal to the direction of flow. The scales on such a series of stepped gauges should have adequate overlap.

An inclined gauge is installed so as to follow the contour of the river bank. The profile of the bank may be such that a gauge of a single slope may be installed; frequently however, it may be necessary to construct the gauge in several sections, each with a different slope.

3.3.5 Needle gauges

3.3.5.1 General

A needle water-level gauge consists of a point and some means of determining its exact vertical position relative to a datum. It is mainly used for checking or calibrating other gauges or recorders. The two types of needle gauges are:-

i. the point gauge whose tip approaches the free surface from above, and

ii. the hook gauge which is hook-shaped and whose tip is immersed and approaches the free surface from below.

The vertical position is determined by a graduated scale, a tape with some vernier arrangement, or a digital indicator. The scale is movable and graduated to read downward from top to bottom in metres. Application of needle gauges consists of positioning the needle of the gauge near the water surface and detecting the moment the tip touches the free surface. Setting a point exactly at the water surface may be facilitated by electrical means.

The advantage of water-level needle gauges is their high measuring accuracy, whereas their disadvantage is their small measuring range, usually about 1 metre. However, this disadvantage can be overcome by installing a series of datum plates at different levels.

3.3.5.2 Graduation

The graduations of a hook or point gauge can be in millimetres and a vernier or micrometer head is usually provided to allow readings of 0.1 mm. However, such a reading accuracy is normally only required for laboratory measurements.

3.3.5.3 Installation and use

i. A hook or point gauge is usually mounted over an open water surface at the edge of a channel. If this is not practicable, a suitable permanent stilling bay or stilling well can be installed.

ii. The location of the hook or point gauge should be as close as possible to the measuring section and should be conveniently accessible to the observer.

iii. The gauging point should not be installed in a location where the water surface is disturbed. The vicinity of bridge abutments or piers is generally unsuitable.

iv. Where more than one datum plate or bracket is provided at different levels, it is preferable that all should lie on the line of a single cross section normal to the direction of flow in the channel; if this is not practicable and it is necessary to stagger the points, all should lie within a close distance on either side of the cross section line.

v. Datum plates and brackets should be mounted on a secure foundation which extends below the frost line.

vi. The elevation of the datum plates, with reference to which the level of the free surface is determined, should be established with care. Periodically, this elevation should be checked from the station bench mark. The tolerance on the transfer of level from the station bench mark to each datum plate should not exceed ± 1.0 mm.

3.3.6 Float gauges

Typical float gauges operate within a hut and consist of a float operating in a stilling well, a graduated steel tape, a counterweight, a pulley, and a pointer. The float pulley is grooved on the circumference to accommodate the tape, and mounted on a support. The tape is fastened to the upper side of the float and runs slip-free over the pulley in the gauge shed above the well. It is kept tight by a counterweight at the free end or by a spring. In this way, stage fluctuations are sensed by the float which positions the tape with respect to the pointer.

The mechanical recorder that registers a float gauge reading may be analogue or digital, depending upon the mode used in recording the rotational position of the input shaft. The analogue type produces a graphic record of the rise and fall of parameter values with respect to time, while the digital recorder punches coded parameter values on paper tape at preselected time intervals.

Alternatively, an electrically controlled mechanism may be employed to operate a stylus and a chart transport mechanism. There are basically two types of electro-mechanical recorders, those with a direct operational mechanism and those with a servo-operated mechanism. The low torque and relatively limited output motion of a direct acting mechanism can position only a light, low friction stylus over a limited range, whereas the sturdy servo-operated mechanism has ample power and a much wider motion capability.

The advent of digital data loggers based on micro-computers with calibratable software is tending to displace many of the above mechanical and electro-mechanical recorders.

3.3.7 Wire-weight gauges

The typical wire-weight gauge consists of a drum, wound with a single layer of cable, a bronze weight attached to the end of the cable, a graduated disc and a counter, all housed within a cast-aluminium box. The disc is graduated and is permanently connected to the counter and the shaft of the drum. The cable is guided to its position on the drum by a threading sheave. The reel is equipped with a pawl and ratchet for holding the weight at any desired elevation. The gauge is set so that when the bottom of the weight is at the water surface, the gauge height is indicated by the combined readings of the counter and the graduated disc.

Installation and use:

i.   The wire-weight gauge is used as an outdoor instrument where other outside gauges are difficult to maintain. The wire-weight gauge is normally mounted where there is a bridge deck, or other structure over the water.

ii. The gauging point should not be installed in a location where the water surface is disturbed. The vicinity of bridge abutments or piers is generally unsuitable.

iii. The check bar elevation of the wire-weight gauge should be read frequently to ensure the reliability of a correct base elevation.

3.3.8 Crest stage gauges

The crest stage gauge is used to obtain a record of the peak level reached during a flood when other methods of recording levels cannot be used. Peak discharges may be calculated from the water levels at two gauges installed some distance apart in a stretch of channel, providing that the time lag between measurements is negligible. These gauges do not have high accuracy.

Basically they may be a tube about 50 mm internal diameter down the centre of which runs a rod. The tube is perforated to permit rising water to enter, the perforations being located so as to prevent draw down or velocity head from affecting the static water level. The top of the tube must be closed to prevent the entry of rain, but it should have an air vent to permit water to rise up the tube without significant delay. Powdered cork in the bottom of the tube floats on the surface of the floodwater being deposited on the centre tube as the water recedes; alternatively the centre tube is coated with a paint whose colour is permanently affected by water. Electrically recording devices based on the change in conductivity or dielectric constant as the water rises in a tank are also practicable and can give more detailed information about whether there are a series of crests.

3.3.9 Pressure gauges

Pressure gauges are frequently used at sites where it would be too expensive to install stilling wells. They are also used on sand-channel streams because the intake line can be extended to follow a stream channel that shifts its location, and if the gas-purge technique is used, the gas flow tends to keep the orifice from becoming plugged with sand.

The method of transmitting pressure from the water column to the sensor may be direct or indirect. When the sensor is located below the point in the water column at which the pressure is to be measured, the water pressure may be transmitted directly to the sensor. However, if the sensor is located above the water column, the direct method is usually not satisfactory because gases entrained in the water can create air locks in the line. Also, if the water is highly corrosive, it is undesirable to bring it into direct contact with the sensor.

3.3.9.1 Gas-purge (bubbler) technique

The most successful and widely used method of transmitting pressure is the gas-purging technique. This technique may be used regardless of the elevation of the pressure device with respect to the water column; and because the water does not come into direct contact with the pressure sensor, it is suitable for use in highly corrosive waters.

In the gas-purge technique, a small discharge of noncorrosive or compressed gas is allowed to bleed into a tube, the free end of which has been lowered into the water and fixed at an elevation below the water column to be measured. The sensor, which is located at the opposite end, detects the pressure of the gas required to displace the liquid in the tube; this pressure is directly proportional to the head of liquid above the orifice.

3.3.9.2 Pressure bulb system

Where no gas supply is available, a pressure bulb system can be used to transmit pressure to the sensor. This device, frequently referred to as an elastic pressure bulb, is usually made of casting in the form of a short hollow cylinder with one open end. The open end is sealed with a slack, highly flexible diaphragm, and the cylinder is connected by means of tubing to the pressure sensor. The whole unit forms a closed gas system with pressure initially equal to atmospheric. The cylinder is lowered into the water and fixed at an elevation below the water column to be measured. The diaphragm permits water pressure to compress the gas in the cylinder until the pressure within the system is proportional to the height of the water column above. One of the major disadvantages of this device is that ultimately an excessive amount of gas will escape from the system with a resultant stretching of the diaphragm. When this occurs the pressure within the system will no longer be equal to the pressure head. This disadvantage can be overcome by periodic renewal of the gas in the system by opening and resealing under atmospheric pressure and checking the calibration. It is difficult to maintain the desired degree of accuracy with this device.

3.3.9.3 Servo-manometer and servo-beam balance

Both the servo-manometer and the servo-beam balance are pressure sensors that convert the pressure detected to a rotational shaft position proportional to the height of the column of water; the shaft position is used for driving a recorder and a water-level indicator. The servo-manometer is essentially a manometer with a servo-system detecting and following the liquid differential within the manometer. The servo-beam balance is a beam balance with pressure bellows on one side of the beam and a weight on the other. The servo system positions the weight so that the beam is in balance and detects this position.

3.3.9.4 Compensation for water and gas density

Since the density of the water which the sensor is to measure will vary with temperature and also with chemical and silt content, either automatic or manual means of compensating for these changes should be provided.

If one of the gas techniques is used to transmit pressure, provisions should be made for compensating for changes in the density of the gas, as all gases vary in volume with temperature and pressure changes.

3.3.9.5 Other pressure sensors

There are numerous other pressure sensors available including strain gauges and piezo-electric transducers. Most of these have an electrical output which is proportional to the pressure. They are occasionally used for the detection of water level. The proper selection is dependent upon the particular application involved. Their application is very versatile and capable of high accuracy.

3.3.10 Stilling wells

The functions of a stilling well are:

i.   to provide an accurate representation of the water level in the channel;

ii.   to accommodate the instrument and protect the float system; and

iii.   to damp out oscillations of the water surface.

Some specific design points:

i.   The well should be firmly anchored.

ii.   The well and all construction joints of well and intake pipes should be watertight so that water can enter or leave only by the intake itself.

iii. The well may be placed in the bank of a channel or directly in the stream when attached to a bridge, pier or abutment. It should not, however, be located directly in the channel where flow conditions would lead to separation and stagnation effects. When placed in the bank, the well should be connected to the channel by intake pipe(s).

iv. Intake pipes should be laid at a constant gradient on a suitable foundation which will not subside.

v. The intake should be so orientated in the stream that it can sense the true water level.

vi. Means of cleaning the intakes should be provided. Intake pipes more than 20 m in length should be provided with an intermediate manhole filled with internal baffles to act as a silt trap and provide access for cleaning.

vii. The well should not interfere with the flow pattern in the approach channel and if set in relation to a control, it should be located far enough upstream or downstream to be outside the area affected by the control.

viii. The dimensions of the well should be such as to allow unrestricted operation of all equipment installed in it. In silt laden rivers, it is an advantage to have the well large enough to be entered and cleaned.

ix. For precautions to be taken under ice conditions see Section 3.7.

3.3.11   Gauge datum

The datum of the gauge is normally a recognised datum, such as mean sea level, or an arbitrary datum plane selected for the convenience of using gauge readings of relatively low numbers. It is generally desirable to avoid negative values for these readings, therefore, the datum selected for operating purposes should be below the elevation of zero flow on the control. At sites that are subject to severe scour, care should be taken to select a datum that is sufficiently low.

If an arbitrary datum plane is used, it should be referred to a bench mark of known elevation above sea level by accurate levelling so that the arbitrary datum may be recovered if the gauge and reference marks are destroyed. A permanent datum should be maintained so that only one datum for the stage record is used for the life of the station.

3.3.12   Gauge zero

The zero of the gauge is normally correlated with a national datum through a station bench mark. The relation between the gauge zero and the station bench mark should be checked periodically. The relation between the gauge zero and other gauge sections should also be checked. The uncertainty in the transfer of the level from the station bench mark to the gauge should not exceed ± 1.0 mm.

3.3.13   Station bench mark

The station bench mark is set in a position offering maximum security against disturbance. It should be securely fixed to a level free from disturbance, such as frost. It should be correlated with a national survey datum by accurate levelling. To facilitate accurate levelling between the station bench mark and the gauge zero, the bench mark should be located in a position such that the transfer of the level may be carried out by reciprocal levelling or with equally balanced foresights and back sights on the setting of the level. Where it is not feasible to correlate the bench mark with the national survey datum more than one station bench mark should be established in significantly different locations.

3.3.14   Accuracy

The accuracy recommended in ISO 4373 (5) is as follows: for the measurement of stage, in certain installations an accuracy of ± 3 mm or better may be required; however, in no case should the accuracy be worse than ± 10 mm or ± 0.1% of the range whichever is greater.

3.4 Methods for making individual measurements of discharge

The following methods are most suitable for a single measurement of discharge or for a limited number of measurements.

3.4.1 Velocity-area method for the measurement of discharge

The velocity-area method is almost universally employed for measuring discharge in open channels. In some countries, however, notably those in arid regions, open channels are usually unstable and resort has to be made to a combination of methods to suit the flow conditions. The United Kingdom hydrometric network is probably unique in that about half the stations are velocity-area stations, the other half being measuring structures. The latter are necessary mainly in eastern and southern areas of the country where backwater conditions prevail. Velocity-area measurements may be made by wading, from a cable way by cable car or trolley, from a bridge or from a boat (7). The actual method used depends on the hydraulic conditions and the size of the river.

Each gauging involves measurements of velocity and depth at a number of verticals, spaced transversely along a cross-section and measurements of width from a reference point on the bank. The cross-section is therefore divided into segments by selecting verticals at a sufficient number of points to ensure an adequate sample of both velocity distribution and bed profile (see Figure 8). The spacing of the verticals is important for accurate measurement of discharge and usually the interval between verticals should not be greater than one-fifteenth of the width in the case of regular bed profiles, or one-twentieth of the width in the case of irregular profiles (8).

In special cases such as small lined channels with regular geometric profiles, the number of verticals may be reduced. In addition, however, the spacing should be such as to ensure that the difference between mean velocities on adjacent verticals does not exceed 20%, or that the discharge through one segment does not exceed 10% of the total discharge. It is clear therefore that the accuracy of a velocity-area measurement depends on the number of verticals used in the measurement. However, the harsh environmental conditions for open channel measurement are such that other factors often require to be considered. For example, increasing the number of verticals increases the time required for a measurement, and where stage is fluctuating a balance between the need for accuracy in the gauging and for an accurate determination of mean stage is required. In addition, cost factors require to be considered.

3.4.2 Measurement of velocity

3.4.2.1 The velocity distribution method

In this method, velocity observations are made in each vertical at a sufficient number of points distributed between the water surface and bed in order to define the vertical velocity curve; the mean velocity being obtained by dividing the area between the curve and the plotting axis by the depth. The number of points required depends on the degree of curvature, particularly in the lower part of the curve, and usually varies between 6 and 10. Observations are normally made at 0.2, 0.6 and 0.8 of the depth from the surface, so that the results from the vertical velocity curve can be compared with various combinations of reduced points methods, and the highest and lowest points should be located as near to the water surface and bed as possible. In this respect, the horizontal axis of the current meter should not be located at a distance less than one and a half times the rotor height from the surface, nor at a distance less than 3 times the rotor height from the bed of the channel (8).

This method is the most accurate if done under ideal, steady-stage conditions but is not considered suitable for routine gauging due to the length of time required for the field observations and for the ensuing computation. It is used mainly for checking velocity distribution when the station is first established and for checking the accuracy of the reduced points methods.

3.4.2.2 The 0.6 depth method

Velocity observations are made at a single point at 0.6 of the depth from the surface and the value obtained is accepted as the mean for the vertical. This assumption is based on theory and results of analysis of many vertical velocity curves, which showed that in the majority of cases, the 0.6 method produced results of acceptable accuracy. The value of the method is its essential reliability, the ease and speed of setting the meter at a single point and the reduced time necessary for completion of a gauging.

3.4.2.3 The 0.2 and 0.8 depth method

Velocity is observed at two points at 0.2 and 0.8 of the depth from the surface and the average of the two readings is taken as the mean for the vertical. Here again this assumption is based on theory and the study of vertical velocity curves, and experience has confirmed its essential accuracy. Generally the minimum depth of flow should be about 1 m when the 0.2 and 0.8 depth method is used.

3.4.2.4 Six point method

Velocity observations are made by taking current meter readings on each vertical at 0.2, 0.4, 0.6 and 0.8 of the depth below the surface and as near as possible to the surface and bed (see velocity distribution method above). The mean velocity may be found by plotting in graphical form and using a planimeter, or from the equation:

$$v = 0.1 \ (v_{surface} + 2v_{0.2} + 2v_{0.4} + 2v_{0.6} + 2v_{0.8} + v_{bed})$$

3.4.2.5 Five point method

Velocity observations are made by taking current meter readings on each vertical at 0.2, 0.6 and 0.8 of the depth below the surface and as near as possible to the surface and bed (see velocity distribution method above). The mean velocity may be found by plotting in graphical form and using a planimeter, or from the equation:

$$v = 0.1 \ (v_{surface} + 3v_{0.2} + 3v_{0.6} + 3v_{0.8} + v_{bed})$$

3.4.2.6 Three point method

Velocity observations are made by taking current meter readings on each vertical at 0.2, 0.6 and 0.8 of the depth below the surface. The average of the three values may be taken as the mean velocity in the vertical. Alternatively, the 0.6 measurement may be weighted and the mean velocity obtained from the equation:

$$v = 0.25 \ (v_{0.2} + v_{0.6} + v_{0.8})$$

However, many rivers do not necessarily follow the theoretical velocity distribution even when the time of exposure of the meter is several minutes. In such situations, and where sufficient depth is available special gaugings are sometimes taken using the 5 point or 6 point method using a single rod with 5 or 6 meters attached to it and employing a special counter box to record the current meter observations.

3.4.2.7 Current meters

Current meters (9, 10) may be used with an individual rating or a group rating (10). Generally, meters on an individual rating require to be re-rated each year. A group rating, on the other hand, is established from at least 20 new and used meters and although the confidence limits are wider than for an individual rating, the uncertainty is acceptable for routine flow measurement. The cost saving in using a group rating may be significant since only a sample batch requires re-rating each year to check that the ratings are still within the original confidence limits.

The minimum speed of response of current meters is generally of the order of about 0.03 m/s^{-1}, at which speed the uncertainty of the rating is about $\pm$ 20%. Thereafter, the uncertainty improves to about $\pm$ 1% at speeds of 0.25 m/s^{-1} and over for individual ratings. For group ratings, the uncertainty at the lower speeds is similar but is about $\pm$ 2% at speeds of 0.45 m/s^{-1} and over. However, a meter which is inadequately maintained or which has suffered damage cannot be expected to give correct results particularly at low velocities. A meter which has been only slightly damaged may still be usable if it is re-calibrated. If, however, a group calibration is being relied upon there will be an uncertainty whether a slightly damaged meter will continue to operate within the chosen tolerance.

3.4.2.8 Computation of discharge

The computation of discharge from a current meter gauging is normally carried out by the mean-section method or the mid-section method. The latter is usually preferred because it is slightly quicker and therefore, over a period, less costly (8).

Mean-section method

The cross-section is regarded as being made up of a number of segments each bounded by two adjacent verticals. The discharge, q, through each segment is then:

$$q = \left(\frac{v_1 + v_2}{2}\right)\left(\frac{d_1 + d_2}{2}\right) \times b$$

where v_1 is the mean velocity in the first vertical
         v_2 is the mean velocity in the second vertical
         d_1 is the depth in the first vertical
         d_2 is the depth in the second vertical
         b is the width of the segment

The summation of all segment discharges gives the total discharge.

The mean velocity in each of the two segments nearest the banks may be calculated by assuming zero depth and velocity at the water's edge.

Mid-section method

In this method, the product of v and d taken at each vertical is multiplied by the segment width taken as half the distance to adjacent verticals. The segment discharge is then (see Figure 8):

$$q = vd\left(\frac{b_1 + b_2}{2}\right)$$

where b_1 is the width of segment on one side of the vertical and
         b_2 is the width of segment on the other side of the vertical.

In most cases, the v·d values at the end sections next to the banks are negligible and the first and last verticals are placed as near as possible to the banks.

Graphical methods

Graphical methods are appropriate when the velocity distribution method is used, or when it is required to investigate the flow characteristics at the measuring section. They are described in reference 8.

After making a current meter measurement it is advisable to compute the measurement before leaving the site. This gives an on the spot quality control check on the measurement. A typical computation for a current meter measurement is shown in Table 2 (11) where it will be seen that:-

i.   the number of verticals (column 1) is 22, the distance between verticals (column 2) is 1 m and the width of measuring section is 26.5 m, the interval between verticals is therefore less than 1/20 of the width;

ii.   the difference between mean velocities on adjacent verticals (column 8) does not exceed 0.595 m/s^{-1};

iii.   the discharge in any one segment (column 11) does not exceed 10% of the total discharge (0.595 m/s^{-1});

iv.   when the depth is more than 1 m the 0.2 + 0.8 method is used; and

v.   the minimum time of exposure of the meter is approximately one minute and a preset number of revolutions are timed to compute velocity.

3.4.2.9   Stage-discharge relation. Determination of the rating curve

In the majority of cases, the stage-discharge relation may be expressed by an equation of the form:

$$Q = C (h + a)^{\beta}$$

where Q is the discharge;
  h the gauge height;
  C and β are coefficients; and
  a is the stage at zero flow (12).

This equation may be transformed by logarithms to

$$\log Q = \log c + \beta \log (h + a)$$

and by plotting log Q against log (h + a) a straight line is obtained and the constants C and β are computed.

The transformation to a mathematical equation is convenient for computer programming and for the analysis of uncertainties when the standard error may be calculated. When a change in calibration occurs, however, the equation requires to be recalculated (13, 14).

It is good practice to provide a graphical plot of the stage-discharge curve in the instrument house so that each time a gauging is made it is calculated and plotted on the curve before leaving the site. It is at this time that any discrepancy either in the curve or in the gauging may be conveniently discovered and investigated before leaving.

If several break points are required to fit a curve it is usually more convenient to plot the curve and to prepare a rating table or 'look-up' table for further manual or computer processing. In this case, the curve cannot conveniently be mathematically analysed for uncertainties, and resort is sometimes made to setting a tolerance on the gaugings. Usually this tolerance is made so that no gaugings are more than $\pm$ 5% from the curve.

3.4.3   The moving boat method

The moving boat method was introduced by Smoot (15) for the US Geological Survey. Essentially the moving boat method is a speeded-up velocity-area method, the main difference being in the method of data collection. A propeller type current meter is suspended from a boat at about one metre below the surface and the boat traverses the channel normal to the stream flow. During the traverse an echo sounder records the geometry of the cross-section and the continuously operating current meter records the resultant of the stream and boat velocities. A vertical vane aligns itself in a direction parallel to the movement of water past it and an angle indicator attached to the vane assembly indicates the angle between the direction of the vane and the true course of the boat. The velocity, V_b, of the boat is the velocity at which the current meter is being pushed through the water by the boat. The force exerted on the current meter is a combination of two forces acting simultaneously; one force resulting from the movement of the boat through the water and the other a consequence of the streamflow.

The velocity measurement taken at each of the sampling points (verticals) in the cross-section is a vector quantity which represents the relative velocity past the vane and meter. This velocity, V_v, is the vector sum of V, the component of stream velocity normal to the cross-section at the sampling point and V_b.

A rate indicator unit is used in conjunction with a current meter rating table to obtain V_v while the angle reading representing the angle the vane makes with the cross-section path, defines the direction of the vector (see Figure 9).

Stream velocity, V, perpendicular to the boat path at each vertical can be determined from

$$V = V_v \sin \alpha$$

where

$$L_b = \int V_v \cos \alpha \, dt$$

L_b, is the distance that the boat has travelled along the true course between two consecutive verticals. It can be assumed that α is approximately uniform over the relatively short distance between verticals and can be treated as constant. The equation then becomes

$$L_b = \cos \alpha \int V_v \, dt$$

and

$$\int V_v \, dt = L_v$$

L_v is the relative distance through the water between two consecutive verticals as represented by the output from the rate indicator and counter and

$$L_b = L_v \cos \alpha$$

Finally, d, the stream depth at each vertical can be obtained from the echo sounder chart and upon obtaining V, L and d for each vertical across the measuring section, the mid-section method of computation is used to obtain the discharge.

Since the method uses a current meter measurement at about 1 m below the surface (sub-surface method) the computed discharge requires to be multiplied by a coefficient. In larger rivers (rivers over 3 m deep) it is found that the vertical velocity profile is usually vertical for most of its depth and a single coefficient is normally satisfactory. This coefficient has been found to vary between about 0.90 and 0.95. Normally at least six runs are made, each with 30 to 40 verticals, and the results averaged.

The limitations of the moving boat method concern the minimum width and depth of channel, and the shape of the vertical velocity curve. The channel width should preferably be of the order of at least 100 m and the depth at least 3 m. The vertical velocity curve should be stable for an individual run and the vertical distribution of velocity should be such as to be able to estimate the sub-surface coefficient with acceptable uncertainty

The moving boat method is dealt with in more detail by Smoot (15, 16). See also Herschy (17), Charlton (18) and ISO 4369 (19).

3.4.4 Measurement by floats

The speed of the current can be measured by recording the time taken for a float to travel a known distance along the channel. Observations are made using floats at different positions across the channel. The width and depth are measured at the same time in shallow channels which may be waded, or at some other convenient time in deeper channels.

The floats used may be surface, sub-surface, double or rod floats as described in ISO 748 (8).

The procedure for the measurement of the width, depth and velocity, and the computation of discharge is described in ISO 748 (8).

3.4.5 Dilution gauging methods

3.4.5.1 Principle

A tracer liquid is injected into a stream and at a point further downstream, where turbulence has mixed the tracer uniformly throughout the cross-section, the water is sampled. The change in concentration between the solution injected and the water at the sampling station is a measure of the discharge. The tracer may be injected gradually (constant rate method) or suddenly (gulp, pulse or integration method), and may be chemical, radioactive or a fluorescent dye. The procedure is described in ISO 555 Parts I and II (20, 21).

3.4.5.2 Preliminary survey

A preliminary survey is carried out to determine the hydraulic and mixing characteristics of the site, paying due regard to the need to establish a stable stage-discharge relation, and the requirement of obtaining a satisfactory measuring reach necessary to obtain good mixing of the chemical or tracer.

3.4.5.3 Selection of site

The site selected is such that it is possible to measure the whole range and all types of flow which may be encountered or which it is required to measure. Great care is required to make a satisfactory choice of a site suitable for the measurement of discharge by the dilution method.

There should be no loss or gain of water in the measuring reach (for example by a tributary joining or a distributary leaving the main flow, or overflow from or to the banks of the stream). Its length should be such that, by the natural mixing action of the stream, the solution injected becomes uniformly diluted throughout the sampling cross-section.

In addition to the above requirements it is desirable that the distance between the injection and sampling sections be as short as possible. This allows time gain and economy of tracer.

To comply with the above requirements a reach is chosen in which the river is as narrow and as turbulent as possible, free of dead water zones, with numerous transverse currents to promote lateral mixing. Mixing may be improved by disturbances such as bends, narrows, shelves, falls etc. Very wide channels and vegetation-grown zones should be avoided, and reaches where the stream divides into a number of branches should not be used.

When examining a potential measuring reach, it is advisable to make preliminary tests to ensure that efficient mixing in the river will be achieved, to choose the injection and sampling cross-sections, and, once these have been chosen, to determine the duration of the injection period. In most cases, the sampling cross-section will be chosen for the water level recorder.

For determining the length of the measuring reach a concentrated solution of, for example the dye, fluorescein, may be injected for a relatively short time at a point on the potential injection section. Study of the diffusion of the dye will show whether there are any dead zones or similar and be a rough guide to the minimum distance between the injection and sampling cross-sections.

A guide to the length of the measuring reach which may be required is given by the following formulae.

i.   If the injection rate across the channel is proportional to the flow through the panels forming the section, then

$$l = rh$$

where   l = mixing length
r = ratio of mean velocity to friction or shear velocity
h = mean depth.

ii.   If the injection is at a point in the channel

$$l = \frac{0.12b^2C(0.7C + 2g)}{gh} \qquad \text{in SI units}$$

where   b = mean width of wet section in the measuring reach (metres)
h = mean depth of water in the reach (metres)
C = Chezy coefficient

3.4.5.4 Design and construction

The gauging station consists of a measuring reach and a reference gauge.

In many instances, the equipment necessary to make a measurement of discharge will be transported to and from the permanent installation. Details of such equipment necessary for this purpose are given in ISO 555 Parts I and II (20, 21).

3.4.6 Slope-area method

3.4.6.1 Principle

The water surface slope and the mean area of cross-section of the channel are measured in a selected reach which is as straight and uniform as possible. Assuming a coefficient of roughness, the mean velocity is computed using a flow formula relating to velocity, roughness, hydraulic mean radius and slope. The discharge is then the product of mean velocity and mean area of cross-section of flow. The method is covered in ISO 1070 (22).

3.4.6.2 Preliminary survey

A preliminary survey is made to ensure that the physical and hydraulic features of the proposed site are satisfactory (22).

3.4.6.3 Selection of site

The river should be fairly straight and uniform in section, free from obstructions and vegetation, show no progressive tendency to scour or accrete, and be free of the effect of tributaries.

The length of the reach should be such that the difference in water levels is not less than ten times the uncertainty in the stage measurement and the flow should be contained within defined boundaries.

After the preliminary survey, a topographical survey can be made when selecting a permanent site. This should include a plan of the site indicating the width of the water surface at a stated stage, the edges of the natural banks of the channel, the line of any definite discontinuity of the slope of these banks and the toe and crest of any artificial flood bank.

All obstructions in the channel or floodway should be indicated.

A longitudinal section of the channel can be drawn from a point downstream of a control, where this exists, to the upstream limit of the reach showing the level of the deepest part of the bed and water surface gradients at low and high stages.

The reach containing the measuring section can be checked to ensure that it contains no discontinuities that may affect the measuring results. At least five cross-sections should be surveyed in the measuring reach, two cross-sections upstream from the measuring section and two downstream, at distances upstream and downstream of not less than one bank-full width of the channel.

The detailed survey of the reach can be extended through the floodway to an elevation well above the highest anticipated flood level. The spacing of levels or soundings should be close enough to reveal any abrupt change in the contour of the channel and the bed of the reach should be examined carefully for the presence of rocks or boulders, particularly in the vicinity of the measuring section.

3.4.6.4 Design and construction

The gauging station consists of a natural or artificial measuring section and two reference gauges.

The positions of the cross-sections can be marked on the banks and the sections surveyed at intervals, and before and after floods.

The loss of water from the main channel by spillage can often be avoided by constructing flood banks to confine the flow in a defined floodway. Minor irregularities in the bank or bed causing local eddies may be eliminated by trimming the bank to a regular line and a stable slope, and by removing from the bed any large stones or boulders.

Where possible a suitable access to the site should be available to provide safe passage at all stages of flow and in all weathers for personnel and for any vehicles used for the conveyance of instruments and equipment.

All key points at the site can be permanently marked on the ground by markers sunk to such a depth below the surface as will ensure them against movement. Cross-section markers should be set on the line of the cross-section to facilitate the repetition of levels or soundings when the section is checked.

3.4.6.5   Definitive survey

After the gauging station has been constructed a definitive survey can be made. Gauges should be precisely levelled and the levels related to a common datum and the distance between the gauges should be accurately measured.

3.5   Methods for continuous measurement of discharge

The following methods are most suitable for relatively frequent measurements often made over a long period.

3.5.1   Stage-discharge station

3.5.1.1   Principle

In a stable channel with satisfactory downstream control of water level there can be a relation between stage and discharge. In such channels it is more economic to establish the relation between stage and discharge and thereafter to deduce the discharge from measurements of stage only. The station can be calibrated by the velocity-area method using a stationary current meter (8), moving boat (19), floats (8), or by dilution gauging methods (20, 21).

3.5.1.2   Preliminary survey

A preliminary survey can be made to ensure that the physical and hydraulic features of the proposed site conform to the requirements for the method selected to measure discharge for the calibration of the station. The survey should establish that the proposed site is in a stable stretch of river and free from standing waves at high flow, weed growth and adverse ice conditions.

3.5.1.3   Selection of site

The site selected should be such that it is possible to measure the whole range and all types of flow which may be encountered or which are required to be measured. The range of measurement may be referred to one reference gauge, or certain ranges of discharge may be referred to different gauges. Different methods of calibration may be employed for separate parts of the range, the particular conditions relative to each of the methods of calibration being specified appropriately (20,21).

The operation of a station depends upon the assumption that the elevation of the free surface for practical purposes is a function of the discharge. In the case of stations affected by hysteresis, the rise and fall should be calibrated separately by discharge measurement. It is desirable to select a site where the relationship between stage and discharge is substantially consistent and stable, where there is no variable backwater effect and where the channel itself is stable. However, this may not be possible on all alluvial rivers. For such rivers, the stage-discharge relation is generally applicable only for the period for which it has been determined.

The site should be sensitive, such that a significant change in discharge, even for the lowest discharges, should be accompanied by a significant change in stage. Small errors in stage readings during calibration at a non-sensitive station can result in large errors in the discharges indicated by the stage-discharge relation.

A comparison can be made between the change in discharge and the corresponding minimum change in stage to ensure that the sensitivity of the station is sufficient for the purpose for which the measurements are required.

Sites where weed growth is prevalent should be avoided. There should be no vortices, dead water or other abnormalities in flow. Sites where poor ice conditions are prevalent should also be avoided. Access to the site should be feasible under most conditions.

3.5.1.4 Survey for a permanent gauging station

After the preliminary survey, a topographical survey can be made when selecting a permanent site for a suitable measuring section. This should include a plan of the site indicating the width of the water surface at a stated stage, the edges of the natural banks of the channel(s), the line of any definite discontinuity of the slope of the banks and the toe and crest of any artificial flood bank.

All obstructions in the channel or floodway should be indicated.

A longitudinal section of the channel can be drawn from a point downstream of a control, where this exists, to the upstream limit of the reach showing the level of the deepest part of the bed and water surface gradients at low and high stages. The reach containing the measuring section can be checked to ensure that it contains no discontinuities that may affect the measurement results. At least five cross-sections should be surveyed in the measuring reach, two cross-sections upstream from the measuring section and two downstream, at distances upstream and downstream of not less than one bank full width of the channel.

The control can be defined by one or more cross-sections or by a close grid of levels over the area.

The detailed survey of the reach can be extended to an elevation well above the highest anticipated flood level. The spacing of levels or soundings should be close enough to reveal any abrupt change in the contour of the channel. The bed of the reach can be examined carefully for the presence of rocks or boulders, particularly in the vicinity of the measuring section.

When the station is to be calibrated using current meters, exploratory measurements of velocities should be made in the proposed measuring section and in the cross-section immediately upstream and downstream. The method of velocity distribution described in ISO 748 (8) can be used for these measurements, to determine the feasibility of using reduced point methods.

When floats are to be used for velocity measurements, trial runs of floats should be closely spread across the width of the channel. When dilution techniques are to be used to calibrate the station, trial measurements should be made to check the efficiency of mixing (20, 21).

Velocity measurements should be repeated at more than one stage to ensure that any abnormality of flow is detected.

3.5.1.5 Design and construction

The gauging station consists of one or more measuring sections and a reference gauge. Normally, a water level recorder can be installed to produce a continuous record of stage. It may be desirable to establish gauges at both banks particularly when there is any risk of differential level.

The position of each cross-section should be defined on the banks of the river by clearly visible and readily identifiable permanent markers, and a station bench mark should be established.

If a control regulates the stage at low discharges at the gauging section, it should be situated at the downstream end of the reach, and any measuring section should be sufficiently remote from it to avoid any distortion of flow which might occur in that vicinity. It should be close enough to ensure that a variable stage-discharge relation will not be introduced through the effect of wind or weed growth in the channel. Higher discharges are most often controlled by the general characteristics of the channel for a considerable distance downstream.

The reference gauge and water level recorder can be located as closely as possible to the measuring reach unless floats are used to measure the velocities, in which case the reference gauge and water level recorder are located near the midpoint of the measuring reach.

Where the main requirements necessary for a suitable gauging site, as specified, are not present, conditions may be improved as follows:

i.   The loss of water from the main channel by spillage can often be avoided by constructing flood banks to confine the flow in a defined floodway.

ii.   Minor irregularities in the bank or bed causing local eddies may be eliminated by trimming the bank to a regular line and a stable slope and by removing from the bed any large stones or boulders.

iii.   Unstable banks should be protected wherever possible. Such protections should extend upstream and downstream of a measuring section for a distance equal to at least one quarter of the bank-full width of the channel in each direction. In the case of float gauging, the whole of the measuring reach should be protected.

iv.   Instability of the bed may sometimes be corrected by introducing an artificial control which may also serve to improve the stage-discharge relation (sensitivity) or to create conditions in the measuring section for instruments to be effectively used. Occasionally, it may be possible to eliminate variable backwater effect by introducing an artificial control. Artificial controls, are, however, not practicable in large alluvial rivers.

Note:

An artificial control is a simple structure built in a channel for the reasons given in (iv) above. It may be a low dam or a contraction which is seldom designed to function as a control throughout the entire range of stage. Such artificial control structures should be designed in accordance with the conditions at the site where it is to be built. In the design of controls, the following major points should be considered:

i.   the shape of the structure should permit the passage of water with minimum disturbance of the flow regime upstream or downstream of the controls;

ii.   in order to provide adequate sensitivity, the profile of the crest of a control should be designed so that a small change in discharge at low stages will cause a measurable change in stage;

iii.   the control should have structural stability and be permanent;

iv.   if any alterations are made to the natural conditions, the subsequent re-establishment of stability may take some time; and

v.   care should be taken to monitor the stability effect of a control by periodic surveys.

A suitable access to the site should be available where possible, to provide safe passage at all stages of flow and in all weathers for personnel and for any vehicles used for the conveyance of instruments and equipment.

All key points at the site should be permanently and securely marked on the ground. Cross-section markers should be set on the line of the cross-section to facilitate the repetition of levels or soundings when the section is checked.

3.5.1.6   Definitive survey

The definitive survey, repeated as required, should include the accurate determination of the elevations and the relative positions of all the station installations and any other key points or significant features of the site. It is desirable to correlate the elevation with the national survey datum through the station bench mark. Bed profiles should be checked after a flood.

3.5.1.7   Operation of station

The production of a satisfactory record, depends on the station being maintained in full operating order at all times. This requires attendance on the recorder and proper maintenance of the station, its equipment and its calibration.

Where a station is only fitted with a reference gauge or reference gauges (vertical, inclined, wire weight or hook) and no water level recorder, local observers are required to furnish readings at specified intervals of all the gauges. Readings should be made at fixed hours. The intervals between the readings are determined by the rate at which the water level at the site usually changes, but arrangements should be made to have additional readings when the water level is changing more abruptly than usual.

The observer should record the time of each gauge observation.

When a recorder is provided, visits by the observer should be made throughout a period to verify that the recorder is operating satisfactorily. The observer should be required to record observations of the water level by the reference gauge and also the exact time for comparison with the recorder clock. At all stations, the observer notes any casual obstruction of the channel, inlet pipe(s), measuring structure or transducer mountings and pays particular attention to the legibility of the reference gauge.

Every gauging station should be inspected whenever any incident which might affect its accuracy is reported by the observer. All recorders and recorder clocks should be cleaned and lubricated in accordance with manufacturers' instructions.

The elevation of all key points (including the zero of the reference gauge) which are surveyed in the definitive survey should be checked by reference to the station bench mark particularly following any flood when equipment might have been damaged. At the same time, any vertical gauge should be tested. Where feasible, the correlation of the station bench mark with the national survey datum should be checked at periodic intervals.

3.5.2   Slope-stage-discharge or fall-discharge method

3.5.2.1   Principle

In a stable channel with a varying downstream control of water level when there is no unique relation between stage and discharge there may be a relation between the water surface slope, stage and discharge. In such channels it is economic to measure both water surface slope and water level from which the discharge is deduced. The station may be calibrated using a stationary current meter (8), moving boat (19), floats (8), or by dilution gauging methods (20, 21).

3.5.2.2   Preliminary survey

See stage-discharge station (Section 3.5.1.2).

3.5.2.3   Selection of site

The site selected should be such that it is possible to measure the whole range and all types of flow. Different methods of calibration may be employed for separate parts of the range, and the particular conditions relative to each of the methods of calibration being specified.

At any gauging station with twin gauges, the site should be sensitive such that a significant change in discharge should be accompanied by a significant change in fall between the two gauges. See also Section 3.5.1.3.

3.5.2.4   Survey for a permanent gauging station

See stage-discharge station (Section 3.5.1.4).

3.5.2.5 Design and construction

The gauging station consists of one or more measuring sections and two water level gauges one of which is the reference gauge. Water level recorders may be installed to produce a continuous or an intermittent record of stage.

The position of each cross-section is defined on the banks of the river by clearly visible and readily identifiable permanent markers and a station bench mark is established. It may be desirable to establish gauges at both banks particularly when there is any risk of differential level.

The length of the reach should be sufficient to make any observational error negligible relative to the fall of level between the two gauges. Furthermore, there should be no additions to or withdrawals from the flow between the two gauges.

If a control regulates the stage at low discharges at the gauging sections, it should be situated at the downstream end of the reach, and any measuring section should be sufficiently remote from it to avoid any distortion of flow which might occur in that vicinity. It should be close enough to ensure that a variable stage-discharge relation will not be introduced. Higher discharges are often controlled by the general characteristics of the channel for a considerable distance downstream.

The reference gauge and water level recorder should be located as closely as possible to the measuring reach unless floats are used to measure the velocities in which case the reference gauges and water level recorder are located near the midpoint of the measuring reach.

Where the main requirements necessary for a suitable gauging site, as specified, are not present, conditions may be improved as described earlier for the stage-discharge station. See also Section 3.5.1.5.

3.5.2.6 Definitive survey

See Section 3.5.1.6.

3.5.2.7 Operation of station

See stage-discharge station (Section 3.5.1.7)

3.5.3 Weirs and flumes

The basis of the method is to establish a relation between head and discharge, usually in the laboratory, and apply this relation to the field installation. A measurement of head is therefore required at the gauging station and this value inserted in the appropriate formula to obtain a corresponding value of discharge. A selection of weirs have been check calibrated in the field and relations which have been developed in the laboratory have shown no significant departure from their original calibration. By far the most serious uncertainty in this form of gauging is the inaccuracy in the measurement of head especially at low flows where, by comparison, any small uncertainty in the coefficient becomes insignificant. For design purposes reference should be made to (24) and (25) and (26–31).

Weirs or flumes are most common in the middle and upper reaches of watercourses. In the lower reaches, the width of rivers usually makes the size and hence cost of a structure prohibitive. In any case, the shallow longitudinal slope of the lower reach normally means that the afflux associated with a structure could not be tolerated from a flooding point of view.

In very general terms, conventional hydraulic structures can be used in natural watercourses where the longitudinal slope is between 0.003 and 0.0003, while specialist structures may be used in streams where the longitudinal slope is as high as 0.02. This specification ensures that for typical natural channels the Froude number, Fr, prior to installing a conventional hydraulic structure, is within the range $0.1 < Fr < 0.5$.

3.5.3.1 Modular and non-modular flow

The philosophy of using a hydraulic structure to measure flow is based on the premise that the relationship of discharge to a measure of water level (or pressure) can be forecast from basic physical principles or from empirical evidence on performance. The water level is gauged at a prescribed location upstream of the structure, and an equation or graphical relationship is applied to convert this to flow. This is the simplest case where, because the water level downstream of the structure is below some limiting condition (the modular limit), there is a unique relationship between these two quantities. Under these circumstances flow conditions are said to be modular.

If the tail water conditions affect the flow, the weir is said to be drowned or operating in the non-modular range. Two independent measurements relating to upstream and downstream water levels are required in order to determine the discharge at the structure under these circumstances.

The dividing line between modular and non-modular flow conditions is defined as the modular limit. It is quoted for each individual structure as the submergency ratio (the ratio of downstream to upstream total heads, both relative to weir crest or flume invert level) when the flow is 1% below the equivalent modular value.

3.5.3.2 Installation

The complete flow measuring installation consists of an approach channel, the structure itself and the downstream channel. The structure plays the most important role in determining the accuracy of the measured discharge but the condition of the approach and downstream channels also makes a contribution.

The structure should be rigid, watertight and capable of withstanding peak flows without damage and its axis should be in line with the natural direction of flow. The surfaces of the structures should be smooth, particularly in the vicinity of the crest or throat, and the alignment and dimensions of the structure should be set out with care. Parallel and vertical side walls should flank the structure and these should extend upstream at least as far as the head measurement position.

The main requirement for the approach channel is that it should be straight and reasonably regular for a distance upstream of the structure of at least 5 times its surface width. This ensures that the velocity distribution upstream of the structure is not heavily distorted and, more important, that there is no appreciable variation in water level across the width of the approach channel.

Flow conditions downstream of the structure are important in that they determine tail water levels which in turn influence the choice of elevation for the structure. It is important, therefore, to survey the downstream channel at the design stage and either measure or calculate the variation of tail water levels with discharge.

3.5.3.3 Measurement of heads

The discharge at a gauging structure depends on the geometry of the structure and water levels relative to the structure. The geometry of the structure is usually fixed and hence the accurate determination of its dimensions is relatively straightforward. Water levels relative to the structure (gauged heads) present a more difficult problem, particularly at low flows.

The best place to measure the water level should be determined, this being defined as that position which will yield the most accurate and reliable values for computed discharges. The water surface profile upstream of a gauging structure may not be horizontal and hence the choice of the location for the water level measurement materially affects computed flows. Immediately upstream of the structure, the water surface profile takes the form of a draw down curve and pressures may not be hydrostatic. Further upstream, frictional forces produce a water surface slope towards the structure. In general, the position for measuring the upstream water level, commonly referred to as the gauging section, should avoid the area of draw down but should not be so far upstream of the structure that frictional losses play a significant role. Common practice is to specify the distance to the gauging section as a multiple of the maximum head to be expected, typical values being two to four times the maximum head.

Having determined the location for the gauging section, it is necessary to consider how and with what type of instrumentation the water level is to be measured.

It is usual to measure the water level in a separate gauge well which is connected to the approach channel at the gauging section by a pipe. This pipe may or may not have a perforated cover plate on the outer end. This system reduces the effects of water surface irregularities in the approach channel to the structure, but the dimensions of the well and connecting pipe (and cover plate) must be chosen such that significant differences between river and well water levels do not occur during the critical periods when discharge is changing rapidly with time. An alternative system is to set an open-ended vertical damping tube in the approach channel with instrumentation recording water levels within it. This system is cheaper, but causes undesirable disturbances to the flow. Yet another system is to record the water level directly in the approach channel. This method is common in laboratories and is also used in the field as a check on gauge well levels or as a basic manual method where automatic instrumentation is not considered justifiable.

The computation of discharge depends on a knowledge of water levels relative to the elevation of the structure. In particular, the water levels must be known relative to the crest level of weirs (lowest level for V-notches and flat-V weirs) and the throat invert of flumes (lowest level of flumes). This means that the instrumentation for measuring water levels must be accurately zeroed to the level of the structure. The most convenient method is to set metal datum plates on the walls of the structure and on the top of the gauge well where applicable. An accurate survey of the structure then relates crest and invert levels to these datum plates. Carefully carried out manual measurements then relate the water levels to these datum plates and the readings of the head measuring instruments. Regular checks on zeroes should be carried out, particularly where instruments are moved or replaced. A zero check based on the water level, either when the flow ceases or just begins, is liable to serious errors due to surface tension effects.

3.5.3.4 Computation of discharge

Discharge equations are usually quoted in terms of total head values, although there are some exceptions. Theoretical and experimental studies suggest that total head (or energy) is the more fundamental variable and discharge coefficients are more readily presented within this framework. Data recorded at gauging structures are, however, of gauged heads and total heads must be deduced using one of two methods. The first uses successive approximation techniques and is particularly suited to computer analysis. An alternative manual method exists which is particularly useful at the design stage. The approach, known as the coefficient of velocity method, is graphical and considers the structure and flow geometries and their effect on the relationship between gauged and total heads.

As an example, a straightforward 2-dimensional weir is considered, ie a weir with a horizontal crest line operating in the modular flow range. The argument to the special case of a triangular profile weir operating in the drowned flow range can then be extended.

3.5.3.4.1 Modular flow conditions

The common discharge equation for a 2-dimensional weir, in terms of total head is

$$Q = C_d b H^{3/2} \sqrt{g}$$

where $Q(m^3 s^{-1})$ is the discharge;
C_d the effective coefficient of discharge;
$g\ (ms^{-2})$ the acceleration due to gravity;
$b\ (m)$ the crest breadth; and
$H\ (m)$ is the effective upstream total head.

The corresponding gauged head equation is

$$Q = C_v C_d b h^{3/2} \sqrt{g}$$

where C_v is the coefficient of velocity, and

h (m) is the effective upstream gauged head.

3.5.3.4.2   Non-modular flow conditions

A 2-dimensional weir of triangular profile with 1:2 and 1:5 upstream and downstream slopes, respectively, may be used in the non-modular range and the total head and gauged head equations are as follows:

$$Q = C_d bfH^{3/2}\sqrt{g}$$

where   f is the drowned flow reduction factor and

$$Q = C_v C_d bfh^{3/2}\sqrt{g}$$

It has been shown that the drowned flow reduction factor, f, is dependent upon the ratio b/h and the weir and flow geometries (h is the head within the zone of flow separation which forms just downstream of the crest and is recorded as well as the upstream gauged head). The coefficient of velocity, C_v, is dependent upon f and the weir and flow geometries.

3.5.3.5   Thin plate weirs

The standard thin-plate weir or notch has a crest profile consisting of a narrow surface at right angles to the upstream face of the plate and a 45-degree chamfer at the downstream edge. The upstream edge must be accurately machined to a 90 degree angle. Rounding, rust pitting and damage by debris or sediment can affect the flow, and consequently the role of thin-plate devices is restricted to those circumstances where maintenance is good and there is little risk of damage or deterioration. Naturally, if only a rough measure of flow is needed, less stringent standards of manufacture and maintenance can be accepted, but the various equations given later presuppose a stringent regard for the accuracy of the upstream corners of the weir.

Because the performance of a thin-plate device is dependent upon the full development of the contraction below the nappe, any obstructions to the flow as it converges towards the crest can affect the relationship of discharge to upstream level. Thus, projections such as bolt heads, stiffening brackets or other supporting structures cannot be permitted on the upstream face of the plate near the crest. Moreover, the nappe must be at atmospheric pressure on all its surfaces; it has to be well ventilated and cannot be submerged by a tailwater level above crest level without radically altering the flow. If sediment or other deposits accumulate upstream of the weir, the geometry of the approaching flow is affected and this in turn influences the contraction of the nappe and hence the coefficient.

The range of application for thin-plate weirs is restricted, if reasonable accuracy is desired, to the following situations:

i.   clean water, not carrying debris that might damage the crest or sediment that could settle in the approach to the weir; and

ii.   sites where adequate fall can be made available to ensure free discharge over the whole range to be gauged and where energy dissipation can be achieved satisfactorily.

Although these devices find some use in the field they are most frequently used in hydraulic laboratories. The attraction is their cheapness and the ease with which they may be made. Thin-plate devices fall into three main categories, depending on the cross-sectional shape presented to the flow.

i.   Full-width weirs occupying the complete width of a vertical sided channel. (Positive steps have to be taken to ensure ventilation of the underside of the nappe to achieve atmospheric pressure there). They present a rectangular cross-section.

ii.   Weirs with side contractions. These also present a rectangular cross-section, but do not occupy the full width of the approach channel. Thus, the boundary geometry is contracted at each flank and this in turn makes the nappe contract in a horizontal direction at each side. This type of weir is sometimes called a rectangular notch.

iii.   The V-notch. This is a symmetrical triangular version of the thin-plate weir with apex downwards. Its advantage lies in the ability to measure low discharges accurately and to cover a wide range of flows, albeit small ones. An included angle of 90° is common, but other angles are permissible for particular situations.

3.5.3.5.1 Rectangular thin plate weirs

Categories (i) and (ii) comprise a group known as rectangular thin plate weirs and the following equations are recommended.

Fully and partially contracted weirs (Kindsvater and Carter):

$$Q = \frac{2}{3} C_d b_e h_e^{3/2} \sqrt{2g}$$

Where Q (m³s⁻¹) is the discharge;
g (ms⁻²) the acceleration due to gravity;
C_d the coefficient of discharge;
b_e (m) the effective breadth of notch; and
h_e (m) is the effective gauged head.

$$b_e = b + 0.003$$

$$h_e = h + 0.001$$

where b is the breadth of notch and h is the gauged head.

$$C_d = \alpha = \beta \frac{h}{P}$$

Where P(m) is the height of the crest above upstream bed. Values of α and β depend on the ratio b/B, where B is the upstream breadth as follows, see Table 3.

Full-width weirs (Hydraulics Research Station):

$$Q = 0.564 \left(1 + \frac{0.150h}{P} \right) b(h + 0.001)^{3/2} \sqrt{g}$$

(units are metres and seconds).

3.4.5.2 Triangular (V-notch) weirs

The recommended discharge equation is

$$Q = \frac{8}{15}(2g)C_d \tan \frac{\theta}{2} h_e^{5/2}$$

where θ(deg) is the angle included between the sides of the notch.

$$h_e = h + k_h$$

For fully contracted V-notches, C_d and k_h vary with the notch angle, θ, as follows:

θ(deg)	20	40	60	80	100
C_d	0.592	0.582	0.576	0.576	0.581
k_h(m)	0.0028	0.0016	0.0011	0.0010	0.0009

For partially contracted V-notches, data are only available for 90° notches, k may be taken as 0.0009 (m) but C varies in a complex way with h/P, P/B and Q.

3.5.3.6 Broad crested weirs

3.5.3.6.1 Round-nose horizontal broad crest weirs

This type of weir has a horizontal surface at the crest which spans between vertical abutments. The upstream corner is rounded across the breadth of the weir in such a way that flow separation does not occur up to and including the design maximum head. The length of the horizontal section of the crest should not be less than 1.75 H_{max}. This geometry ensures that flow separation will not occur at the upstream corner and that parallel flow conditions will be developed at some point on the horizontal crest.

At the downstream limit of the horizontal crest there is a rounded corner, a downward slope or a vertical face. The geometry of the downstream section of the weir does not affect the modular discharge characteristics of the weir, but does affect the modular limit. In general, the more gradual the expansion of the flow, the higher the modular limit. In round figures, weirs with vertical downstream faces have a submergence ratio of 70% at the modular limit: a rounded downstream corner can increase this to 75% and a gradual slope downstream of the structure may, under favourable circumstances, produce figures of up to 95%.

The modular flow characteristics of round-nose horizontal-crest weirs can be predicted because the pressure distribution on the horizontal crest is sufficiently close to hydrostatic for basic critical depth theory to apply. Boundary layer theory predicts the variation of discharge coefficients with the relevant hydraulic flow characteristics, and the geometric and surface roughness properties of the weir itself.

The basic discharge equation for this type of weir may be written as

$$Q = \left(\frac{2}{3}\right)^{3/2} C_d b H^{3/2} \sqrt{g}$$

The coefficient of discharge is given by the expression

$$C_d = \left[1 - \frac{0.006L}{b}\right]\left[1 - \frac{0.003L}{h}\right]^{3/2}$$

3.5.3.6.2 Rectangular-profile broad crest weirs

The crest of the rectangular-profile weir is a horizontal rectangular plane surface and the upstream and downstream faces are vertical. It is important that the upstream face forms a sharp, right-angle corner where it intersects the plane of the crest. The submergence ratio at the modular limit is generally quoted as 65–70% and there is a dearth of experimental evidence to support these figures.

The basic discharge equations used for rectangular-profile weirs are similar to that used for round-nosed horizontal crest weirs, viz

$$Q = \left(\frac{2}{3}\right)^{3/2} C_d b H^{3/2} \sqrt{g}$$

The coefficient of discharge, C_d, for a rectangular profile weir is variable but it has been shown that C_d can be taken as a basic (constant) coefficient of 0.855 within the limited range

$$0.08 < h/L < 0.3$$

and

$$0.18 < h/(h+P) < 0.36$$

3.5.3.7 Triangular-profile weirs

Triangular-profile weirs have become very popular and are used in both the laboratory and the field.

The Crump profile weir has a 1:2 upstream slope and a 1:5 downstream slope. This type of weir has the advantages of a stable and constant coefficient of discharge in the modular range, together with an option to operate in the drowned flow range without *in situ* calibrations. The 1:5 downstream slope produces a strong, controlled hydraulic jump in the modular range which simplifies energy dissipation problems. Two dimensional weirs have the advantage of ease of construction and simplicity in operation.

If it is assumed that operation in the drowned flow range is undesirable, then one solution is a compound weir in which low discharges are measured by containing flow within a relatively narrow lower crest section, and high afflux at peak flows is avoided by incorporating a much wider crest section at a higher elevation. The main disadvantage of this type of weir is that divide piers are necessary between crest sections at different elevations, if there is to be complete confidence in applying the standard 2-dimensional calibration to individual crests.

An alternative method of avoiding large afflux at peak flows is to operate a simple single-crested weir in the drowned flow range. This method involves the use of two gauges rather than a single gauge recording upstream water levels, the second measurement being the downstream water level or, preferably, the pressure within the separation pocket which is formed just downstream of the weir crest. This latter position provides a more sensitive means of measuring flow and has the advantage that it is not affected by the geometry of the downstream section of the weir installation.

These two possible ways of measuring a wide range of flows without incurring difficulties at either end of the range have been combined and compound weirs have been operated in the drowned flow range.

3.5.3.7.1 Two-dimensional weirs

The discharge equation for 2-dimensional weirs operating in the modular flow range takes the form

$$Q = C_d b H_1^{3/2} \sqrt{g}$$

The coefficient of discharge, C_d takes a constant value of 0.635.

In the drowned flow range, a drowned flow reduction factor, f, is introduced. Thus

$$Q = C_d f b h_1^{3/2} \sqrt{g}$$

The drowned flow reduction factor is determined from a measurement of the downstream water level or (preferably) from the pressure head, H, measured within the separation pocket which forms just downstream of the crest.

3.5.3.7.2 Flat-V weirs

Two modular flow discharge equations are obtained for flat-V weirs; one for conditions when flow is confined within the V and a second, at higher discharges, where the presence of the vertical side walls has to be taken into account. These are as follows:

$$Q = 0.8 C_d n H^{5/2} \sqrt{g} \text{ when } H \leq H^1$$

and

$$Q = 0.8 C_d n H^{5/2} \sqrt{g} \left[1 - \left(1 - \frac{H^1}{H} \right)^{5/2} \right] \text{ when } H > H^1$$

where $C_d = 0.63$ for weirs with a 1:2/1:5 longitudinal profile;
H^1 (m) is the difference between lowest and highest crest elevation; and
n is the crest cross-slope (1 vertical: n horizontal)

Flat-V weirs are occasionally used in the drowned flow range with a crest tapping (24, 25). The modular limit for Crump profile flat-V weirs occurs at submergence ratios between 0.67 and 0.78.

3.5.3.7.3 Compound weirs

When a weir is compounded, individual weir sections have different crest elevations and they are separated by divide piers. This ensures that 2-dimensional flow is preserved at each section and, as a consequence, calibrations can be derived from the basic equations for 2-dimensional weirs.

General practice is to record upstream water levels at one position only. Hence, in calculating total river flow, it is necessary to make assumptions about the relationships between flow conditions at the various individual crest sections. Three possibilities have been investigated and these may be summarised as follows.

i.   Total head level is assumed constant over the full width of the weir. It is obtained by adding, onto the observed static head, a velocity head based on the mean velocity of approach to the structure as a whole.

ii.   Water level is assumed constant over the full width of the weir. Thus, the observed static head is applied to each crest section (taking into account differences in crest levels) and individual total heads can be obtained by adding velocity heads appropriate to each crest section.

iii.   Total head level is assumed constant over the full width of the weir. It is obtained by adding, on to the observed static head, the velocity head appropriate to the individual crest section at which the water level is observed.

Field experiments covering a wide range of conditions have indicated that the third method is the most accurate (24, 25).

Several compound weirs have been built with crest tappings in the lowest crest section. This facilitates operation in the drowned flow range but, because of the complex geometry of compound weirs, the accuracy of flow measurement in the drowned flow range is reduced (32).

3.5.3.8   Flumes

The discharge in an open channel may be measured by means of a flume, consisting essentially of constrictions in the sides and/or bottom of the channel forming a throat. When the reduction in cross-sectional area exceeds a certain value, critical depth occurs in the constriction and the stage-discharge relationship becomes independent of conditions in the channel downstream of the structure.

The device is then said to be 'free-flowing' and constitutes a critical depth-measuring flume. If the throat is prismatic over a significant length in the direction of flow, critical depth will always occur at a similar section and the calibration of the flume becomes amenable to theoretical derivation. Such a flume is said to be long-throated, and three basic types are to be found in general use: rectangular-throated, trapezoidal-throated and U-throated.

The type of flume which is used depends on several factors, such as the range of discharge to be measured, the accuracy requirements, the head available and the estimated sediment load of the stream. The rectangular-throated flume is probably the simplest geometry to construct and its calibration is straightforward. The trapezoidal-throated flume is more appropriate to large installations, particularly where a wide range of discharge is to be measured with consistent accuracy. This shape of throat is particularly suitable where it is necessary to work to a given stage-discharge relationship. The U-throated flume is useful for installation in a U-shaped channel or where discharge is from a circular section conduit. It has found particular application in sewers and at sewage works. The versatility of all three types may be enhanced by raising the invert of the throat above upstream bed level.

Critical depth theory, augmented by experimental data, may be used to deduce the basic equations for free discharge through long-throated flumes. The theory relates to the frictionless flow of an ideal fluid, and an additional coefficient has to be introduced in practice, either based on experiment or deduced by considering boundary layer development within the throat of the flume. When the velocity distribution is uniform within the throat and that there is no significant curvature of the streamlines, considerations of minimum energy yield the general expression:

$$Q = \left(\frac{gA_c^3}{W_c} \right)^{1/2}$$

where A_c (m²) is the cross-sectional area of flow at the critical section, and
W_c (m) is the water surface width at the critical section.

The equation above gives discharge in terms of depth at the critical section, but in practice it is necessary to measure heads upstream of the throat of the structure. Thus, an essential step is to convert the formula into one which relates upstream gauged head to discharge. The effective total head, H_e, measured relative to the invert of the flume, relates to the conditions at the critical section as follows:

$$H_e = d_c + \frac{A_c}{2W_c}$$

where d_c (m) is the depth of flow at the critical section.

Using the previous two equations, a theoretical calibration for a gauging structure over the full range of discharge can be derived by considering flow conditions in the throat of the flume and deducing corresponding heads and discharges. The principle of the method is to select a series of values of d_c, the critical depth in the throat, and calculate corresponding values of Q and H. Total heads are then converted to gauged heads using successive approximation techniques (32).

An explicit relationship may be derived for rectangular-throated flumes from the previous two equations as follows:

$$Q = \left(\frac{2}{3}\right)^{3/2} C_v C_d b_e H^{3/2} \sqrt{g}$$

where b_e (m) is the effective width of the throat.

Shape coefficients have to be introduced for trapezoidal and U-throated flumes and the explicit method becomes more cumbersome. Graphical solutions are, however, available.

The modular limit of long-throated flumes depends to a large extent on the severity of the expansion downstream of the throat of the flume. A rapid expansion results in the modular limit occurring at a submergence ratio of around 75%, whereas a very smooth and gradual expansion can increase this figure to as high as 95%.

3.5.3.9 Range of the discharge measured by weirs and flumes

Table 4 (11) shows the minimum and maximum discharges measured by the weirs and flumes described above for the prescribed conditions and limitations given. The maximum height of a weir, (P), is normally designed to be about one metre and the minimum head used in the table follows the limitation given for each device.

3.5.4 Ultrasonic (acoustic) gauging station

3.5.4.1 Principle

The principle of the ultrasonic method (33, 34) is to measure the velocity of flow at a certain depth by simultaneously transmitting sound pulses through the water from transducers located on either side of the river. The transducers, which are designed to transmit and receive sound pulses, are not located directly opposite each other but staggered so that the angle between the pulse path and the direction of flow is between 30° and 60°. The difference between the time of travel of the pulses crossing the river in an upstream direction and those travelling downstream is directly related to the average velocity of the water at the depth of the transducers. This velocity can then be related to the average velocity of flow of the whole cross section. By incorporating an area factor in the electronic processor the system produces an output of discharge.

3.5.4.2 Theory

Referring to Figure 10 and assuming

L = path length (m)
θ = path angle (degrees)
V_1 = line velocity at transducer height (ms^{-1})
V_p = velocity component along acoustic path (ms^{-1})
V = average velocity of flow of river (ms^{-1})
D = depth of water (m)
W = width of river (m)
t_1 = time taken for pulse to travel from A to B (s)
t_0 = time taken for pulse to travel from B to A (s)
Q = discharge of river (m^{3}s^{-1})
C = velocity of sound in water (ms^{-1})

The time taken for a pulse to travel from A to B is

$$t_1 = \frac{L}{C + V_p}$$

Similarly, the time taken for a pulse to travel from B to A is

$$t_2 = \frac{L}{C - V_p}$$

from which

$$t_2 - t_1 = t = \frac{2LV_p}{C^2 + V_p^2}$$

Note that C^2 is large compared to V_p^2.

Therefore

$$\Delta_t = \frac{2LV_p}{C^2}$$

also

$$V_L = \frac{V_p}{\cos\theta}$$

From the last two equations

$$V_L = \frac{C^2 \Delta_t}{2L\cos\theta}$$

If the transducers are positioned to give the average velocity of flow then

$$V = \frac{C^2 \Delta_t}{2L\cos\theta}$$

Now Q = WDV, and therefore Q = L sin θ DV, and from these equations

$$Q = \frac{1}{2\Delta_t C^2 D \tan\theta}$$

3.5.4.3 Available systems

The systems at present available consist of one pair of transducers (single path) or several pairs of transducers (multipath). The former is adaptable to rivers where changes in stage are small for a large percentage of the time and where the vertical velocity distribution is regular. The multipath system is used where large changes of stage predominate and where irregular vertical velocity distributions prevail. Generally 4 to 6 paths may prove satisfactory in most instances.

3.5.4.4 Limitations

Ultrasonic gauging stations can be sited on most rivers possessing difficult hydraulic conditions but precautions should be taken against the following factors:

i.   weed growth;

ii.   high sediment load;

iii.   temperature gradients;

iv.   salinity gradients; and

v.   air entrainment.

Where the above factors are significant, a loss of signal is to be expected.

Other factors to be allowed for in the computation of discharge are oblique flow and changes in bed level.

3.5.4.5 Selection of site

The site selected should conform to the requirements of Section 3.3.3. It should be such that it is feasible to measure the whole range and all types of flow. The following factors should be considered.

i. Mains power should be available.

ii. There should be good access to the site, preferably to both banks.

iii. Abrupt bends in the channel should be avoided, but these may be acceptable provided that condition (iv) is satisfied.

iv. At cross-sections taken in the area between the upstream and downstream transducer mountings, the velocity distributions should be similar.

v. The bed should preferably be stable. If it is not, regular bed surveys should be carried out to determine the change in area in order to compute the discharge.

vi. The section should be free of weed growth which attenuates the acoustic signal.

vii. For rivers up to 100 m wide there should be at least 1 m depth of water in the river at all times. The following table gives approximate minimum required depths for rivers over 100 m wide.

Path length (m)	Minimum total depth (m)	
	Acceptable	Preferred
200	2.5	7
300	5	10
400	7	15
500	12	25
600	18	40

The table is based on an operating frequency of 100 kHz.

NOTE: this table is based on consideration of the refraction problem only. It shows that the depth of water required increases as the path length increases. For example, for a path length of 200 m the preferred acoustic performance would be expected for depths greater than 7 m, acceptable performance would be anticipated for depths between 2.5 m and 7 m, but for depths less than 2.5 m, on-site investigation of the characteristics of acoustic transmission would be necessary.

viii. Refraction of the acoustic signal can be caused by temperature gradients of the order of as low as 0.01°C per 30 mm depth and the signal may be lost due to this cause alone. A water temperature survey should therefore be made at the proposed site.

ix. Attenuation of the acoustic signal may also be caused by reflection and scatter of the propagated pressure wave from entrained air bubbles. Sites immediately downstream of dams, weirs or waterfalls should therefore be avoided.

x. Suspended solids may have a significant effect on the signal attenuation, caused by both reflection and scatter from sediment particles suspended in the stream. Generally, sections having concentrations of over 1000 mg/l^{-1} for significant periods of time should be avoided. The following table gives approximate values of attenuation, expressed in decibels, for the corresponding values of suspended sediment loads but due regard should be given to the operating frequency used, size of sediment, distribution, water temperature and length of acoustic path.

Acoustic signal attenuation in decibels per 100 m path length	Sediment concentration (mg l⁻¹)
1	120
2.5	250
12	1300
25	2600

NOTE: the table is based on an operating frequency of 100 kHz.

3.5.4.6 Design and construction

The gauging section consists of:

i. (a) one or more pairs of transducers installed on each bank and fixed permanently in position; or
(b) one or more pairs of transducers installed on each bank and having the facility of movement in the vertical or on an incline;

ii. a console containing a data processor and a data recorder;

iii. a water level recorder interfaced with the data processor where an output of stage or discharge, or both, is required;

iv. an armoured cable, to transmit the signals from the transducers and the water level recorder (where part of the system), normally installed in the bed;

v. a reference gauge.

For the method of fixed transducers, a path or index velocity can be obtained which is related to stage and area to obtain discharge. Calibration by current meter is required in this method.

For the method whereby the transducers are designed to move on a vertical or inclined assembly, the system is self-calibrating. This is performed by establishing vertical velocity curves by moving the transducers to various paths and obtaining a series of path velocities in the vertical. This should be performed at different values of stage and the resulting curves analysed to determine the optimum location of the transducers.

In the multipath system, where several pairs of transducers are employed, the optimum positions of these are determined from a preliminary examination of vertical velocity curves obtained by current meter. The transducers should then be fixed as in (i) (a) or installed on an assembly as in (i) (b) above.

Where the transducers are to be permanently fixed in position they should be securely mounted into the river bed in a vertical position. Where they are designed to slide on an assembly, the construction of the mountings and guides should be such as to withstand damage. The guides should be securely fastened to the bed or banks and set in concrete so as to be free from sinking, tilting or washing away. The anchorages should extend below ground surface to a level free of disturbance by frost. In both methods the construction should be sufficiently rigid to be capable of withstanding the effects of floods.

A detailed level survey can be made of the bed and banks extending for one river width upstream of the proposed upstream transducer mounting and one river width below the downstream transducer mounting. Depending on the result of this survey, consideration should be given to the improvement of the bed and banks by cleaning or dredging, after which the local survey should be repeated.

When the position of the transducer mountings has been decided, the angle between the mountings should be carefully surveyed for ultimate wiring into the processor. A level survey can be made of the bed between the transducer mountings along the path length and the average bed level obtained also for wiring into the processor where discharge is being processed on-site.

This survey should be repeated periodically.

3.5.4.7   Operation and maintenance

The output from an ultrasonic station may be recorded in any one of the following modes:

i.   path velocity (or an index which is numerically proportional to the path velocity);

ii.   path velocity and stage;

iii.   discharge and stage;

iv.   velocity and discharge; or

v.   velocity, discharge and stage.

If stage is not included in the mode, it can be recorded separately by a water level recorder for subsequent off-site processing.

When operating in the discharge mode a manual facility can be provided in the electronic processor to make any adjustment necessary for a change in bed level.

3.5.5   Electromagnetic method

3.5.5.1   Principle

The basic principle of the electromagnetic method is the measurement of the electro-motive force produced by a conductor moving in a magnetic field. In the case of a river, the conductor is the flowing water and the magnetic field is artificially produced by installing a coil below the bed (see Figure 11). In the case of a small channel or culvert the coil may be placed above the water surface.

3.5.5.2   Preliminary survey

A preliminary survey can be made to ensure that the physical and hydraulic features of the proposed site conforms to the requirements for the application of the method.

3.5.5.3   Selection of site

The following factors should be considered:

i.   the site should not be liable to interference from strong electric currents, for example, from a nearby generating station;

ii.   mains power should be available; and

iii.   the width of river should be less than 100 m.

3.5.5.4   Theory

From the law of electromagnetic induction

$$E = HVb$$

where   E is the emf generated in volts,
           H is the magnetic field in tesla,
           V is the average velocity of flow in ms^{-1}, and
           b is the river width in metres.

It can be shown that

$$Q = K_1 \left(\frac{Eh}{I} \right)^n$$

where   I is the coil current in amperes
           h is the stage in metres
           K_1 is a dimensional coefficient
           n is an exponent.

3.5.5.5 Design and construction

An electromagnetic gauging station consists essentially of a coil, voltage probes, noise cancellation probes (where necessary) and the necessary recording equipment. The positions of the coil and probes are related to the bank-full width, w, of the river. The coil is located below the bed with about 0.5 m minimum cover and is square in plan. In a trapezoidal section, the coil may be taken up the banks, again allowing 0.5 m minimum cover. It has been found that the best design of coil is one having 3 or 4 turns of 4 core cable, excited with 20–25 amperes, giving a total of about 300 ampere turns.

The voltage probes may be installed in a vertical or sloping position depending on the geometry of the cross-section and they are taken down to the level of the coil. The electromagnetic measuring section is contained between the water surface, the voltage probes and the coil. The emf is integrated within this area and the effect of silt, weeds (zero velocity) or negative flow is allowed for. The coil and probe cables can be threaded through preformed and jointed PVC ducts laid in trenches excavated in the bed.

The probes can be of stainless steel with a diameter of 50 mm. The voltage probes that sense the emf produced by the coil are located centrally with respect to the coil. An additional two pairs of noise cancellation probes can be installed if the ambient electrical noise is a problem at the site. The emf produced from this source is then deducted automatically from the emf produced by the coil.

3.5.5.6 Calibration

The electromagnetic gauging station requires calibration by current meter so that a relation is established between Q, as measured by current meter, and

$$\frac{Eh}{I}$$

3.6 Compilation of records

The collection of field data in the form of records of gauge readings and of velocity or discharge measurements, is only the first step in the compilation of a station record. While it is important that field observations should be made accurately, no less importance should be attached to the work of reducing the transcribed information. Both operations must be performed with meticulous care, as negligence in either operation can invalidate the value of the record.

Where recorders are installed, readings of water levels are taken at such intervals as may be necessary to define the hydrograph adequately. The conversion from water level to discharge by the use of the stage-discharge curve and station rating table in the case of a velocity area station, and the weir or flume equation in the case of a measuring structure, are made for each water level. For the computation of daily mean discharge, the assumption is often made that changes in water level which take place between readings vary directly with them. This may not necessarily be the case.

The extrapolation of discharges from rating curves should be avoided, if possible, otherwise it can be done as indicated in ISO 1100 Part II (12). Discharges derived by extrapolation are distinguished from those derived by interpolation. They should not be regarded as standard discharges themselves. Notwithstanding this, a record may be considered a standard record, provided the sum of the estimated quantities does not exceed 5% of the total run-off for the year.

Annotations of the record should also indicate any day on which the flow suffered interference.

3.7 Measurement and computation of discharge under ice conditions

3.7.1 Design and construction

3.7.1.1 Stilling well

The stilling well and inlet pipes should be constructed in such a manner that the system will remain operational during extended periods of freezing temperatures. Methods of achieving this include the following.

i.   Construct well of non-conductive materials, or insulate to prevent frost penetration.

ii. Where necessary and feasible, the lower inlet pipe is wrapped with electrical heating tape, or the tape is placed inside the inlet pipe, so that it may be kept free of ice. A steaming apparatus may also be used.

iii. Inlet pipes are positioned such that the lower pipe is below the bottom of the ice sheet, and the upper pipe is above the ice sheet. In this way, the recorder will operate on the lower inlet during the freezing period, and should the lower inlet become frozen, the upper inlet will become operative during the snow melt freshet while the lower intake thaws.

iv. Stilling wells which are constructed far enough into the bank to be below the frost line may be kept free of ice through use of a removable insulated sub-floor. The sub-floor is positioned below the frost line but above the maximum likely water level during the freezing period. Provision is made for free passage of the float and counterweight wires. The sub-floor is removed prior to the snow melt freshet.

v.   As an alternative to (iv), an open-ended waterproof cylinder, larger than the float diameter, should be fixed vertically in the well and partially filled with a non-volatile petroleum distillate. The cylinder should be of sufficient length and installed such that the lower end will be substantially lower than the minimum anticipated water level and the upper end higher than the maximum anticipated water level for the period over which freezing temperatures occur. Care should be taken to ensure that the float will ride freely in the cylinder and travel of the counterweight is not impeded. The cylinder and petroleum distillate are removed before the spring freshet. If the petroleum distillate escapes from the cylinder, errors in stage record will result because of the specific gravity difference between water and distillate.

vi. Stilling wells may be heated by means of electrical or propane heaters. In some instances, it may be necessary to mount the heater on a separate float system or to incorporate an electric immersion heater into the recorder float to prevent freezing of the well. The quantity of heat provided should be the minimum required to keep the stilling well ice-free. Overheating of the well will result in production of excessive water vapour which will condense as frost in the recorder shelter, possibly causing jammed doors or recorder and clock malfunctions.

It may be necessary to heat the water stage instrumentation to ensure continuous operation under severe temperatures, although some instruments will operate at temperatures of -45°C if special cold temperature lubricants are used.

3.7.1.2 The pneumatic recorder

i.   The orifice from which the compressed gas escapes into the stream is mounted at an elevation below that of the bottom of the ice sheet that would normally form at the gauging station.

ii. The orifice is located away from locations where anchor ice will form, such as above rapids, to prevent blockage of the orifice.

iii. Where the possibility exists of the orifice becoming frozen in the ice, the gas feed pressure is reduced to a value less than the pressure equivalent of the full scale range of the instrument. This will prevent possible instrument damage in the event of the orifice becoming blocked.

iv. The line to the orifice is buried in the bank to a depth sufficient to prevent damage from ice scour during the freshet.

v.   Instrumentation is heated to the minimum operating temperature stated by the manufacturer if uninterrupted operation is required. Battery power supplies may be waterproofed and placed in the stream to obtain satisfactory performance during times of extremely low temperatures.

3.7.1.3   Notches, weirs and flumes

Where necessary and feasible these structures are heated during the freezing period to ensure that the head-discharge relation is applicable during the winter. This may be accomplished by suspending an array of electric or propane radiant heaters from a hood over the structure, or by enclosing the entire structure, leaving openings for the free inflow and outflow of water. The space enclosed in this manner may then be heated.

The elevation of the structure is checked during the ice period to ensure the structure remains secure.

3.7.2   Compilation of records

Daily discharge records, computed for periods when ice conditions affect the stage-discharge relation, are normally subject to a higher error than under open water conditions. However, ice effects at a given gauging station tend to follow a similar pattern and reliable computations can normally be made by careful interpretation of the type of ice regime, hydrometric data, meteorological data and a knowledge of previous ice effects.

The difference in stage between the effective gauge height and the recorded height (backwater) is computed for each discharge measurement. Backwater values between discharge measurements are interpolated using air temperature, ice thickness, or other hydrologic information as a guide. Effective gauge heights can then be determined by subtracting the backwater from daily mean gauge heights. Daily mean discharges can be computed using the effective gauge heights and the open water stage-discharge relation.

3.7.2.1   Recession curve

Larger streams, particularly those which have significant lake storage, may exhibit a semi-logarithmic form of recession from the time of formation of an ice cover until breakup of the ice cover. The general mathematical form of the equation is:

$$Q_2 = Q_1 K^{-\Delta t}$$

where Q_2 = discharge at time t_2,
            Q_1 = discharge at time t_1,
            K = recession constant
            Δt = elapsed time interval $(t_2 - t_1)$.

If the slope of the recession line is invariant from year to year, a single discharge measurement can be used to define the recession. Daily mean discharges are computed utilising the recessing equation or a graphical semi-logarithmic plot.

3.7.2.2   Methods of computation for streams having intermittent ice cover

Some streams do not form a permanent ice cover and are subject to cycles of formation and dissipation of ice cover, frazil ice and anchor ice throughout the winter. These cycles can occur on a daily basis and will result in a highly irregular water stage record. Frequent discharge measurements are necessary, especially at new gauging stations, to develop a better understanding of the stage-discharge interactions that occur under varying climatic conditions. Continuous operation of a recording current meter at a point in the cross-section, or time lapse photography may provide useful information for interpretation of the stage record.

Table 2　Typical computation for a current meter measurement by the mid-section method

	Distance from initial point (m)	Depth (m)	Meter position	REVS	Time in seconds	Velocity At point (m s⁻¹)	Velocity Mean in vertical (m s⁻¹)	Width (m)	Area (m²)	Discharge (m³ s⁻¹)
RB	4	0		0	0	0	0	0	0	0
1	5	0.31	0.6	40	60	0.193	0.193	1	0.31	0.060
2	6	0.4	0.6	45	59	0.219	0.219	1	0.40	0.089
3	7	0.51	0.6	51	61	0.238	0.238	1	0.51	0.121
4	8	0.85	0.6	52	61	0.243	0.243	1	0.85	0.206
5	9	1.23	0.2	55	60	0.260	0.235	1	1.23	0.289
			0.8	44	60	0.211				
6	10	1.58	0.2	58	62	0.265	0.240	1	1.58	0.379
			0.8	46	61	0.216				
7	11	1.69	0.2	60	61	0.278	0.251	1	1.69	0.424
			0.8	48	61	0.225				
8	12	1.71	0.2	65	62	0.295	0.274	1	1.71	0.468
			0.8	51	63	0.253				
9	13	1.87	0.2	70	62	0.317	0.287	1	1.87	0.537
			0.8	58	64	0.257				
10	14	1.84	0.2	69	62	0.313	0.287	1	1.84	0.528
			0.8	58	63	0.262				
11	15	1.71	0.2	66	61	0.305	0.278	1	1.71	0.475
			0.8	55	62	0.252				
12	16	1.65	0.2	62	61	0.287	0.262	1	1.65	0.432
			0.8	52	62	0.238				
13	17	1.50	0.2	60	61	0.278	0.258	1	1.50	0.387
			0.8	50	60	0.238				
14	18	1.36	0.2	58	62	0.265	0.241	1	1.36	0.328
			0.8	47	62	0.217				
15	19	1.19	0.2	55	61	0.257	0.228	1	1.19	0.271
			0.8	42	63	0.193				
16	20	1.17	0.2	51	62	0.235	0.211	1	1.17	0.247
			0.8	39	60	0.188				
17	21	0.92	0.6	46	61	0.216	0.216	1	0.92	0.199
18	22	0.81	0.6	41	63	0.188	0.188	1	0.81	0.152
19	23	0.70	0.6	39	61	0.184	0.184	1	0.70	0.129
20	24	0.63	0.6	36	63	0.167	0.167	1	0.63	0.105
21	25	0.55	0.6	31	61	0.150	0.150	1	0.55	0.082
22	26	0.48	0.6	26	64	0.125	0.125	1	0.36	0.045
LB	26.5	0	0	0	0	0	0	0	0	0

RB=Right bank
LB=Left bank

Σ 24.54　5.953

Table 3

b/B	0.1	0.2	0.3	0.4	0.5	0.6	0.7	0.8	0.9	1.0
α	0.588	0.598	0.590	0.591	0.592	0.593	0.594	0.596	0.598	0.602
β	-0.002	-0.002	0.002	0.006	0.011	0.018	0.030	0.045	0.064	0.075

Table 4 Maximum and minimum discharges for weirs and flumes for given conditions

		P (m)		Discharge per metre of crest (m^3 s^{-1})	
				minimum	maximum
Weirs:					
Thin plate full		0.2		0.005	0.667
width		1.0		0.005	7.7
Thin plate		0.2		0.009	0.45
contracted		1.0		0.009	4.9
Thin plate V notch θ=90°				0.001	1.8
Triangular		0.2		0.01	1.17
profile		1.0		0.01	13
(Crump)					
Flat V	b		Slope		
	4	0.2	1:10	0.014	5.0
	80	1.0	1:40	0.055	630
Rectangular		0.2		0.026	0.60
		1.0		0.15	6.5
Round nosed		0.15		0.026	0.11
		1.0		0.1	8.2
Flumes:	b (m)	m (slope)	L (m)		
Rectangular,	0.5	0	1.0	0.009	0.30
trapezoidal	1.0	5	4.0	0.27	41
U-shaped	D				
	0.3		0.6	0.002	0.07
	1.0		2.0	0.019	1.4

4 Measurement of flow in closed conduits

4.1 Introduction

A summary is made of the main methods of closed conduit flow measurement (pipes running full). For more detailed information the reader is referred to the references provided.

4.2 Differential pressure meters

4.2.1 General

Although differential pressure meters are the oldest kind of flow meter, these are still by far the most commonly used. They are based on the principle that when a fluid passes through a contraction in a pipe it accelerates; the resulting increase in kinetic energy is balanced by a decrease in the static pressure at that point in the pipe, and the pressure drop caused by the contraction is proportional to the square of the flow rate for a given flow meter. The general relation between flow rate and pressure drop for a differential pressure meter is:

$$Q = \frac{C_d A_2}{\left[1 - \frac{A_2{}^2}{A_1{}^2}\right]} (2gH^{1/2})$$

(1)

where   Q is the volume passing in a given time,
          A_1 is the cross-sectional area of the pipe,
          A_2 is the cross-sectional area of the contraction in the flow meter,
          g is the acceleration due to gravity, and
          H is the head difference between contraction and adjacent pipe.

C_d is an empirical constant known as the discharge coefficient which has to be introduced mainly to compensate for the fact that the fluid does not fill the full cross-sectional area of the contraction in the plane of the pressure measurement. Occasionally, the flow coefficient a, is used instead of C_d. This is defined by

$$a = \frac{C_d}{\sqrt{(1 - m^2)}}$$

where $m = A_2/A_1$, the area ratio of the flow meter. C_d or a must be obtained by calibration (35, 36). The value of C_d is a function of Reynolds number, but usually becomes virtually constant above a Reynolds number of about 3×10^5 (based on the diameter of the contraction).

4.2.2 Types of differential pressure meters

The most common types are the square-edged orifice plate (Figure 12), the venturi tube (Figure 13) and the nozzle (Figure 14). Typical values of the discharge coefficient for these are 0.6, 0.99 and 0.98 respectively.

The orifice plate is simply a plate installed transversely in a pipe with a hole in it and with differential pressure tappings before and after the plate. Usually this is a concentric square-edged orifice, but other types exist for specialised applications.

Three types of tappings may be used for orifice plates and these are illustrated in Figure 15. Whichever type is chosen, there should be at least four tappings in each plane of pressure measurement, distributed evenly around the pipe. This applies to all types of differential pressure meter, so that a check can be made that the pressure distribution is constant across each of the two planes of pressure measurement. This is a necessary, but not sufficient, condition to ensure that the flow-meter is being presented with good velocity distribution in the flow.

Venturi tubes (Figure 13) consist of a cylindrical 'throat' section preceded by a short contraction and followed by a longer expansion to allow pressure recovery. Although more expensive than an orifice plate, the pressure recovery means that there is a much lower irrecoverable head loss than with an orifice plate.

The nozzle (Figure 14) has a curved entry to its cylindrical throat, but no divergent outlet section and so the discharge coefficient is similar to that of a venturi but the irrecoverable head loss is like that of an orifice plate with the same pressure difference. The head loss can be reduced by adding a divergent section and the flow-meter is then classed as a venturi nozzle (Figure 16).

The irrecoverable head losses incurred by these differential pressure meters are a function of the area ratio of the device and Figure 17 gives the values for each, as a percentage of the differential pressure generated.

The use of a differential pressure meter which has a low head loss has obvious advantages. One of the earliest developments was the Dall tube (37), Figure 18. It consists of two cones, each with a substantial included angle, between which is a circumferential slot. The abrupt change of boundary contour results in a flow curvature which increases the differential head produced and the sudden reduction in cross-sectional area at the upstream pressure tapping gives a local pressure increase which also augments the pressure differences.

A significant reduction in pressure loss has been achieved by the GEC Elliot-Nathan flow tube (38), Figure 19, for which the pressure loss is only about 1.5% of the differential pressure, compared with 14% and 50% for the equivalent venturi or orifice respectively.

4.2.3   Limitations of differential pressure flowmeters

A serious disadvantage of these devices is their small range ability (turndown) in comparison with other flow meters. Because of the square-law relationship between flow rate and differential pressure, a 3:1 flow range is about the most which can conveniently be measured without changing the manometers or pressure transducers. The head loss of the meter can also be a problem.

Manometers are most commonly used to measure the differential pressure and these have their own limitations. In particular, great care must be taken to ensure that the leads to the manometer are free from air bubbles. Frequent 'bleeding' of the leads to eliminate bubbles is essential. Note also that the quantity 'H' in equation 1 (section 4.2.1) must be expressed in metres (or feet) of the flowing fluid. If a U-tube manometer is used to measure the differential pressure, the effective density of the manometer liquid is mercury density minus water density, or water density minus compressed air density, depending on which type of manometer is used.

4.3   Other types of flow meter

The choice of flow meter, other than a differential pressure device, is usually made because of a requirement to have low head loss, a wider range ability or, occasionally, for simplicity in obtaining an electrical output as a continuous indication of flow rate.

4.3.1   Electromagnetic flow meters

Electromagnetic flow meters are becoming more popular because of their minimal head loss, because of their large range (typically 30:1) and because they are claimed to be less sensitive to pipe work installation effects, although they become increasingly more expensive than differential pressure meters as the pipe diameter increases.

Papers on electromagnetic flow meters have been reported by Shercliff (39), Balls and Brown (40), Baker (41), Scott (42) and Taylor (43).

The principle of an electromagnetic flow meter is that an electrically conductive liquid flowing through a magnetic field generates an electrical current the magnitude of which is proportional to the velocity of the liquid. Flow meters employing this principle are now well established, but frequent checking of the calibration is required if the highest accuracy is to be maintained.

4.3.2   Turbine flowmeters

In this type of flow meter, a free-spinning rotor is mounted axially in the pipe and a magnetic pick-up is used to measure the speed of rotation, which is practically proportional to flow rate, except at very low flows (44, 45). Turbine meters have a range of about 10:1 and have a much lower head loss than differential pressure types, although higher than electromagnetic flow meters. Their main attribute is very good short term repeatability, but if used in abrasive or dirty fluids, excessive bearing wear can occur and the calibration coefficient can change markedly. They are relatively insensitive to any asymmetry in the flow, but are affected if there is the slightest amount of swirl present.

A typical turbine meter is shown schematically in Figure 20.

4.3.3   Ultrasonic flowmeters

Only with the development of transducers, has the principle of the ultrasonic meter become attractive. Whilst a major advantage is that there is virtually no resistance to the flow, perhaps the most important is that the cost for really large pipes (0.5 m diameter and above) is little different from that for smaller pipes and indeed, the accuracy of these devices deteriorates as the pipe size diminishes. Other advantages are that the response is virtually independent of viscosity and that these instruments are very durable, having no moving parts.

There are two main principles on which these flow meters may work: the 'time of flight' principle or the Doppler effect.

For the former, one beam of ultrasound is sent at an angle to the flow towards a receiver, so that the velocity of the beam is increased if the direction of the beam is downstream. A second beam, at an equal angle to the flow, but directed upstream, has its velocity diminished by the component of the flow velocity along the beam (Figure 21). It is then possible to show that the difference in the times of flight of the two beams, $\triangle t$, is given by

$$\triangle t = \frac{2\ VD}{C^2\ \tan\ \theta}$$

where   V is the velocity of the liquid,
               D is the pipe diameter,
               C is the speed of the ultrasound beams in the still fluid, and
               θ is the angle the beams make to the direction of flow.

This is the simplest description of this approach, but refinements exist such as using only one pair of transducers, each of which transmits and receives a pulse alternately, or using four such pairs across chords of the pipe, which do not pass through the pipe centre line and averaging the answer to give a mean pipe velocity.

The second approach, using the Doppler effect, relies on a single beam being reflected from particles moving with the flow, and the frequency with which these reflected signals are received is then a function of the frequency of the transmitted beam, the velocity of the fluid and the speed of the ultrasound. This is, however, less accurate than the time of flight method, which is more commonly used in commercial instruments.

A typical range for ultrasonic flow meters is 5:1 for single path devices or 10:1 for multiple path types.

4.3.4 Vortex flowmeters

Vortex meters make use of the principle that vortices are shed alternatively from opposite sides of a bluff body introduced into a flowing fluid, giving rise to a von Karmen vortex street (46). The frequency with which these vortices are shed, f, is given by

$$f = \frac{SV}{d}$$

where   V is the velocity of the fluid,
               d is the transverse dimension of the bluff body, and
               S is the 'Strouhal number'.

S is virtually constant for a wide range of Reynolds numbers.

In practice, the bluff body extends across the diameter of a pipe and some typical examples of the shapes used are rectangular, triangular and 'T' shaped, with the cross-piece of the 'T' facing the flow. A number of methods of detecting the frequency of the vortices can be used.

Vortex meters are again relatively new, but successful designs have the advantages of offering little obstruction to the flow, having an inherently digital output, and having a linear performance over wide ranges (about 15:1).

One of the main disadvantages for pump testing purposes is that they are not commonly made in large sizes, ie greater than about 0.2 m.

4.4 Indirect methods

4.4.1 Velocity integration techniques

Several indirect methods of measuring flow rate can be used, the most common of which is the velocity integration technique, where the local velocity is measured at a number of positions in a plane normal to the flow and a graphical or numerical integration method used to calculate the mean velocity in the pipe.

The traditional instrument used is the pitot-static tube, and full details are available (47). For very large pipes (greater than about 1.5 m in diameter) current meters can be used (48).

A useful method of obtaining the various local velocity measurements is to use a pitot cylinder which has a number of tappings for measuring the total pressure (Figure 22) in conjunction with a set of wall tappings about 1 diameter upstream of the cylinder for the measurement of static pressure. In this way, the various local velocity pressures can be fed into a manometer bank. Each tapping must have its own lead to an individual manometer limb.

Measurements should be made along at least two diameters (perpendicular to each other) and preferably three (equally spaced around the pipe), with a minimum of three measurements per radius; where possible, there should be five measurements per radius.

Graphical methods of determining the mean velocity are time-consuming and require experienced staff to achieve the highest accuracy. For circular ducts, the best methods are the log-linear (49), the log Tchebychev (48, 50) and the method of cubics (48, 50, 51).

When only an approximate indication of flow rate is required, the 'three-quarter radius' pitot tube (52) may be used. The velocity at a distance of three-quarters of the radius from the pipe centre line is approximately equal to the mean velocity in the pipe for fully developed turbulent flow and so a single pitot tube or current meter placed at that position will give a reasonable indication of the mean velocity.

The use of velocity integration techniques is most common where there are very large pipes or where only an occasional measurement of flow rate is required, such as with acceptance tests *in-situ*, or where the nature of the velocity distribution is to be checked. They are cheap from the point of view of equipment, but expensive in manpower.

4.4.2 Tracer methods

The essence of these methods is to inject a small amount of concentrated substance into the flow and deduce the flow rate, either from the rate at which the substance is swept along with the main flow or from the extent to which it is diluted. The tracer may be a chemical, a dye or a radioactive isotope.

4.4.2.1 Constant rate injection method

In the constant rate injection method, a tracer of concentration C_1 is injected with a flow rate q into the main flow which has an unknown flow rate Q and a tracer background concentration of C_0. Then

$$Q = q \left(\frac{C_1 - C_2}{C_2 - C_0} \right)$$

where C_2 is the concentration of the tracer at the sampling station.

This method requires thorough mixing of the tracer before the sampling station is reached, so it is common to inject and sample upstream and downstream of a pump respectively. This in itself is the greatest advantage of constant rate injection methods: they do not require straight lengths of pipe as do most other methods. High accuracy (better than 1%) can be achieved with this method (53, 54).

4.4.2.2 Integration method

The integration (or sudden injection or gulp) method consists of injecting a known quantity of tracer over a short time and obtaining a concentration-time distribution at a downstream sampling position where thorough mixing has taken place. The flow rate, Q, is then given by

$$Q = \frac{vC_1}{t(C_2 - C_0)}$$

where v is the volume of the injected tracer,
C_2 is the mean concentration of the tracer at the sampling station over a time t, and
t is the period over which the concentration time distribution is obtained.

A third method, the transit time method, measures the time of transit of a pulse of tracer between two sampling stations to give the mean velocity in the pipe. This method differs from the other two in that a long straight length of pipe is required, since the tracer must not become dispersed in the main flow. It does, however, have the advantage that the concentration of the tracer does not have to be measured.

All tracer methods are similar in that they do not provide a continuous measurement of flow rate. They are, like velocity integration techniques, most commonly used in large pipes for 'one-off' investigations where the cost of the exercise will be less than that for the provision of a permanent flow meter. The constant rate injection and gulp methods are particularly useful where complicated pipe work geometry makes conventional flow metering difficult.

4.5   Absolute methods

Absolute methods collect the flowing water for a measured time interval and either the volume or the weight of the collected water is determined. Such methods are inherently more accurate than the use of flow meters or indirect methods, but are of course practicable only when used in a permanent test installation. Even then, the cost is such that they are justified only if the very highest accuracy (better than 0.5%) is necessary.

The system most commonly used employs a mechanical diverter to deflect the flowing stream into a weighing tank or a volumetric measuring tank for a period, the time of diversion being indicated by an electronic timer triggered by the diverter movement. Advice on the design and operation of such systems has been given by Spenser (55).

4.6   Error sources and accuracy

All flow meters have their own sources of error, but one common to almost all is the deviation from straightness in the upstream pipework. The effects of bends, valves etc are important and it is vitally important to make sure that no swirl exists at the flow meter inlet, since this can cause errors of as much as ±20% in some flow meters. A review of the problems which can arise with both asymmetry and swirl is given by Kinghorn (56). As a general rule, any differential pressure flow meter should have as small an area ratio as possible in order to minimise the effects of flow disturbances, although the acceptable head loss restricts the area ratio which can be used.

Cavitation in the meter should be avoided. When considering this, it should be borne in mind that the pressure inside a flow meter is almost always lower than downstream of it, so it is not always sufficient to use a pressure gauge a few pipe diameters from the flow meter to control cavitation.

The accuracy attainable is governed by a number of factors. If more accurate measurement is required then individual calibration of the flow meter by an absolute method is necessary, in which case an uncertainty of 0.5% should be achievable. It is, however, essential to ensure that the conditions under which the flow meter is used are identical to those under which it was calibrated.

5 Groundwater flow and load determination

5.1 Introduction

Determination of the load of substance contained in underground water is dependent on several inter-related variables. In the simplest case, the water is at rest, the substance is uniformly distributed throughout the water and the aquifer is saturated. In such a case determination of the load depends on measuring the substance concentration in the ground water and making an estimate of the amount of water contained in the aquifer, which latter amount is dependent on the porosity of that aquifer, which may not be uniform. One way of ascertaining the amount of water in an aquifer, provided that undamaged cores are available which have not been affected by the drilling necessary to obtain them, is to carry out moisture content determinations (loss to constant weight on drying at 105°C, see ref. (57)) on a selection of samples. Section 5.2 discusses the factors which affect the distribution of solutes in groundwater. These are the degree of saturation of the ground, the nature of the pores and cavities available in the ground, how they interconnect and the consequent effect on fluid flow, diffusion processes in the liquid in the pores, and solid liquid interactions.

5.2 Effects causing variations in saturation of the aquifer

When water falls onto a surface it may be absorbed or run off depending on the nature and state of that surface. If the rate at which the water falls onto the surface is greater than the rate at which it is absorbed into or penetrates that surface, then the surplus will run off. For some soils, the initial rapid absorption may produce a surface layer which has a much lower rate of steady absorption.

The water which passes into the ground can be absorbed into the minerals making up the ground, or displace the air and vapour trapped in the pores and voids between and in the mineral grains. If not bound to the mineral surface or lattice or held in the pores by surface tension effects, the water will slowly percolate downwards until it reaches an impermeable stratum. Thereafter, it will either flow along that stratum or fill up the aquifer from the bottom, or both depending on the shape of the aquifer.

The above processes produce two distinct zones in the aquifer; the lower one where the aquifer is saturated with water, usually called the Saturated Zone, and where water contained in this zone is sometimes called Phreatic water. Above this is a zone where the aquifer is not yet fully saturated and water is still descending slowly displacing air and vapour. This is usually called the Unsaturated Zone and water in this region is sometimes called Vadose water.

The level at which the aquifer becomes saturated is known as the Water Table. The saturated and unsaturated zones are said to be below and above the water table respectively. Above the water table, general water movement is downwards but with a tendency to spread out sideways to some extent, dependent on the way the mineral grains are arranged in the aquifer. What happens below the water table is dependent on the boundaries of the aquifer. Water will flow along the aquifer under its own hydraulic head pressure until it either emerges as a spring at the surface of the ground or in the bed of the sea or a lake or river, or alternatively it is contained by the aquifer walls. Below ground, lateral flow can be stopped by the porous rock ending or by a rise in the floor of the aquifer creating a natural basin. Seasonal rise and fall of the water table level with rainfall can cause intermittent appearances of streams in normally dry valleys through porous strata. Such streams are known as Winterbournes. A series of springs may appear where impermeable strata underlying a large aquifer outcrop at the surface. Such a boundary is sometimes called a spring line. Sometimes strata may be folded into U-shapes (synclines) or inverted U-shapes (anticlines). If water entering a porous stratum flows into such a fold with impermeable strata both above and below, the situation resembles flow in a packed pipe, and syphons and artesian basins may develop with quite high hydrostatic pressures forcing water upwards at a considerable distance from where it first fell. Such journeys may take a very long time if the aquifer is big and if its pores are narrow and tortuous.

The whole process is complicated by the formation of fissures and voids due to solution or washing away of mineral grains and sometimes by fracturing of the rocks. The extreme examples are caves and underground rivers. Although the above phenomena are chiefly associated with sedimentary rocks, some volcanic rocks such as tuffs can have the same porous properties.

Aquifers are filled either by rain falling on to porous ground or by insoaking of water from rivers, streams and lakes through their beds. Rivers and streams may disappear into fissures in the ground, but these usually interconnect to form underground systems, If porous strata are exposed in the sea bed, the water soaking in may be saline. Rivers often lay down beds of river gravel and porous sediments which form a shallow aquifer in which, for practical purposes, the river level controls the water table level. There is evidence that interchange of water between the river itself and such water in the banks is continually occurring. Aquifers are known in which stored water has since been sealed by the deposition of impermeable strata over the top. Without some form of recharge, such fossil water is subject to exhaustion in the same way as mineable minerals.

During severe winters and in areas where ground temperatures at depth are sub-zero (permafrost), frozen water in an otherwise porous rock can render it impermeable.

The number and size of pores per unit volume in a rock and the degree of convolution in such pores varies with the constituents of the rock and its past history. Not all pores form continuous passages. Usually, these voids are formed by gaps between compacted grains or shells or where molten liquid has drained away from crystals. The overall phenomena, called porosity and tortuosity, considerably affect the flow of liquids through a rock. For more information, see refs 58 and 59. With rocks that have been under pressure due to depth these voids may be squeezed smaller unless solution or cracking also occurs.

5.3   Equations governing flow through porous strata

Two sets of phenomena govern the flow of a solute through porous strata, the actual flow of the water itself and the diffusion of the solute across that water. These will be discussed in turn.

The flow of a fluid, in this instance water, but also air displaced by the water through a capillary, is given by the Darcy equation, which in its simplest form is:-

$$V = \frac{Q}{A} = k \frac{\Delta p}{\mu l}$$

where   V is the apparent velocity in cms^{-1},
Q is the discharge in cm^3s^{-1},
A is the cross-sectional area in cm^2,
k is the permeability, expressed as an area in cm^2,
μ is the viscosity in $gcm^{-1}s^{-1}$,
l is the distance of flow in cm,
and Δp is the pressure drop in a distance of 1 cm in $dynescm^{-2}$.

For a perfectly uniform bore cylindrical capillary, this becomes the viscous flow equation:-

$$Q = \frac{\pi r^4 \Delta p}{8\mu l}$$

Where the terms are as above and r is the capillary radius.

In the Darcy equation, the permeability factor encompasses both the permeability factor and tortuosity effects. It is possible to determine the porosity experimentally by taking a suitably shaped section of the stratum, fitting it into a suitable holder and forcing water through it under a known pressure drop. Q, A, p, μ and l are measured or known. Ideally, to convert for direction effects, flows should be measured through samples in three directions at right angles relative to the original sample position in the stratum. Reproducibility is rarely better than ± 50%, the chief sources of error being the difficulty of making water-tight joints surrounding the sample to prevent bypassing and changes in porosity due to the cutting out and preparation of the sample for the test. Usually, experimental values on laboratory specimens give higher porosities than are subsequently found in the stratum, except when major fissures occur in the aquifer.

Porosity is usually expressed in units of Darcy. A porosity of one Darcy allows $1\ cm^3$ of a liquid, of viscosity 1 centipoise, to flow through a 1 cm thick sample, of 1 cm cross-section, in 1 second. The viscosity of water is almost 1 centipoise at 20°C.

Diffusion of a solute through a liquid is governed by the general Kinetic Diffusion equation:-

$$PV = KT$$

where　P is the osmotic pressure difference between the two solutions,
　　　　V is the volume, in litres, containing one gram mole of the solute,
　　　　T is the absolute temperature in degrees Kelvin (degrees Centigrade + 273) and
　　　　K is a factor to allow for differences in molecular shape, and size attraction between molecules of solute and water, and also for ionisation.

For very dilute solutions of simple hydrocarbon gases such as methane, K is reported to have almost the same value as R, the Gas Law Constant. Large variations occur with both organic solutes, and inorganic ions and complexes. An iterative approach using differential equations to take account of the existence of concentration gradients is:

$$\frac{dc}{dt} = D\,\frac{d^2c}{dl^2}$$

for both electrolytes and non-electrolytes, or

$$\frac{dc}{dt} = D\,\frac{d^2c}{dl^2} \cdot \frac{RT}{F^2} \cdot \frac{(n_1 + n_2)\,(\lambda_1^0 + \lambda_2^0)}{n_1 Z_1 \lambda_1^0}$$

for an ion in a strong electrolyte

where　c is concentration in moles per litre,
　　　　t is time in seconds,
　　　　l is the distance diffused in cm,
　　　　D is the diffusion coefficient in cm^2s^{-1},
　　　　R is the Gas Law Constant,
　　　　T is the absolute temperature in degrees Kelvin,
　　　　n_1 and n_2 are the number of cations and anions (or vice versa) formed from the compound under study,
　　　　λ_1^0, and λ_2^0 are the respective equivalent ionic conductivities at infinite dilution for the ions formed,
　　　　F is Faraday's constant,
　　　　and Z_1 is the ionic charge on the ion under study (without sign).

Rock strata permeability is usually determined by pumping tests on partially lined bore holes drilled from the surface, measurements being made either at a constant head or over a fixed change of head.

For more complex treatments including combinations of both the above processes, see ref. 60.

5.4　Additional complications

Three additional factors can affect the underground transport of substances. These are multi-phase systems, solid-liquid interactions and turbulence.

In the unsaturated layer, there are always two phases in the voids, water and gas or vapour (usually air). It is also possible for pores to be blocked even when below the water table. Likewise, if the cap rock in an anticline is impervious to gas, it is possible for gas to be trapped there and, like blocking a syphon, it prevents liquid from flowing further along an aquifer.

Immiscible or only partially soluble liquids, such as hydrocarbons, will seek their own level relative to the groundwater and displace the water accordingly (61). Relatively saturated solutions may have a similar effect. Examples are known where fresh water rafts over the top of brines, sea water and highly alkaline waters due to a sill or dyke at the point of ingress.

Ion exchange can occur with a variety of minerals, especially clays, though there are limitations due to ionic size. Thus, some silicate lattice minerals will leach or exchange sodium ions but not potassium ions, as the latter cannot pass out of the silicate cages.

Absorption is also well known. Some clays such as bentonite and kaolinite can absorb considerable quantities of water and other liquids, sometimes with considerable lattice expansion and consequent swelling.

Precipitation and leaching are also important, but are very dependent on the form in which the substance is complexed in the water. Thus, calcium sulphate (gypsum) will almost always remove lead from a water, and hydroxy-apatite will remove fluoride, but while calcite (common calcium carbonate) will remove copper coordinated by water or chloride, it has no reaction at all with soluble copper carbonate complexes. The same is true for many transition metals.

Turbulent flow changes the rate of flow and improves mixing. However, it only occurs when the voids are large enough, as in fissures and caves.

5.5   Practical measurements

5.5.1   Well sampling

If a well penetrates more than one aquifer or if the water in an aquifer is layered, the water in a well may not be homogeneous and may flow at different rates at different levels. This information can be very useful, especially if, during contamination studies, water seeping in the unsaturated zone is collected. There are several methods for obtaining a sample from a specific depth in a borehole. These are by lowering a bottle to a pre-arranged depth and opening it, by lowering a tube through which water flows until a messenger weight or control line is used to activate spring located stoppers at the top and bottom of the tube, by sealing the bore with plugs (usually removable) activated from the surface and pumping out the water in between, or by pumping up samples from known depths either by dip tubes or by some other container device. Several, but not all of these devices are illustrated in Figures 5 and 10 of reference 7. For more details on underground water sampling, see the first part of this booklet (62).

5.5.2   Tracing water flows

Although the confines of an aquifer may appear to be obvious, and springs and streams may be evident, the actual direction and source of water underground may not always as expected. Quite thin bands of a different rock can change flow patterns and even replenish wells in areas seemingly with no aquifer. Faults and dykes can also cause unforeseen discontinuities. It is sometimes necessary to trace underground waters. This is usually done by adding an indicator substance capable of easy detection. Radioisotopes are sometimes used (58), but only when no risk is involved. Dyes such as fluorescein have also been used, but much material may be needed. Other tracers are stable isotopes such as nitrogen-15 and uncommon readily detectable elements such as lithium (63,64) iodine or iodide, sulphur hexafluoride or where polluted water or sewage are involved, microbes and bacteriophages. Infra red photography, revealing temperature differences, and soil conductivity can sometimes be used. This is especially useful for detecting flows into open water, such as rivers, lakes or the sea. Because of solution of minerals, trace element comparison is of more use for surface rivers. If underground water originating from a suspected burst in a treated water supply or sewer carrying treated water has to be identified, comparisons of the trihalomethane ratios between known and suspect samples can be made (65).

5.5.3   Flow measurement

Actual measurements of flow are very difficult to make and are expensive. The most direct method is to note the rate of movement of a known contaminant (or added marker) along a series of boreholes drilled along the suspected lines of flow. The direction can be difficult to judge and sideways diffusion can complicate detection of the marker. Pumping tests are usually used instead.

5.5.4   Pumping tests

For information on these see ref 66.

5.5.5 Down-well inspection

If an underwater camera is lowered down a borehole (preferably attached to a well logging depth measuring cable) it is sometimes possible to observe and estimate underwater flows by their turbulence, suspended solids content, or colour. This is especially useful when water is leaking down the outside of a well lining and entering at the bottom of the lining, a screen, or at a break in the lining.

5.5.6 Additional bibliography

For further details see refs 67–72.

6 Sediment transport

6.1 Definitions

(Note: ISO Standard 6107 in numerous parts, defines many of these terms.

6.1.1 Introduction

Sediment may be transported in an open channel in different ways depending on the size and density of the material and the transporting ability of the water. Figure 23 illustrates the methods of transport.

6.1.2 General definitions

6.1.2.1 Sediment

Those solid particles transported by liquid flow and derived from erosion in the catchment or erosion of the boundaries of the channel.

6.1.2.2 Bed material

That material found in the bed which is of such particle size as to be affected by water borne transport, including spates.

6.1.2.3 Load

The general term describing the rate at which some substance is transported by a liquid, normally water, past a given point. The substances constituting the load can be insoluble (sediment load) or in solution (solute load).

6.1.2.4 Sediment transport

The movement of solids by a flowing liquid either as suspended load or bed load.

6.1.2.5 Sediment concentration

The ratio of the mass or volume of the dry sediment in a mixture of water and sediment in transport, to the total mass or volume of the suspension.

6.1.3 Particular definitions

See also Figure 23.

6.1.3.1 Total load

The total amount of sediment transported by the flowing water. It is the sum of the bed material load and the wash load, and is expressed as mass or volume per unit time.

6.1.3.2 Wash load

That part of the suspended load which is composed of particle sizes smaller than those found in appreciable quantities in the bed material. It is in near permanent suspension and is transported through the channel without deposition unless the flow ceases. The discharge of a wash load through a reach depends only on the rate with which these particles become available in the catchment and not on the transport capacity of flow. It is generally expressed as mass or volume per unit of time.

6.1.3.3 Bed load

The sediment moving in almost continuous contact with the bed either by rolling, sliding or hopping. It is usually expressed as mass or volume per unit of time.

6.1.3.4 Suspended load

That part of the total sediment transported which is maintained in suspension by turbulence of the flowing water for considerable periods of time without contact with the stream bed. It includes the wash load and the suspended bed material load, and moves at practically the same velocity as that of the flowing water. It is generally expressed as mass or volume per unit of time.

6.1.3.5 Bed material load

That part of the total sediment transported which consists of the bed material and whose rate of movement is governed by the transporting capacity of the channel. It may be carried in suspension as suspended bed material load or in almost continuous contact with the bed as bed load.

6.1.3.6 Suspended bed material load

That part of the bed material load which is transported in suspension by the flowing water for considerable periods without contact with the stream bed. It is generally expressed as mass or volume per unit of time.

6.2 Sediment surveys

6.2.1 Purpose

Sediment surveys may be made to establish one or more of the following:

i. the bed load;

ii. the suspended bed material load;

iii. the wash load;

iv. the grading of the bed material;

v. the grading of the suspended material; and

vi. other physical and chemical characteristics of the bed and suspended materials.

6.2.2 Stages in determination

There are usually 3 stages in a sediment survey;

i. field observations and collection of samples;

ii. laboratory analyses; and

iii. computations and processing of field and laboratory measurements.

6.2.3 Field measurements

The procedure and equipment for field measurements will vary depending on the data required. Estimates of sediment load are usually made indirectly and require the measurement of depth and speed of liquid flow, and sediment concentration. Samples extracted to establish the grading or other physical and chemical characteristics of the sediment can be easy to take, and the effect of the sampling equipment on the distribution of the sediment throughout the flow is usually minimal. Care should be taken to ensure representative sampling of suspended sediment and water.

The field measurements may, therefore, be grouped in the following categories, the procedures and equipment being different in each case.

i.   Suspended sediment sampling to determine the grading or other physical and chemical characteristics of the sediment.

ii. Suspended sediment sampling to determine the sediment concentration, and hence the sediment transport rate.

iii. Bed sampling to determine the grading or other physical and chemical characteristics of the sediment. This can be split into two categories:
     a. fine-grained material (clay, silt, and sand); and
     b. coarse-grained material (gravel and boulders).

iv. Bed sampling to determine the sediment transport rate.

v.   Bank sampling to determine the grading or other physical and chemical characteristics.

6.2.4 Accuracy

The concentration of suspended sediment usually varies across a channel, in elevation above the bed, and with time. The concentration of bed load also varies across the channel and with time.

Due to the spatial and temporal variations in sediment concentration, surveys must be carefully planned to ensure the correct choice of

i.   sampling site,

ii. sampling programme (in time),

iii. sampling pattern (in time),

iv. sampling and handling procedures, and

v.   data analyses.

These variations also affect the degree of accuracy with which the sediment load may be determined. Whereas the uncertainty of measurement of liquid flow normally ranges between 2% and 10% depending on the method, equipment and observers, the uncertainty of suspended load measurements is often of the order of 100%. Bed load measurements are more difficult to make and are even less reliable.

The effect of time of sampling on the accuracy of sediment load measurements in rivers is reported in ref 73. The distribution of suspended solids with particle size in flow through a pipe is reported in ref 74. Results from channel flow would be somewhat similar.

6.3   Suspended sediment measurements

6.3.1   Introduction

In classifying methods of estimating the suspended sediment load it is important to recall the difference between sediment concentration and load (see Section 6.1).

The suspended sediment load may be estimated in two ways.

i.   Concentration Velocity Method. The concentration of the suspended sediment and the velocity of the liquid flow are measured independently. The product of these two values is the suspended sediment load at a point. By integration in width and depth, the total suspended sediment load over the channel is obtained.

ii. Computational Method. The grading and specific gravity of the bed material, and the velocity of the flowing water are measured. A suitable sediment transport formula is then used to calculate the suspended bed material load but not the wash load.

6.3.2 Suspended sediment samplers

There are many different instruments available for the measurement of the concentration of suspended sediment (suspended bed material load plus wash load).

6.3.2.1 Direct measuring instruments

These may be classified under:

i.   Radiation, obscuration and scattering.
       a. Visible light.
       b. Infra-red or ultra violet.
       c. Gamma, or X-rays.

ii.   Differential pressure.

iii.   Electrical.

iv.   Acoustic or ultrasonic.

Such instruments are usually calibrated in advance to display the concentration of suspended sediment. If, however, the type of sediment or the quality of the water change, it may be necessary to re-calibrate the instrument. Instruments are available for use in dredging where sediment concentrations are very high, which measure the liquid density and discharge, and hence a mass rate of flow.

Optical measuring instruments are best suited to continuous monitoring of suspended load where it is not necessary to differentiate between wash load and suspended bed material load. They are useful where the suspended load is predominantly wash load and measurements at one point in a channel are sufficient to estimate the suspended load. They may also be used where a measure of concentration only is required.

6.3.2.2 Indirect measuring instruments

There are many different types of suspended sediment sampler available. All of them may be used to obtain a sample for grading, but not all are suitable for determining the sediment concentration and hence the suspended load. They may be broadly grouped under three headings:

i.   instantaneous point samplers;

ii.   time integrating point samplers, (point integrating samplers); and

iii.   depth integrating samplers.

The choice of the sampler is dependent on the information required, the skill of the operator, the ancillary sampling facilities available, and the properties of the river.

Instantaneous point samplers are usually the least accurate but the simplest to use, and may be used by unskilled observers with little loss of accuracy. They range from a simple bottle to carefully designed instruments.

Depth integrating samplers are cheaper than point integrating samplers, but are less accurate and more difficult to use. They are designed to be lowered to the bed of the channel and raised to the surface with the minimum of disturbance to the flow patterns.

6.3.3 Ancillary equipment

The ancillary equipment required for the operation of a sampler depends to some extent on the size of the channel, speed and depth of flow, and the sampling procedure. It may include:

i.   bridge over the channel;

ii.   cable way across the channel;

iii.   suitable boat;

iv.   temporary bridge of planks over narrow channels; and

v.   winch and suspension equipment.

6.3.4   Location of samplers

When a channel conveys a uniformly distributed wash load of very fine material, the concentration need only be measured near the surface and near the bank. More observations are desirable to improve the accuracy. These simple measurements will be adequate to estimate the average sediment concentration, or in conjunction with a measure of the discharge, to estimate the suspended sediment load.

When the suspended load is composed of both wash load and suspended bed material load, then the latter will vary across the channel and over the depth. Sampling at one or two points will therefore be inadequate. Samples must be taken at several verticals spaced across the channel, and at not less than two points on each vertical. The velocity must also be measured at these points in order to calculate the suspended sediment load.

6.3.5   Bibliography

See Table 5 for the references associated with the particular topic identified.

6.4   Bed material measurements

6.4.1   Introduction

The equipment and techniques needed to obtain a sample of bed material for grading are different from those required to collect a sample for determining the bed load.

6.4.2   Samplers for grading

It is very important that the type of sampler used in extracting a sample of bed material to determine the grading is suitable for the type of material to be sampled. In particular, to sample soft silts or clay from the bed surface, it is important that

i.   the sampler does not disturb the bed unduly on contact, and

ii.   the soft, loosely consolidated material is retained in the sampler and not washed out as it is raised.

Available equipment may be classified under three headings

i.   grab;

ii.   sampling tube; and

iii.   scoop or drag bucket.

The grab and the scoop or drag bucket are best suited for sampling sands and fine gravels. The sampling tube, with additional attachments to prevent loss of material on extraction, may be used for sands, silts and clays.

Samples of gravels and cobbles for grading may be collected by picking up individual stones according to a pre-determined pattern to avoid a subjective selection of stones.

Samples of both fine and coarse materials may also be obtained by excavation. Usually about 1 kg of material is sufficient, but when the material is very coarse, a larger quantity may have to be removed.

6.4.3   Samplers for bed load

There is no satisfactory practical method of measuring bed load, but the following methods may be useful:-

i.   Direct measurements:
        a. bed load samplers;
        b. sediment traps;

c. accretion in reservoirs

d. accretion upstream of obstructions;

e. turbulence flume;

f. radioactive tracer techniques;

g. fluorescent tracer techniques;

h. movement of dunes;

i. acoustic meters;

j. collision meters.

ii. Indirect methods:

a. computations using sediment transport theories;

b. physical hydraulic models.

Bed load samplers are of three basic types:

i.   pan;

ii.   bucket; and

iii. full wall.

The methods are not suited to routine data collection. Handling the sampler and its load presents many problems, and the difficulties increase as bed loads increase and heavier lifting gear becomes necessary.

Sediment traps are sometimes used for specific investigations. They provide a long-term, rather than an instantaneous, rate of sediment transport. The same is also true of measuring rates of accretion in reservoirs and upstream of obstructions.

The turbulence flume converts bed load to suspended load and makes it possible to measure the transport rate using suspended sediment load methods of measurement. It is a method which can rarely be used due to the cost of constructing a flume, and is thus suitable for research purposes only.

Radioactive and fluorescent tracer techniques are suitable for special investigations only, and they would not be used for routine regular surveys. They provide information on the long term movement of sediment but not instantaneous rates. The methods may be classified under three headings depending on injection techniques:

i.   steady dilution;

ii.   time integration; and

iii. spatial integration.

The movement of dunes on the bed of a channel provides a record of long-term movements of sediment, but in rivers where the dunes are moving rapidly, measurements may be made frequently at short intervals. This is really only suitable for the specific rather than the routine survey.

Acoustic meters and collision meters can be used to measure instantaneous rates of transport.

6.4.4 Bibliography

See Table 6 for the references associated with the particular topic identified.

6.5 Sampling bank material

6.5.1 Introduction

The material in a river bank varies widely in size, grading, cohesive strength, specific gravity and shear strength. These variations have been observed between the toe and top of a bank, along a bank, and between one bank and another.

6.5.2 Location of sampling sites

Due to the variations in bank material, the choice of suitable sampling sites and the number of samples to define the physical properties of the bank is difficult. The selection usually depends on the properties considered to be most important for a particular investigation or the particular location in the channel which requires investigation.

6.5.3 Sampling methods and equipment

The methods of sampling bank material may be summarised as follows:

i.   extract a disturbed or an undisturbed sample using a spade or other digging tool;

ii.   extract a disturbed sample using an earth auger, the type depending on the material;

iii.   extract an undisturbed sample using a sampling tube.

6.5.4 Bibliography

See refs 85, 93 and 96.

6.6 Laboratory techniques for grading of soil

6.6.1 Methods

The method chosen to grade a sample of material depends on the size of the material and the amount available for analysis.

The methods of grading may be classified as follows.

i.   Hydraulic.
       a. settling tube (gravity or centrifugal);
       b. pipette;
       c. hydrometer;
       d. elutricator.

ii.   Sieving.
       a. wet;
       b. dry.

iii.   Electrical sensing zone (Coulter principle).

iv.   Measurement of length of the three main axes of the particles.
       a. direct;
       b. image analyser.

Table 7 shows a guide to the choice of the methods of grading depending on grain size.

6.6.2 Description of grading

When a material has been graded by a hydraulic or sieving method, the results are expressed in terms of weight finer than a specified size, either directly or as a percentage of the whole.

When a coarse material has been graded by measuring the length of the three principal axes of the particle, the results may be expressed as a weight or a number of particles finer than a specified size. If a bulk sample is used, grading by weight is recommended. If stones are selected from the surface, grading by particle size is recommended.

6.6.3 Bibliography

For information on grading using hydraulic methods, sieving, or by the measurement of axes, see references 78, 83, 87, 100 and 101.

Table 5

Subject	References
Direct measuring instruments	
(i) Radiation, obscuration and scattering	
(a) visible light	75a, 76–79
(b) infra-red, ultraviolet	78
(c) gamma, X-rays	77–80
(ii) Differential pressure	75e
(iii) Electrical	75f, 77
(iv) Acoustic or ultrasonic	81
Sediment samplers	
(i) Instantaneous	75a, 75d, 77, 82–85
(ii) Point integrating	75a-d, 77, 82–88
(iii) Depth integrating	75a-b, 75d, 77, 82–88
Selection of sampling site	8, 85, 89
Selection of verticals for sampling	8, 75a, 75d, 84, 87
Frequency of sampling	75a
Sampling at points on vertical	75a, 75d, 87, 90
Sampling by integration over a vertical	90
Measurements for computation of suspended load from formulae	91
Computation of sediment load using samplers	
(i) measurements at a point	90, 92
(ii) measurements over a vertical	90, 92
(iii) computation from formulae	91
Sediment transport equations	91
Ancillary equipment for sampling	6
Tracing fine grain sediments	71

Table 6

Subject	References
Samplers for grading bed material	75d, 77, 83, 86, 93
Sampling coarse material for grading	92, 94, 95
Samplers for measuring bed load	75d, 77, 83, 86, 87, 93
Selection of sampling site	8, 85, 86, 89, 90, 93
Measurement of bed load using:	
(i) samplers	75d, 77, 85, 86, 96
(ii) accretion in traps, reservoirs and obstructions	75d, 77, 83, 86, 96
(iii) turbulence flumes	75d, 97
(iv) tracer techniques	77, 98
(v) movement of dunes	86, 87
(vi) acoustic meters	77, 87, 96
(vii) collision meters	(experimental stage only)
Determination of bed load by:	
(i) computation using sediment transport theories	75d, 84, 92
(ii) physical hydraulic models	99
Sediment transport theories	83, 91

Table 7

Grain size (mm)	Description of material	Method
<0.06	Silt and clay	Hydraulic
0.06–50	Sand and gravel	Sieving
>10	Gravel and boulders	Measurement of axes

Figure 1

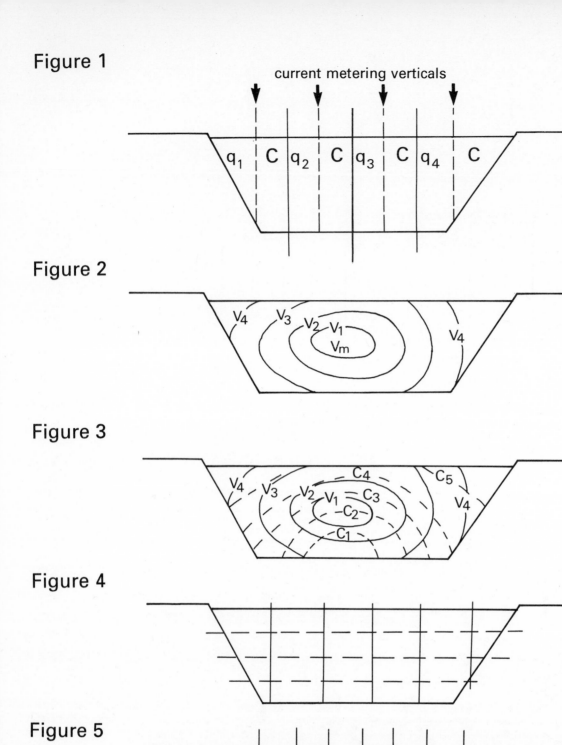

current metering verticals

Figure 2

Figure 3

Figure 4

Figure 5

V_n C_n

current metering verticals

Figure 6

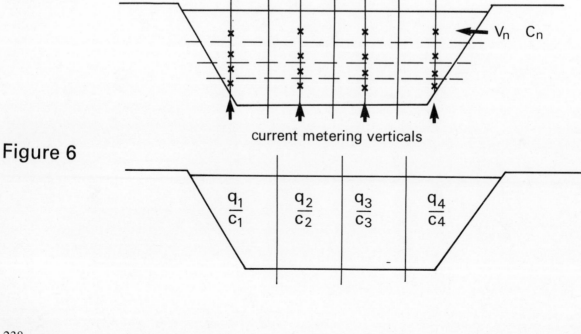

Figure 7

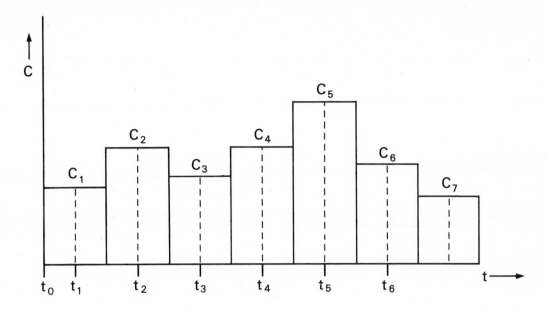

Figure 8

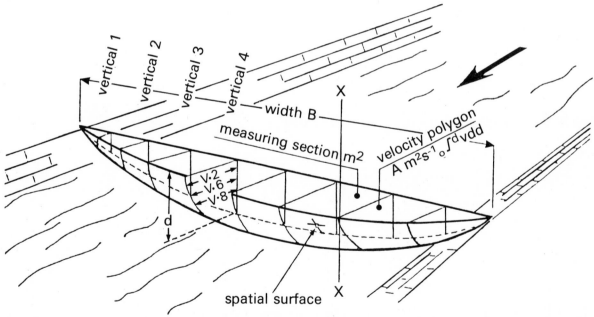

Figure 9

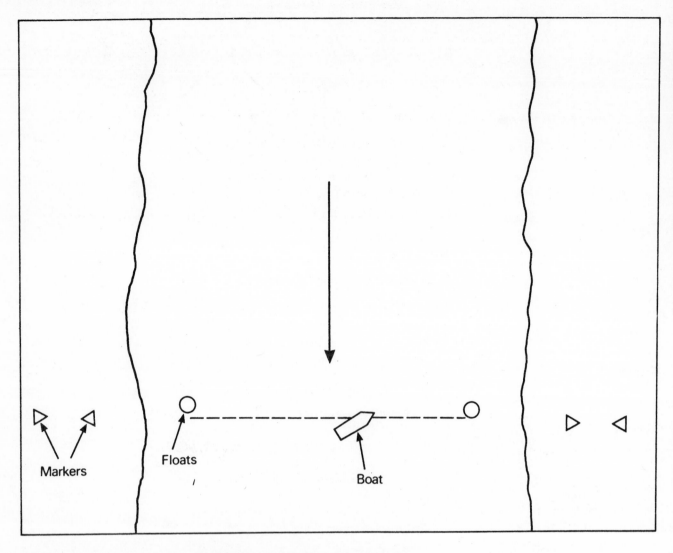

a) sketch of stream with markers

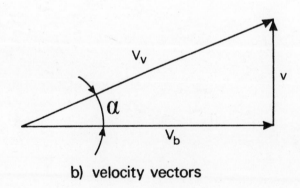

b) velocity vectors

Figure 10

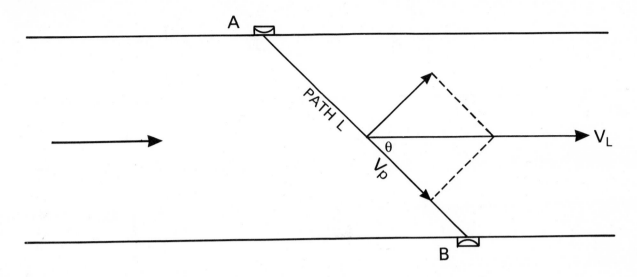

Figure 11

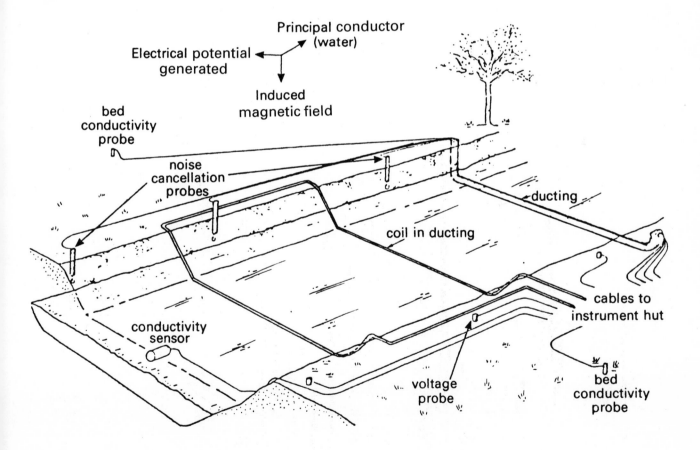

Figure 12   Square-edged orifice plate

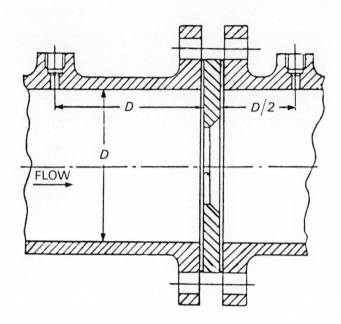

Figure 13   Venturi tube

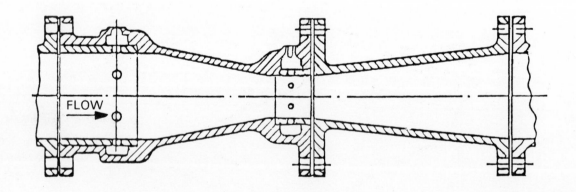

Figure 14   Nozzle type

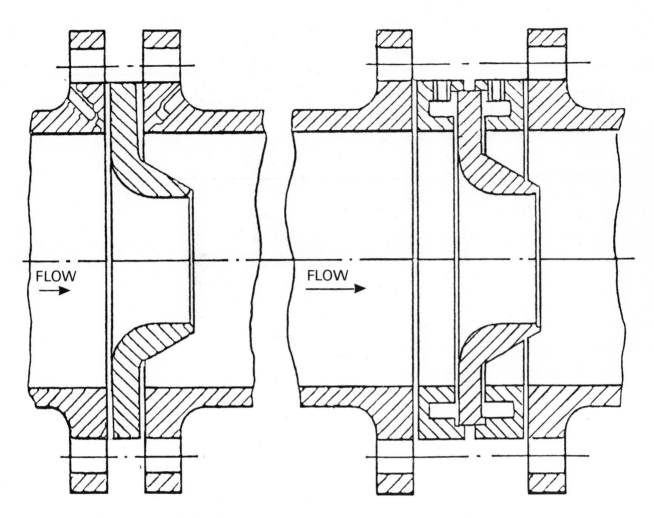

a) mounted between pipe flanges   b) mounted in carrier ring

Figure 15   Tapping

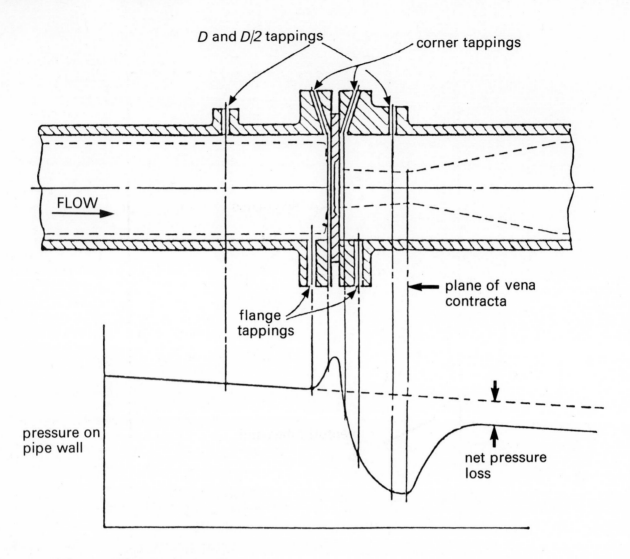

Figure 16   Venturi nozzle

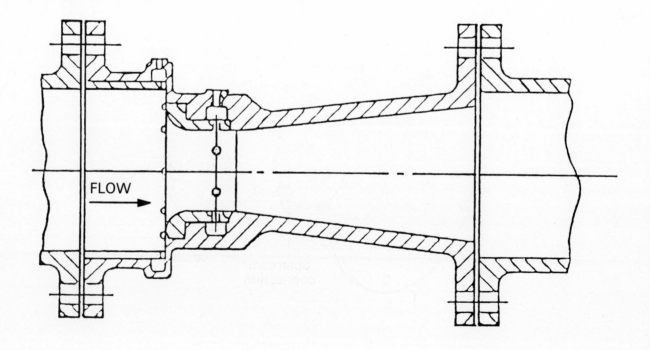

Figure 17

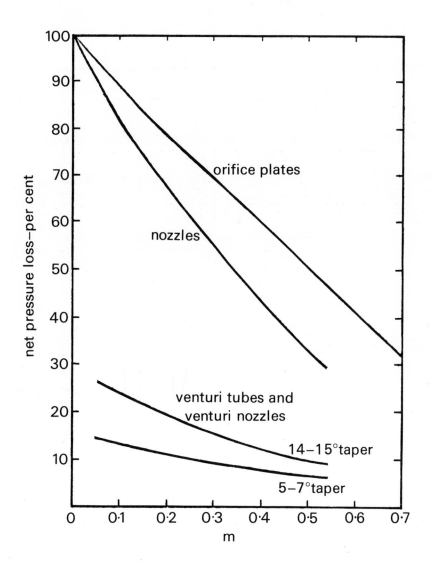

Figure 18   Dall tube

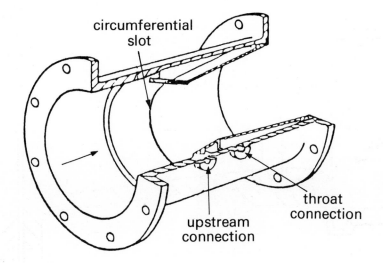

Figure 19   GEC Elliot-Natham flow tube

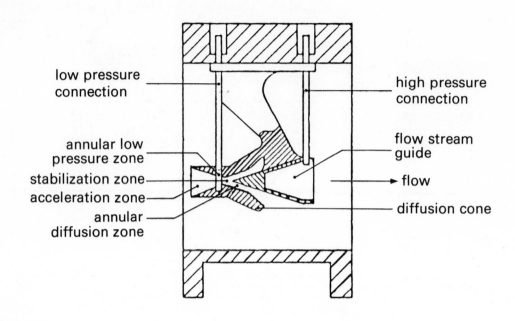

Figure 20   Typical turbine meter

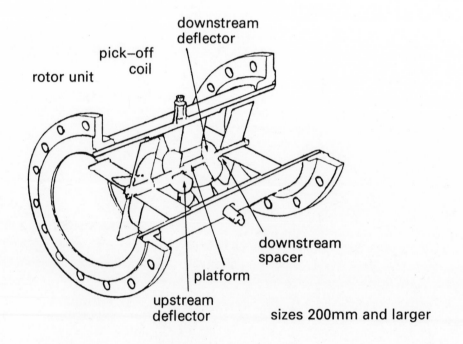

Figure 21

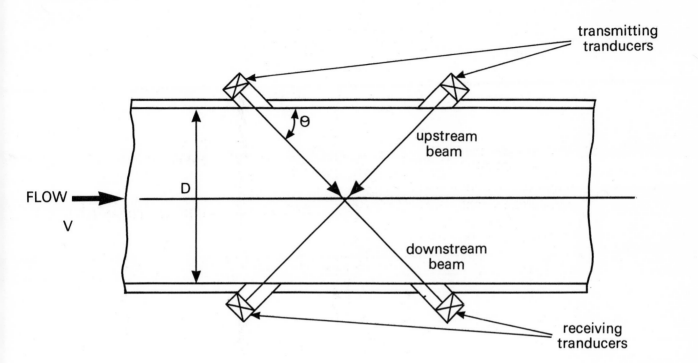

Figure 22   Modified Pitot cylinder

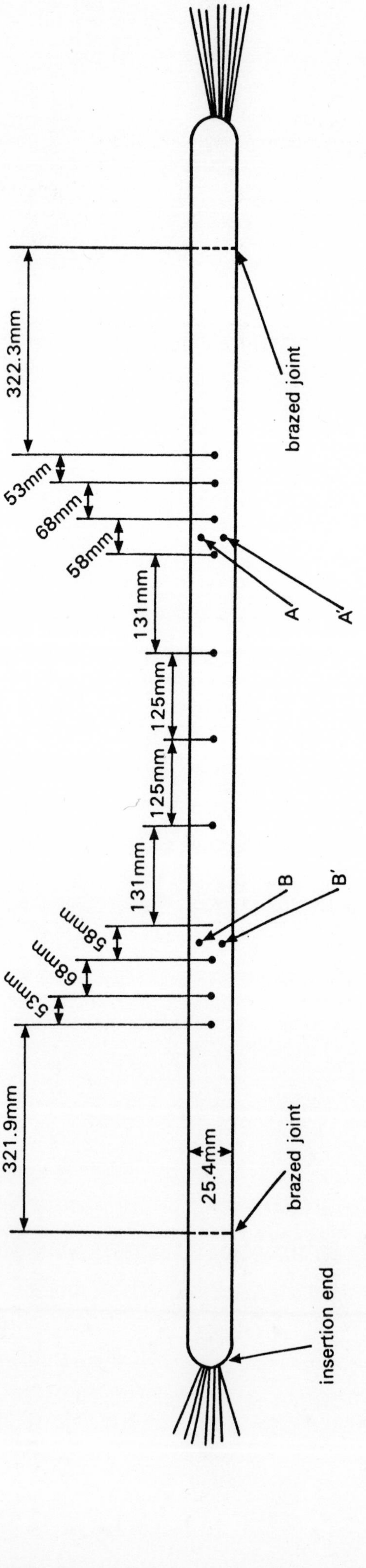

Figure 23   Sediment transportation

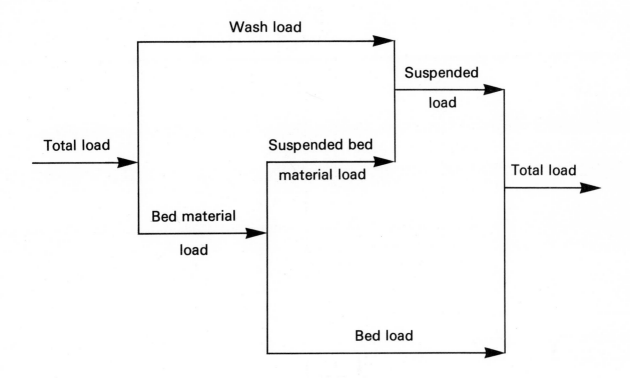

7 References

1. Hawkes HE and Webb JS, *Geochemistry in Mineral Exploration.* Harper and Rowe, New York.

2. Morisawa M, *Rivers.* Longman, London, 1985.

3. Leopold LB, Wolman MG and Miller JP, *Fluvial Processes in Geomorphology.* Freeman, San Francisco.

4. Smoot GF, in *Hydrometry: Principles and Practices,* (ed. Herschy RW). John Wiley and Sons, Chichester, 1978.

5. ISO 4373, *Liquid Flow Measurement in Open Channels. Water Level Measuring Devices,* 1979.

6. ISO 3454, *Sounding and Suspension Equipment,* 1983.

7. Lambie JC, *Velocity Area Methods,* in *Hydrometry: Principles and Practices,* (ed. Herschy RW). John Wiley and Sons, Chichester, 1978.

8. ISO 748, *Liquid Flow in Open Channels. Velocity Area Methods.* 1979

9. ISO 2537, *Cup Type and Propeller Type Current Meters,* 1988.

10. ISO 3455, *Calibration of Current Meters in Straight Open Tanks,* 1976.

11. Herschy RW, *Open Channel Flow,* in *Developments in Flow Measurement,* (ed. Scott RWW). Applied Science Publications, London, 1981.

12. ISO 1100, Parts I and II, *Liquid Flow Measurement in Open Channels, Part I. Establishment and Operation of a Gauging Station.* 1981
Part II. Determination of the Stage-Discharge Relation. 1982

13. Herschy RW, *Accuracy,* in *Hydrometry: Principles and Practices,* (ed. Herschy RW). John Wiley and Sons, Chichester, 1978.

14. ISO 5168, *Calculation of the Uncertainty of Flow Rate,* 1978.

15. Smoot GF and Novak CE, *Measurement of Discharge by the Moving Boat Method. Techniques of Water Resources Investigations of the USGS, Book 3, Chapter A11.* US Geological Survey, Washington, 1968.

16. Smoot GF, *Flow Measurement of some of the World's Major Rivers by the Moving Boat Method.* Proc. International Symposium on Hydrometry, Koblenz. UNESCO, WMO, IAHS Publication No 99, 1970, 149–161.

17. Herschy RW, *Streamflow Measurement*, 2nd edition, Chapman and Hall, London, 1995.

18. Charlton FG, *Current Meters,* in *Hydrometry: Principles and Practices,* (ed. Herschy RW). John Wiley and Sons, Chichester, 1978.

19. ISO 4369, *Liquid Flow Measurement in Open Channels. The Moving Boat Method,* 1979.

20. ISO 9555, *Liquid Flow Measurement in Open Channels. Dilution Methods* Part 1: General, 1994.

21. ISO 9555 Part II, *Liquid Flow Measurement in Open Channels. Dilution Methods* 1992. Also Parts III and IV.

22. ISO 1070, *Liquid Flow Measurement in Open Channels. Slope-Area Method,* 1992.

23. *Estimating the Discharge of Contaminants to Coastal Waters by Rivers*, Wallis DE, Webb BW, Marine Pollution Bulletin Vol 16 No 12, pp388–492 1985.

24. Ackers P, White WR, Perkins JA and Harrison AJM, *Weirs and Flumes for Flow Measurements.* John Wiley and Sons, Chichester, 1978.

25. White WR, *Flow Measuring Structures,* in *Hydrometry: Principles and Practices,* (ed. Herschy RW). John Wiley and Sons, Chichester, 1978.

26. ISO 1438, *Thin Plate Weirs,* 1980.

27. ISO 4360, *Triangular Profile Weirs,* 1984.

28. ISO 4377, *Flat V Weirs,* 1989.

29. ISO 3846, *Rectangular Broad-Crested Weirs,* 1989.

30. ISO 4374, *Round-Nosed Broad-Crested Weirs,* 1989.

31. ISO 4359, *Flumes,* 1983.

32. Herschy RW, White WR and Whitehead E, *Crump Weir Design.* Department of the Environment (Water Data Unit) TM No 8, 1977.

33. ISO 6481, *Liquid Flow in Open Channels. Ultrasonic (Acoustic) Velocity Meters,* 1985.

34. ISO 6416, *Liquid Flow in Open Channels. Measurement of Discharge by the Ultrasonic (Acoustic) Method,* 1992.

35. BS 1042 Part I, *Methods for the Measurement of Fluid in Pipes. Part I: Orifice Plates, Nozzles and Venturi Tubes,* 1964.

36. ISO/DIS 5167, *Measurement of Fluid Flow by Orifice Plates, Nozzles and Venturi Tubes Inserted in Circular Cross-Section Ducts Running Full.*

37. Dall HE, *Flow Tubes and Non-Standard Devices for Flow Measurement with some Coefficient Considerations. Symposium on Flow Measurement in Closed Conduits, Vol. 2.* HMSO, London, 1960, pp 385–394.

38. Lewis DCG and Singer J, *A New Development in Low Loss Metering,* in *Flow—Its Measurement and Control in Science and Industry, Vol. 1 Part 2.* Instrument Society of America, 1974, pp 501–506.

39. Shercliff JA, *The Theory of Electromagnetic Flow Measurement.* Cambridge University Press, Cambridge, 1962.

40. Balls SW and Brown KJ, *The Magnetic Flowmeter. Trans. Soc. Instrum. Tech.,* 1959, **11(2)**, 123–130.

41. Baker RC, *A Review of Some Applications of Electromagnetic Flow Measurement,* in *Flow—Its Measurement and Control in Science and Industry, Vol. 1 Part 2.* Instrument Society of America, 1974, pp 501–506.

42. Scott RWW, *A Practical Assessment of the Performance of Electromagnetic Flowmeters,* in *Proceedings of the Conference on Fluid Flow Measurement in the mid 1970's, Edinburgh.* Paper E-1. HMSO.

43. Taylor PA, *The Development of the Electromagnetic Flowmeter. Process Engng,* November 1969, 144–146.

44. Myles DJ and Harrison P, *A Survey of Turbine Flowmeters.* National Engineering Laboratory, Glasgow, Report No 91, 1963.

45. Watson GA, *The Application of Turbine Meters to Present Day Flow Metering Requirements,* in *Proceedings of the Symposium on the Application of Flow Measuring Techniques, 26–28 April 1977.* Institute of Measurement and Control, Paper 5.

46. Burgess TH, *Flow Measurement using Vortex Principles,* in *Proceedings of the Symposium on the Application of Flow Measuring Techniques, 26–28 April 1977.* Institute of Measurement and Control, Paper 18.

47. BS 1042, *Methods for the Measurement of Fluid Flow in Pipes. Part 2A. Pitot Tubes,* 1973.

48. ISO 3354, *Measurement of Clean Water Flow in Closed Conduits. Velocity-Area Method using Current Meters,* 1974.

49. Winternitz FAL and Fischl CF, *A Simplified Integration Technique for Pipe Flow Measurement. Water Power,* 1957, **9**, 225–234.

50. ISO 3966, *Measurement of Clean Water Flow in Closed Conduits. Velocity-Area Method using Pitot-Static Tubes,* 1976.

51. Kinghorn FC and McHugh A, *An Experimental Comparison of two Velocity Area Numerical Integration Techniques. Water Power,* 1973, 330–335.

52. Preston JH, *The Three-Quarter Radius Pitot Tube Flowmeter. The Engineer,* 1950, **190**, 400–404.

53. Clayton CV and Evans GV, *Experience in the use of Radioisotope Constant Rate Injection Method for Testing the Performance of Hydraulic Machines.* Paper No 5, Int. Conf. on Modern Developments in Flow Measurement. Peter Peregrinus, London, 1972, pp 276–291.

54. Hutton SP and Spenser EA, *Gauging Water Flow by the Salt-Dilution Method.* Paper No 6446. *Proc. Inst. Civil Engrs*, 1960, **16**, 395–346.

55. Spenser EA, *The Accurate Calibration of Flowmeters with Water. Trans. Soc. Inst. Tech.,* 1957, **9(11)**, 1–12.

56. Kinghorn FC, *Flow Measurement in Swirling or Asymmetric Flow.* in *Proceedings of the Symposium on the Application of Flow Measuring Techniques, 26–28 April 1977.* Institute of Measurement and Control, Paper 3.

57. *The Conditionability, Filterability, Settleability and Solids Content of Sludges 1984. Method 1 (Dry Residue at 105fC).* HMSO in this series.

58. Blatt H, Middleton G and Murray R, *Origins of Sedimentary Rocks, 2nd edition.* Prentice Hall, New Jersey.

59. Monkhouse FJ, *Principles of Physical Geography.* University of London Press (especially Chapter 5).

60. *US Geological Survey Professional Paper Series, Papers Issued in Series 411.* US Government Printing Office, Washington DC.

61. *The Sampling of Oils, Fats, Waxes and Tars in Aqueous and Solid Systems,* 1983 (Fig 9 and Ref 20 therein). HMSO in this series.

62. See the first part of this booklet.

63. *Four Essay Reviews on the Application of Radiation Measurement in the Water Industry,* 1984. HMSO in this series.

64. *Lithium in Water,* 1985. HMSO in this series.

65. *(a) Chloro- and Bromo- Trihalogenated Methanes in Water,* 1980, and *(b) Halogenated Solvents and Related Compounds in Sewage Sludges and Waters,* 1985. HMSO in this series.

66. BS 6316, *Code of Practice for Test Pumping Water Wells,* 1992.

67. de Marsily G, *Quantitative Hydrogeology Ground Water Hydrology for Engineers.* Academic Press Inc., Orlando, 1986.

68. Clarke L, *The Field Guide to Waterwells and Boreholes.* Geological Society Handbook. The Geological Society, London.

69. Brassington R, *Field Hydrology.* Geological Society Handbook. The Geological Society, London.

70. BS 7022, *Guide for Geophysical Logging of Boreholes for Hydrogeological Purposes,* 1989.

71. Coakley JP and Long BFN, *Tracing the Movement of Fine Grain Sediment in Aquatic Systems: A Literature Review.* Scientific Series No 174. Inland Waters Environment Directorate, Canada, 1990.

72. Major E, *Applied Chemical and Isotopic Groundwater Hydrology.* Open University Press, 1991.

73. Walling DE and Webb BW, *The Reliability of Suspended Sediment Load Data in Erosion and Sediment Transport Measurement. Proc. of Florence Symposium.* IAHS Publication No 133, 1981.

74. *The Sampling of Oils, Fats, Waxes and Tars in Aqueous and Solid Systems,* 1983 (Fig 11 and Ref 34 therein). HMSO in this series.

75. Federal Inter-Agency Sedimentation Project. *A Study of Methods used in Measurement and Analysis of Sediment Loads in Streams.*
   a. Report No 1. *Field Practice and Equipment used in Sampling Suspended Sediment,* 1940.

    b. Report No 6. *The Design of Improved Types of Suspended Sediment Samplers,* 1952.

    c. Report No 13. *The Single-Stage Sampler for Suspended Sediment,* 1961.

    d. Report No 14. *Determination of Fluvial Sediment Discharge,* 1963.

    e. Report P—Investigations of differential pressure guages for measuring suspended sediment concentrations. June 1961.

    f. Report R—Progress report. Electronic sensing of sediment. December 1964.

76.   Glover JR, Bhattacharya PK and Kennedy JF, *IIHR Report No 120.* Iowa Institute of Hydraulic Research, University of Iowa, 1969.

77.   Stickling W, *Proc. of Hydrology Symposium No 7.* National Research Council of Canada, Victoria BC, 1969.

78.   Allen T, *Particle Size Measurement, 2nd Edition.* Chapman and Hall, London, 1975.

79.   Thorn MFC, *Monitoring Silt Movement in Tidal Estuaries.* XVIth Congress of International Association for Sao Paolo, 1975.

80.   Murphee CE, *Proc. Am. Soc Civil Engineers,* 1968, **94 No HY2**, 515–528.

81.   Soulsby RL, *Sensors for the Movement of Sand in Suspension.* Report No 27. Institute of Oceanographic Sciences, Taunton, 1977.

82.   ISO 3716, *Liquid Flow Measurements in Open Channels. Functional Requirements and Characteristics of Suspended Load Samplers,* 1977.

83.   *Sedimentation Engineering.* ASCE Manual No 54. American Society of Civil Engineers, New York, 1975.

84.   Am. Soc. Civil Engineers, *Sediment Measurement Techniques. A. Fluvial Sediment. Proc. Am. Soc. Civil Engineers,* 1969, **95 HY5**, 1477–1514.

85.   *The Sampling and Initial Preparation of Sewage and Waterworks Sludges, Soil, Sediments, Plants and Contaminated Wildlife, 2nd Edition,* 1986. HMSO in this series.

86.   Guy HP and Norman VW, *Techniques of Water Resource Investigations of the United States Geological Survey. Field Methods for Measurement of Fluvial Sediment.* Book 3, Chapter C2. USGS, Washington, 1970.

87.   Simons DB and Senturk F, *Sediment Transport Technology.* Water Resources Publication, Fort Collins, Colorado, 1976.

88.   Nelson ME and Benedict PC, *Proc. Am. Soc. Civil Eng.,* 1950, **76**, Paper 32. *Trans. Am. Soc. Civil Eng.,* 1951, **116**, Paper 2450, p 891.

89.   *World Meteorological Organisation. Guide to Hydrological Practices.* WMO Report No 168.

90.   ISO 4363, *Liquid Flow Measurement in Open Channels. Methods of Measurement of Suspended Sediment,* 1993.

91.   *Sedimentation Transport Mechanics. Sediment Discharge Formulae.* American Society of Civil Engineers.

92.   Porterfield G, *Techniques of Water Resource Investigations of the United States Geological Survey. Computation of Fluvial Sediment Discharge.* Book 3, Chapter C3. USGS, Washington, 1972.

93.   ISO 4364, *Liquid Flow Measurement in Open Channels. Bed Material Sampling,* 1977.

94.   Wolman MG, *Trans. Am. Geophysical Union,* **35(6)**, 951–956.

95.   Kellerhals R and Bray DI, *Proc. Am. Soc. Civil Engineers,* 1971, **97 HY8**, 1165.

96.   Hubell DW, *Apparatus and Techniques for Measuring Bed Load.* Water Supply Paper No 1748. US Geological Survey, Washington, 1964.

97.   Benedict PC, Albertson ML and Matejka DW, *Proc. Am. Soc. Civil Engineers,* 1953, **79**, No 230.

98.   Crickmore MJ,*Sedimentology,* 1967, **8**, 175–288.

99.   Yalin MS, *Hydraulic Model Techniques.* Macmillan Press Ltd, London, 1971.

100.   BS 3406 Part II, *Methods for the Determination of Particle Size of Powders,* 1984.

101.   Kiff PR, *Particle Size Analysis of Sediments. Laboratory Practice,* April 1973, 259–266.

Quality Control

Although an analytical result can be more reliable, in quantitative terms, than the representativeness of a sample portion used in the analysis, quality control of sampling, sampling preparation and storage prior to analysis is much more complicated than analytical quality control. It is rarely possible to use control charts for accuracy of sampling, though investigation of control charts for a series of analyses may indicate that a sample or series of samples may have been at fault. A typical example is where a highly anomalous result is obtained in a long series of results, for which there is no proper explanation.

Investigation of the quality of sampling and sample storage can be divided into three sections:

i.   the taking of a representative sample or series of samples;

ii.   the storage of samples; and

iii.   any consequent handling, such as filtration, composite preparation and sub-division.

These details are discussed in the earlier part of this booklet, but the essentials are summarised below. Only rarely is it possible to add a known amount or concentration of an easily determined substance prior to sampling, and ascertain whether it is quantitatively found in the sample; although this technique is practicable during storage and handling. One of the most reliable procedures is to investigate thoroughly the whole process in advance and occasionally thereafter.

As far as taking the sample is concerned, a sufficient number of samples ought to be taken and analysed to ascertain the variability of the material being sampled, both with respect to time and location. If only a single sampling occasion is intended, careful planning is needed to ensure that the final sample or series of samples are representative of the whole body of material under study. If any doubt exists, the collection of too many samples at this stage is preferable to the collection of an insufficient number.

Sample stability, pick up from and adsorption by the sample bottle and sampling equipment can be investigated in advance using blanks, real and spiked samples. The effects on storage conditions can be assessed in the same way.

Examination of, or leaching tests on, used bottles and filters may also be useful.

If samples are mixed into a composite, or inhomogeneous samples are being homogenised, it is often possible to ascertain the uniformity of the final sample by spiking one portion of the sample with an easily detected material not interfering with the analysis and checking that the procedure has uniformly distributed that material throughout the final sample. A similar procedure can be used to ensure that portions taken from a large sample are representative.

If solids are being sub-divided or sampled, it is essential to ensure that the particle size is not important or that sub-divisions contain the same proportion of each component. Finely graded particles often differ in composition from larger graded particles. Where grinding may be necessary, contamination from the mill or mortar should be checked. This should be investigated by separately analysing the various sizes of material obtained by various treatments.

To summarise, one of the best quality assurance procedures is a thorough, prior evaluation of all situations that could cause the sample to be non-representative, followed by evaluation, and if necessary, modification of the procedures to give as representative a sample or series of samples as is practicable. For an ongoing sampling programme, there should be periodic reappraisals. Such re-evaluations are essential if changes occur, whether in the sample being taken or in the materials used to take and/or store the samples.

Department of the Environment

Standing Committee of Analysts
Members assisting with this booklet

Grateful acknowledgement is made to all those members and colleagues who contributed draft manuscripts and to those who made comments and helpful suggestions. At some stage, members in all Working Groups contributed to the preparation of this document. As expected in a booklet of this size and in the number of contributions some delay in publication was experienced. In view of this a substantial editorial revision was considered necessary. This exercise was funded by the Department.

Address for correspondence

However well procedures are tested, there is always the possibility of discovering hitherto unknown problems. Users with information on the procedures described in this booklet are requested to write to the Secretary at the address below.

The Secretary
The Standing Committee of Analysts
The Department of the Environment
Drinking Water Inspectorate
43 Marsham Street
LONDON SW1P 3PY
England

Printed in the United Kingdom for HMSO
Dd293034 2/96 C6 G559 10170